SEMICONDUCTOR PLASMA
INSTABILITIES
including Gunn-effect and
Avalanche Oscillations

by

Hans Hartnagel, PhD, CEng, MIEE

Senior Lecturer, Department of Electronic
and Electrical Engineering, University of Sheffield

HEINEMANN EDUCATIONAL BOOKS LTD · LONDON

Heinemann Educational Books Ltd

LONDON EDINBURGH MELBOURNE AUCKLAND
TORONTO JOHANNESBURG SINGAPORE
HONG KONG IBADAN NAIROBI

SBN 435 69390 5

Published by Heinemann Educational Books Ltd
48 Charles Street, London W1X 8AH
Printed in Great Britain by
Spottiswoode, Ballantyne and Co, Ltd, London and Colchester

Foreword

by Hans Pötzl, Dr phil, *Professor of Physical Electronics of the Technical University, Vienna*

Semiconductor plasmas play today a decisive rôle in the development of new telecommunication devices. In the space of the few years which have elapsed since the discovery of the Gunn effect and avalanche diodes, an activity has started, which one can well consider as revolutionary. Frequency limits, which for years appeared to be final for semiconductor devices, have during this period been exceeded by orders of magnitude. One finds an almost bewildering variety of possible applications. One can foresee technical exploration of the millimeter-wave range, in which hitherto only expensive and unwieldy generators had to be employed. Commercial applications of great economic importance can now be expected. The influence has been even more pronounced in the field of data processing, where one relies on the possibility of producing complicated pulse functions with simple semiconducting elements. New aspects are appearing also in the very recent field of optical electronics.

This development makes corresponding demands on the student of applied physics and telecommunications. Quantum mechanics, crystal structures, energy bands, transport theory and plasma waves can no more remain the domain of specializing physicists, but must take their place in the teaching programme on a broad basis. The present book represents an important contribution here. In particular, it presents for the first time a complete treatment of the phenomena known as semiconductor bulk-effects. Starting from the basic principles of physics, the reader is taken through to the present-day level of knowledge. The advantages of a teaching book and a review of the literature are skilfully combined. The fundamental phenomena are treated in a thorough and easily-understandable manner, and subsequently an embracing review is given of the technical literature.

Whereas the treatment of the applications is often rather superficial in books which take full account of the fundamentals of physics, the last chapter of the present volume presents a whole multitude of possibilities now opened up by semiconductor bulk effects. The last two chapters alone deal with more than 300 references.

Only someone who is himself in the forefront of research is able to produce such an outstanding book. I am convinced, that this volume will find an equally enthusiastic reception both from physicists and engineers who are concerned with modern electronics, and I wish the book and the author the success they deserve.

Vienna, April 1968   Hans Pötzl

Contents

Introduction

It is by now well known that semiconductor devices are rapidly replacing vacuum tubes. Transistors are already commonly used for low-frequency electronics and will soon be available for operation at several Gigahertz. Above these frequencies, klystrons and travelling-wave tubes have for a long time had no rival. However, recently, new types of semiconductor diodes have been developed, whose nonlinear characteristics permit generation of microwaves by the production of harmonics from a relatively low-frequency source†.

A more direct approach to the problem of microwave generation by semiconductors is represented by the development of some novel devices which rely on instabilities occurring with charge carriers of the crystal bulk. They are no more related in a primary way to junction effects. It is useful to consider the agglomeration of positive and negative charge carriers as a plasma, in the same way as a neutral system of ions and electrons in the gaseous state is called a plasma. Numerous analogies occur between both types of plasma, which is of advantage. An instability effect was often well known for gaseous plasmas. When one considered a semiconductor with its holes, electrons and ionized impurities as a plasma and searched for the same type of instability, one often found the effect indeed. Several of these plasma instabilities in semiconductors can now be considered for probable useful new devices.

Semiconductor plasmas exhibit also additional features which are not to be found in their gaseous counterpart. Solid-state charge carriers depend very largely on the interactions with the crystal. This can, for example, result in an increase in effective mass for higher carrier energies. This larger mass means a reduction in drift velocity so that a negative differential velocity results as a function of electric field. It is well known that the negative slope of a suitable characteristic causes instabilities. In fact, one has also here the case of the Gunn-effect.

There are several further instability phenomena which are unique in solid-state plasmas. The mathematical methods of analysis are very similar for all types of instabilities. Therefore, a general treatment of the problems involved should be useful and has been attempted here.

The main incentive to write this book was, however, the future importance of semiconductor plasmas. It is clear now, that bulk phenomena enable the

† See Hilsum, *Brit. J. Appl. Phys. (J. Phys. D)*, Ser. 2, 1, p. 265, 1968.

development of cheap, compact and efficient microwave generators and amplifiers. A wide range of books has recently been published on the physics of semiconductors, but hardly any concise treatments of semiconductor-plasma instabilities including the very important fields of the Gunn-effect and the avalanche diode are available.

This book is written mainly for the postgraduate student and research worker who has to introduce himself into this new and wide-ranging subject. It should also be useful for the specialist who wants to broaden his outlook. The first chapter recapitulates the basic facts of semiconductor physics. It will enable the reader either to refresh his knowledge or — in the case of a final-year undergraduate student for example — to obtain some of the background knowledge required for the study of this subject. This book will, therefore, also be of value to anyone with only a very limited knowledge of semiconductors. Only very few general terms are required for the understanding of the five chapters, as concepts which might be new to a physics or engineering undergraduate have been explained carefully.

However, it will usually be necessary for the reader with no previous knowledge of semiconductor physics to consult also one or two of the general teaching books on solid-state physics, as this subject is explained there in greater detail than is possible within the space of one chapter. A range of such books is given at the end of chapter I under the heading 'Additional References (For Further Study)'. For example, the books designated by the following numbers are well-suited for a first introduction: (3), (8), (15),(16), (18), (19).

The second chapter describes the equations relevant for instabilities in semiconductor plasmas, and the third chapter discusses the commonly used methods of studying instability properties.

The content of these three chapters is not subject to such stormy development as that of the following two. It is, therefore, only required to provide a few general references suitable for further studies. The fourth chapter is the longest one. It gives a detailed review of all the instabilities of interest. The amount of detailed information is in some way proportional to the practical importance of the particular effect. Therefore, transferred electron and avalanche effects are treated most extensively. Some of the instabilities proposed on theoretical grounds have only been mentioned briefly in the last section of this chapter. However, everything has been related to references which are consequently very extensive. Only essential references however have been given, and often solely the latest publication at the time of writing this book, so that the reader interested in further studies can find previous references in the publications quoted. They have been carefully checked to see that they do indeed indicate the other relevant references.

The final chapter describes details of technical devices which have either been developed already, or which have been proposed. As the most drastic changes are to be expected in this field, little information is given on the actual numerical values of the device parameters achieved so far. It is felt that the reader will find it is of greater value to be stimulated by the numerous ideas produced in connection with these semiconductor plasmas.

The references of chapters four and five have been quoted together, in order to avoid any duplication.

The author is grateful for the help and advice from colleagues and postgraduate students who have read the manuscript. In particular, he wishes to thank Mr C. Dattatreyan and Mr B. Chambers. The helpful suggestions made by Dr S. W. Fallmann and F. Seifert of Vienna are also gratefully acknowledged.

It is impossible for the author to express adequately his gratitude to Professor H. Pötzl, who read the entire manuscript very carefully and who made numerous useful comments. Thanks are also due to the author's wife, who aided greatly in the preparation of the manuscript.

Sheffield 1969 Hans L. Hartnagel

List of Symbols

A	cross-sectional diameter of diode
A_n	expansion coefficient for $f(x)$
$A_1, A_2, A_3 \ldots A_m$	Gunn diodes with third triggering electrode
$A(x_1)$	cross-sectional diameter of Gunn diode at x_1
a	lattice constant
a_i	acceleration of ith particle
a_i	components of Ψ
a_n	expansion coefficient for ψ
a_x, a_y, a_z	lattice constants in x, y and z directions
$\mathbf{a}_x, \mathbf{a}_y, \mathbf{a}_z$	basic lattice vectors in x, y and z directions
$a_1, a_2, a_3 \ldots$	'and' elements
$\mathbf{a}_1, \mathbf{a}_2, \mathbf{a}_3$	basic lattice vectors
B	magnetic induction
b_1, b_2, b_3	basic vectors of reciprocal lattice
C	capacitor
C	contour of integration
C_d	domain capacitance
C_0	comparator
$C_1, C_2, C_3 \ldots$	capacitors
c	velocity of light
c_d	domain velocity
c_e	elastic constant
D	diffusion constant
D_d	electric displacement
$D_1, D_2, D_3 \ldots$	Gunn diodes
d	interplanar spacing
d	F.M. noise power
d	domain width
d, d^*, d', d''	different delay elements
E	total energy of electron wave
E	energy of particles
$\mathscr{E}$	electric field
$\bar{\mathscr{E}} = V_{B/l}$	
$\boldsymbol{\mathscr{E}}$	electric field vector
$\langle E \rangle$	energy stored

E_A	ionization energy for acceptors
$\mathscr{E}_D$	domain field
$\mathscr{E}_{DM}$	maximum possible domain field of Fig. 4.3.
E_{DO}	ionization energy for donors
E_G	energy gap
$\mathscr{E}_H$	transverse Hall field
$\mathscr{E}_H$	low-conductivity field of Fig. 3.12.
$\mathscr{E}_R$	high-conductivity field of Fig. 3.12.
$\mathscr{E}_R$	field outside the domain
$\mathscr{E}_{R_0}$	value of $\mathscr{E}_R$ for operating point in Fig. 4.4.
E_W	work function
E_a	energy level of acceptors
E_c	lowest level of conduction band
E_d	energy level of donors
E_h	energy coordinate for holes
$\mathscr{E}_t$	threshold electric field for domain nucleation
$\mathscr{E}_{ta}$	threshold electric field for avalanching
$\mathscr{E}_{tn}$	field near threshold for domain nucleation
E_v	top level of valence band
$\mathscr{E}_x$	microwave field in x direction
$\mathscr{E}_z$	microwave field in z direction
$\mathscr{E}(\omega,k)$	Fourier transform in space and Laplace transform in time for $\mathscr{E}$
E_0	Fermi energy
$\mathscr{E}_0$	d.c. electric field
$\mathscr{E}_1$	a.c. electric field
e	electronic charge
e_p	piezoelectric constant
F	general function
$\mathbf{F}$	force
F_b	cross-sectional surface of electron beam
F_l	Liouville's function
f	frequency
f	abbreviated $f(E)$; d.c. part of distribution function
$f(E)$	Fermi-Dirac distribution function
$f(x)$	general function
f_g	maximum Gunn-effect frequency
f_q	phonon frequency
f_t	distribution function of carriers $= f + g$
f_0	resonant frequency
G	gain
g	a.c. part of distribution function
$\mathbf{g}$	reciprocal lattice vector
g_c	carrier generation rate

g_n	reciprocal lattice length
g_x, g_y, g_z	lattice constants of reciprocal lattice in x, y and z directions
$g_j(v,k) = g(v, z, t = 0)$	
H	Hamiltonian
H	denominator of equation (2.31)
$\mathbf{H}$	magnetic field
H_0	external magnetic field
h	Planck's constant
$\hbar$	$= h/2\pi$
I	total current
I_a	avalanche current
I_e	conduction current
I_c	displacement current
I_0	current of electron beam
I_t	threshold current for domain nucleation
I_1	small-signal current
J	current density
$\mathbf{J}$	current density vector
J_D	diffusion current density $[= e \operatorname{grad}(nD)]$.
J_e	$env_d - e \operatorname{grad}(nD)$, current density including diffusion
J_t	total current density, including electric displacement current density $[= J_e + (\partial D_d/\partial t)]$
$\tilde{J}_p, \tilde{J}_n$	a.c. hole and electron current density respectively
$\tilde{J}_t$	total a.c. current density
J_{to}	total d.c. current density
J_1, J_2	small-signal current densities at input and output of system respectively
j $=$	$\sqrt{-1}$
K	electromechanical coupling coefficient
k	electronic wave number
k	propagation constant of electromagnetic wave
$\mathbf{k}$	wave vector
k_i	imaginary part of the propagation constant
k_L	propagation constant owing to lattice alone
k_0	propagation constant of helicons giving boundary between forward and backward wave of Fig. 4.28
k_{max}	maximum value of helicon-propagation constant for gain of Fig. 4.28.
k_r	real part of propagation constant
k_x, k_y, k_z	wave numbers in $x, y,$ and z direction
L	diffusion length
L_D	Debye length
l	length of diode; length of domain trajectory

l	direct lattice vector
l_i	width of layer in which impact ionization occurs
$\|M\|$	a tensor
M_t	transverse magnetoresistivity
m	integer
m	mass of electron
m^*	effective mass
$m_e{}^*$	effective electron mass
m_h	effective hole mass
m_s	plasma charge-carrier mass
N	integer
N	number of gas particles
N_a	acceptor density
N_a	ionized acceptor density
N_c	effective density of states in the conduction band
N_d	donor density
$N_d{}^+$	ionized donor density
N_s	density of states
N_v	effective density of states in the valence band
n	integer
n	electron density
n_i	electron density of an intrinsic semiconductor
n_L	density of electrons in lower-energy valley
n_0	ionized-donor density and trapped-carrier density
$n_0(x_1)$	the value of n_0 at x_1
n_p	plasma density
n_r	index of refraction
n_s	carrier density
n_u	density of electrons in higher-energy valley
O	output terminal
P	output terminal
P	microwave power
$\mathscr{P}$	power density
$\mathscr{P}_1\mathscr{P}_2$	power densities of different waves
p	hole density
p_e	momentum of electron
p_i	hole density of an intrinsic semiconductor
p_x, p_y, p_z	components of momentum in x, y and z directions
Q	Q-factor of a resonant circuit
Q	heat flow vector
q	phonon wave vector
R	'read-out' terminal
R	small-signal diode resistance

R_H	Hall constant
R_L	load resistance
R_a	input resistance for 'and' circuit
R_d	negative diode resistance
R_0	low-field diode resistance
r	recombination rate
$\mathbf{r}$	distance vector, direct lattice vector
S	terminal for triggering pulse
S	density of states
$\mathscr{S}$	strain
S_c	density of energy states in conduction band
S_v	density of energy states in valence band
T	temperature in °K
T^1	period of microwave oscillation
T_c	carrier temperature
T_d	time of domain growth
T_e	electron temperature
T_h	hole temperature
T_l	lattice temperature
$\mathscr{T}$	stress
t	time interval between digits
t	time
t_d	transit time of domain along diode
t_e	electron life-time
t_h	hole life-time
t_p	time interval between triggering pulses in pulsed code modulator
u	lattice displacement
u_a	phase velocity of Alfvén waves
u_o	amplitude of lattice displacement
$\mathscr{V}$	volume of crystal
V_B	applied voltage
V_D	excess domain voltage
V_H	Hall voltage
V_R	$= \mathscr{E}_R.l$
V_a	Alfvén velocity
V_b	breakdown voltage
V_t	threshold voltage for domain nucleation
V_0	cathode-anode voltage
V_1	kinetic voltage
V_1, V_2	kinetic voltages at input and output of system respectively
$V(r)$	potential energy of electron
v	velocity of electron; scattering-limited carrier velocity

$\mathbf{v}$	velocity vector
v_D	domain velocity
v_H	helicon phase velocity
v_R	velocity of electrons outside domain
v_a	average velocity of carriers
v_c	velocity of carriers
v_d	drift velocity
$\mathbf{v}_d$	drift-velocity vector
v_{dm}	drift-velocity for maximum electroacoustic gain
v_e	electron drift velocity
v_g	group velocity
$\mathbf{v}_g$	group velocity vector
$|v_g|$	magnitude of group velocity
v_h	hole drift velocity
$\mathbf{v}_k$	group velocity vector of electronic wave
v_l	velocity of light in absence of a plasma
v_n	scattering-limited velocity of electrons
v_p	scattering-limited velocity of holes
v_{ph}	phase velocity
v_{p3}, v_{p4}	phase velocities
v_s	sound velocity
$v(x_1)$	drift velocity of electrons outside the domain, when the domain is at x_1
v_0	d.c. velocity
v_1	a.c. velocity
v_1, v_2	two different velocities
v_1	random velocity
w	sample diameter for Hall measurements
w_s	width of space-charge region
X	reactance of small-signal impedance
x	cartesian coordinate
$\mathbf{x}$	vector in x direction
x_1	position of domain in Gunn diode
y	cartesian coordinate
$\mathbf{y}$	vector in y direction
Z	characteristic impedance
Z_s	small-signal impedance
α	attenuation constant
α_i	ionization rate of electrons and holes $= g_c/v_d n_s$
α_n	ionization rate of electrons
β	phase constant
β_h	ionization rate of holes
γ	$= 1 - (v_d/v_s)$

Δ	delta operator
Δ	energy difference between the lowest values of central and satellite valleys
Δv_{d}	velocity difference of two electron beams (Fig. 3.10)
$(\Delta\, n\overline{\phi})_{\mathrm{g+r}}$	generation-recombination term in equation (2.33)
$(\Delta\, n\overline{\phi})_{\mathrm{c}}$	collision term in equation (2.33)
∇	nabla operator
∇_{r}	$= \left(\dfrac{\partial}{\partial x}, \dfrac{\partial}{\partial y}, \dfrac{\partial}{\partial z} \right)$
∇_{p}	$= \left(\dfrac{\partial}{\partial p_x}, \dfrac{\partial}{\partial p_y}, \dfrac{\partial}{\partial p_z} \right)$
ϵ	permittivity
ζ	function of expansion for Ψ
η	efficiency
λ	electron wave length
μ	mobility
$|\mu|$	average negative mobility
μ_{M}	magnetoresistance mobility
μ_{e}	electron mobility
μ_{h}	hole mobility
μ_{l}	low-field mobility
μ_{m}	permeability
μ_1	low-field mobility of carriers in central valley
μ_2	mobility of carriers in satellite valleys
ρ	low-field resistivity
ρ_{D}	charge density of ionized donors
ρ_{H}	resistivity in J-direction owing to Hall effect
ρ_{c}	charge density
ρ_{m}	mass density
ρ_0	immobile and trapped charge density
$\rho_{0\mathrm{c}}$	dc charge density
ρ_1	ac charge density
σ_{n}	conductivity by electrons
σ_{p}	conductivity by holes
σ_1, σ_2	conductivities owing to different masses of carriers
τ	relaxation time
τ_{b}	bulk life-time
τ_{d}	dielectric relaxation time
τ_{e}	energy relaxation time
τ_{ep}	collision time between electrons and phonons
τ_{h}	collision time between holes and phonons

τ_1	carrier life-time
τ_m	momentum relaxation time
τ_s	surface life-time
τ_t	transit time of carriers across space-charge region
τ_1	electron transfer time from central to satellite valley
τ_2	electron transfer time from satellite to central valley
τ_+	hole scattering time
τ_-	electron scattering time
ϕ	electrical potential
ϕ	function of equation (2.33)
ϕ_h	angle between helicon propagation and H_0
Ψ	wave function
ψ	time independent wave function
ψ^*	complex conjugate of ψ
ω	angular frequency
ω_D	diffusion frequency
ω_c	cyclotron frequency
ω_d	dielectric relaxation frequency
ω_h	hole plasma frequency
ω_i	imaginary part of ω
ω_m	$= \sqrt{(\omega_c\,\omega_D)}$
ω_m	angular frequency giving uppermost pole of $\mathscr{E}(\omega, k)$
ω_n	electron plasma frequency
ω_p	plasma frequency
ω_r	real part of ω
ω_s	saddle point of Fig. 3.2

CHAPTER I

Semiconductor Physics

1.1 Quantum Mechanics

For a long time, electrons have only been treated as particles. This is correct for all cases where the electron trajectories are very large, as can be shown by experiment.

De Broglie suggested in 1924 that small particles of matter such as electrons behave like waves with a wavelength

$$\lambda = \frac{h}{mv} = \frac{h}{p_e} \tag{1.1}$$

($p_e = mv$ is the momentum, h Planck's constant, m and v the mass and velocity of the particle, respectively). This theory was soon experimentally verified and Schrödinger attempted to develop the wave concept further. He introduced the wave function Ψ into a differential equation whose solution is the expression for a wave, namely $\exp j(kr - \omega t)$, (see (8)), and obtained the wave equation:

$$\left(-\frac{\hbar^2}{2m}\Delta + V(\mathbf{r})\right)\Psi = j\hbar\frac{\partial\Psi}{\partial t} \tag{1.2}$$

Here the fact is used that the kinetic energy, $\frac{1}{2}mv^2$, of an electron is equal to the difference between its total energy and its potential energy $V(\mathbf{r})$. (m is the mass of a free electron, $\hbar = h/2\pi$, $j = \sqrt{-1}$ and Δ is the delta operator.) Assuming a periodic time dependence,

$$\Psi = \psi(\mathbf{r})\exp\left(-\frac{jEt}{\hbar}\right) \tag{1.3}$$

one obtains:

$$\left(-\frac{\hbar^2}{2m}\Delta + V(\mathbf{r})\right)\psi = E\psi \tag{1.4}$$

where E is the total energy of the particle. ψ is the time-independent wave function, which is, by setting $\psi\psi^*$, proportional to the probability of finding an electron at $\mathbf{r}$ (ψ^* is the complex conjugate of ψ). In order to normalize ψ such that it gives the exact probability, one uses the equation:

$$\int_{-\infty}^{+\infty}\psi^*\psi\,d\mathbf{r} = 1 \tag{1.5}$$

The solutions of equation (1.4) for a given potential energy distribution agree precisely with many experimental results, which could not be explained by the classical particle theory.

One can calculate various moments of the corresponding distribution, if one knows $\psi^* \, \psi$. The first moment is the mean position of the particle, i.e.

$$\langle \mathbf{r} \rangle = \int \psi^* \, \mathbf{r} \psi \, d\mathbf{r} \tag{1.6}$$

Such quantitities are called 'observables' and they are directly related to physical measurements. Therefore, they must be real quantities. $\mathbf{r}$ in the above equation is an 'operator', as it operates on ψ.

Similarly, one can obtain the mean momentum of the particle:

$$\langle p_e \rangle = \int \psi^* \, \hat{p}_e \, \psi \, dz \tag{1.7}$$

where $\hat{p}_e = (\hbar/j)/(\partial/\partial z)$, and the mean energy of a particle:

$$\langle E \rangle = \int \Psi^* \, \hat{E} \Psi \, dz \tag{1.8}$$

with

$$\hat{E} = j\hbar \frac{\partial}{\partial t}$$

Owing to the superposition principle, which follows from the linearity of the Schrödinger equation, ψ can be constructed from a number of, say, energy eigenfunctions of the system, i.e.

$$\psi = \sum_n a_n \psi_n \tag{1.9}$$

The coefficients a_n can be found with the use of the orthogonality property, by multiplying this equation by ψ^* and integrating. This gives:

$$a_n = \int \psi_n^* \, \psi \, dz \tag{1.10}$$

Often it was felt that frequency, intensity and polarization of the emitted radiation were preferable to the problems of position and velocity of an electron, i.e. one tried to consider only those quantities which can actually be observed. This approach led to an alternative representation of quantum mechanics, the so-called 'matrix mechanics'. We expand a wave function ψ so that

$$\Psi = \sum_i a_i(t) \, \zeta_i(z) \tag{1.11}$$

with $i \rightarrow \infty$. The orthonormal set of ζ_i functions are treated as coordinate vectors spanning an infinite-dimensional function or vector space, and the coefficients a_i

are called the components of Ψ. As Ψ and ζ_i are usually complex, the corresponding vector space is called a Hilbert space. It is possible to write Ψ in the form of a column matrix

$$\Psi = [a_i] = \begin{bmatrix} a_1 \\ a_2 \\ a_3 \\ \vdots \end{bmatrix} \tag{1.12}$$

It can easily be shown, that

$$1 = \int \Psi^* \Psi \, dz = \sum_i a_i^* a_i \tag{1.13}$$

or

$$1 = [a_i]^+ [a_i] = [a_1^*, a_2^*, a_3^* \ldots] \begin{bmatrix} a_1 \\ a_2 \\ a_3 \\ \vdots \end{bmatrix} \tag{1.14}$$

where $[a_i]^+$ is the Hermitian adjoint of $[a_i]$.

A very useful formalism was developed by Dirac, the well-known bra-ket notation. Instead of $[a_i]$, the ket $|\rangle$ is used to denote a normalized vector, i.e. $|\psi\rangle$. The corresponding adjoint matrix $[a_i]^*$ is represented by the bra $\langle|$. The eigenfunction is written as $\Psi_{lmn} \equiv |lmn\rangle$ and $\Psi_{lmn}^* = \langle lmn|$. A common eigenvector of the operators A and B, corresponding to the eigenvalues a and b, respectively, is represented by $|a, b\rangle$. The scalar product of the vectors $\phi = |a\rangle$ and $\psi = |b\rangle$ is $\int \phi^* \psi \, d\mathbf{r} = \langle a|b\rangle$.

The following equations of Dirac's notation are of importance:

$$A|a^{(J)}\rangle = a^{(J)}|a^{(J)}\rangle$$
$$A|a^{(J)}, b^{(k)}\rangle = a^{(J)}|a^{(J)}, b^{(k)}\rangle$$
$$B|a^{(J)}, b^{(k)}\rangle = b^{(k)}|a^{(J)} b^{(k)}\rangle$$
$$\langle a|b\rangle = \langle b|a\rangle^*$$
$$\langle a|B|b\rangle = b\langle a|b\rangle$$
$$\langle a|C|b\rangle = \langle b|C^*|a\rangle^*$$
$$\langle a^{(k)}|b^{(l)}\rangle = \int \phi^{(k)*} \psi^{(l)} \, d\mathbf{r}$$

$$\langle a|C|b\rangle = \int \phi^* C\psi \, d\mathbf{r} \tag{1.15}$$

where one and two subscripts indicate the component of a vector and the components of a matrix, respectively, where a bracketed superscript denotes one vector or eigenvalue of a set, and where a star * means a complex conjugate value.

1.2. Crystal Structures and their Vibrations

Before applying quantum mechanics to solids, one has to describe crystal structures.

We define the three basic vectors a_1, a_2 and a_3 such that the atomic arrangement of the crystal remains the same at any point given by any integral multiple of these vectors. The points thus described are called 'lattice sites' and form a 'space lattice' or 'Bravais net' (see Fig. 1.1).

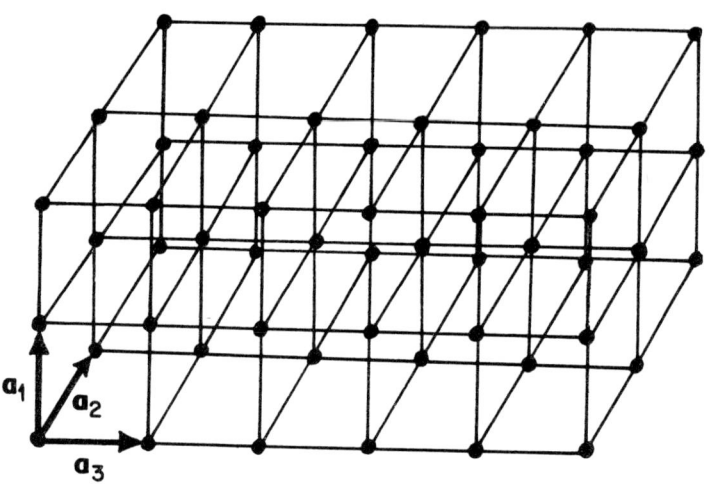

Fig. 1.1   A Bravais net or space lattice with lattice sites defined by the basic vectors a_1, a_2 and a_3.

There is either a single atom or group of atoms (which form a 'unit cell') at each lattice site in an actual crystal.

There are various ways of describing a particular structure. This can easily be demonstrated with the 'body-centred cubic structure' (B.C.C.) (Fig. 1.2). It can also be considered

(a) as a cubic lattice with two atoms per unit cell, or

(b) as two interpenetrating simple cubic sublattices, or

(c) as a cube with the basic vectors

$$a_1 = \tfrac{1}{2}(-a_x + a_y + a_z)$$

$$a_2 = \tfrac{1}{2}(a_x - a_y + a_z)$$

$$a_3 = \tfrac{1}{2}(a_x + a_y - a_z)$$

where x, y and z indicate basic vectors in the direction of rectangular coordinates. This possibility shows that the B.C.C. structure is a Bravais lattice, where each atom is positioned at a lattice site.

(d) Finally, one can describe the B.C.C. structure by the so-called Wigner-Seitz

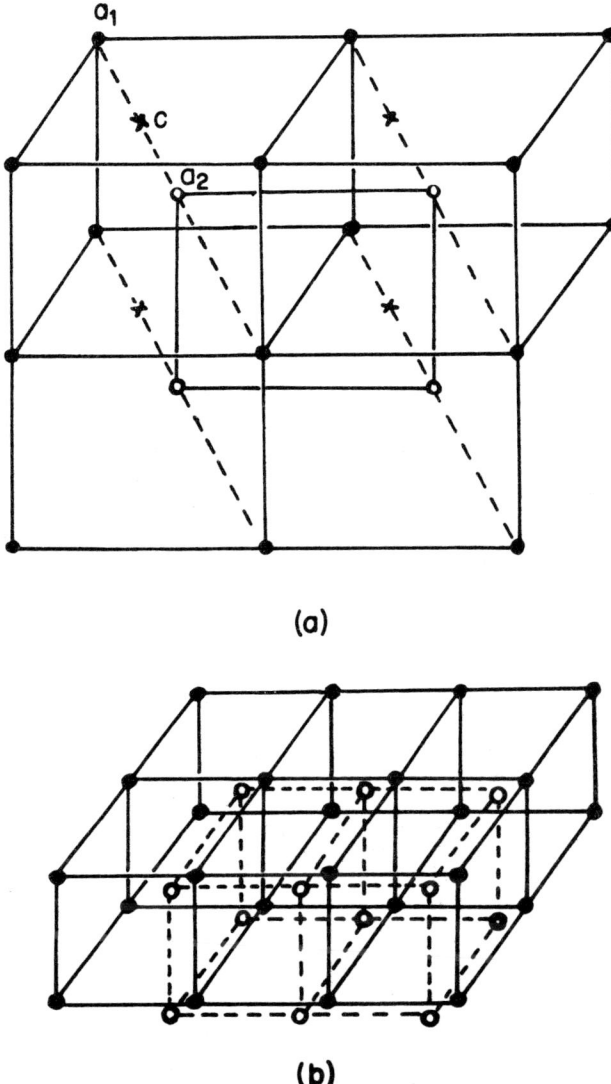

(a)

(b)

Fig. 1.2 The body-centred cubic lattice: (a) the atoms a_1 and a_2 forming a unit cell whose central symmetry is c; (b) two interpenetrating simple cubic lattices.

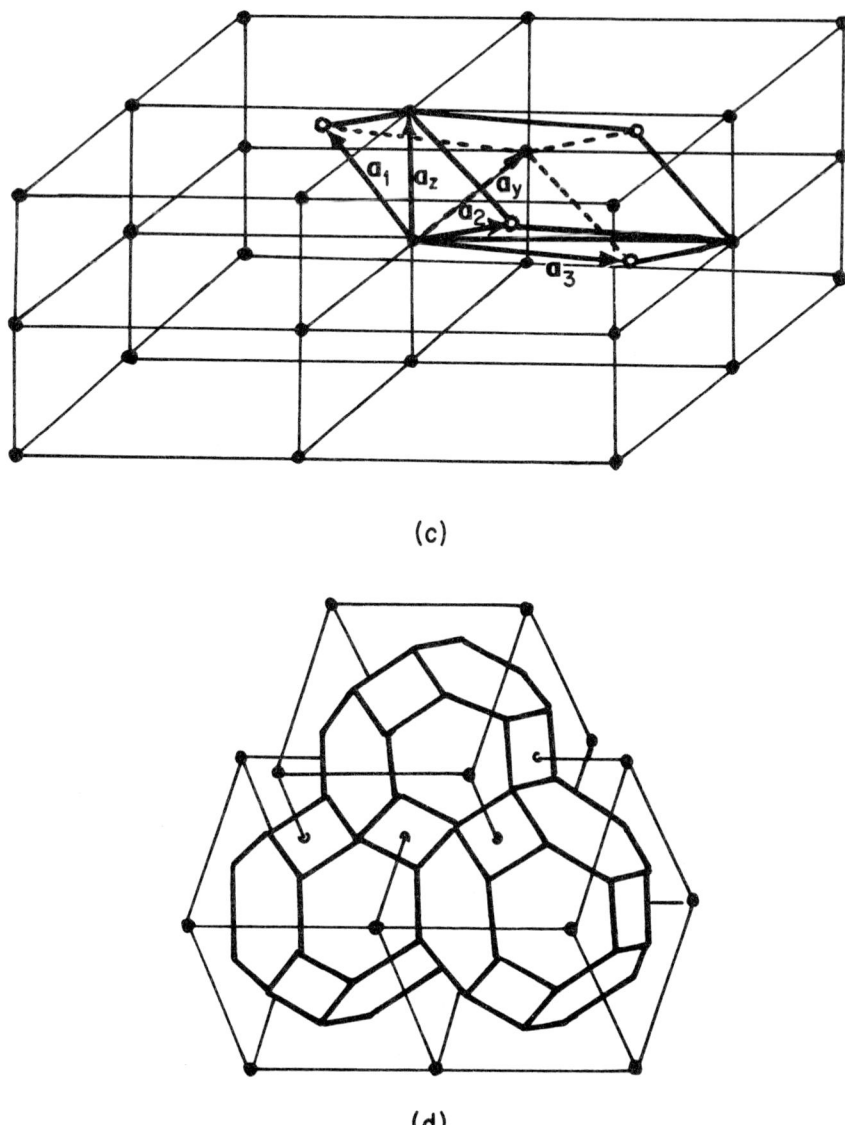

(c)

(d)

Fig. 1.2 *continued* (c) a cube with the basic vectors a_1, a_2 and a_3 forming a Bravais lattice; (d) Wigner Seitz cell, constructed by chopping off all the corners of a cube half way along the diagonal from its centre to the corner.

cells. These are constructed as follows: Every connecting line between two neighbouring lattice points is divided into two equal halves. A perpendicular plane passes through the dividing points. All the planes surrounding one lattice point form a complete enclosure which is a Wigner-Seitz cell. The polyhedra, thus formed from a B.C.C. structure, are shown in Fig. 1.2d.

It is useful to know 'Miller indices', which are defined as follows: Find the intercepts of the plane which has to be described, with the three lattice axes and obtain the distances from a suitable reference point in terms of the number of lattice constants; take the reciprocals of the numbers obtained and reduce to the smallest three integers, which are the Miller indices. Intercepts at ∞ thus become '0' and negative numbers are indicated by a bar across them. The indices are enclosed by round brackets. If all the sets of planes are to be indicated which are equivalent by symmetry, one employs curly brackets. Therefore, $\{110\}$ indicates the planes (110), (101), $(\bar{1}\bar{1}0)$, (011), etc.

If one wants to develop any function describing crystal properties, as for example ψ, one can always assume that these functions are multiply periodic, such as

$$f(x) = \sum_n A_n \exp\frac{2\pi jnx}{a} \tag{1.16}$$

where n is an integer and a is the period of the function. We define

$$g_n = n\frac{2\pi}{a} \tag{1.17}$$

as the reciprocal lattice length. Extended to three dimensions, one obtains:

$$f(\mathbf{r}) = \sum_{g_x, g_y, g_z} A(g_x, g_y, g_z) \exp\{j(g_x x + g_y y + g_z z)\} \tag{1.18}$$

with

$$g_x = \frac{2\pi n}{a_x}, \quad g_y = \frac{2\pi n}{a_y} \quad \text{and} \quad g_z = \frac{2\pi n}{a_z}$$

and a_x, a_y and a_z the periods in x, y and z directions respectively. One can define a vector g with the three components g_x, g_y and g_z and can rewrite the exponential term as follows:

$$\exp(j\mathbf{g}\mathbf{r})$$

g is called the 'reciprocal lattice vector', which defines the 'reciprocal lattice'.

Each direct lattice has also a reciprocal counterpart. The easiest way of finding the reciprocal lattice is by using its fundamental properties, of which the most important ones are given now below:

(a) If l is the direct-lattice vector, which is formed by an integral multiple of the basic vectors a_1, a_2 and a_3, then

$$g \cdot l = 2\pi \cdot \text{integer}$$

(b) If the vector of a non-rectangular direct lattice (e.g. Fig. 1.2c) is

$$l = l_1 \mathbf{a}_1 + l_2 \mathbf{a}_2 + l_3 \mathbf{a}_3$$

and its corresponding reciprocal lattice vector is

$$g = g_1 \mathbf{b}_1 + g_2 \mathbf{b}_2 + g_3 \mathbf{b}_3$$

then

$$g \cdot l = g_1 l_1 + g_2 l_2 + g_3 l_3$$

which is fulfilled if

$$\mathbf{b}_1 = \frac{\mathbf{a}_2 \times \mathbf{a}_3}{\mathbf{a}_1 \cdot \mathbf{a}_2 \times \mathbf{a}_3}; \quad \mathbf{b}_2 = \frac{\mathbf{a}_3 \times \mathbf{a}_1}{\mathbf{a}_2 \cdot \mathbf{a}_3 \times \mathbf{a}_1}; \quad \mathbf{b}_3 = \frac{\mathbf{a}_1 \times \mathbf{a}_2}{\mathbf{a}_3 \cdot \mathbf{a}_1 \times \mathbf{a}_2} \tag{1.19}$$

(c) The projection of l on g has the length

$$d = \frac{l \cdot g}{|g|} = \frac{2\pi N}{|g|} \quad (N = 1, 2, 3 \ldots)$$

One obtains the same value of d, if one replaces l by l', with its component coefficients:

$$l_1' = l_1 - mg_3, \quad l_2' = l_2 - mg_3, \quad l_3' = l_3 + m(g_1 + g_2)$$

$$(m = 1, 2, 3 \ldots)$$

This means all vectors l' with $m = 1, 2, 3 \ldots$ point to lattice sites on one lattice plane, and all have the same projection on g.

Therefore g must be normal to lattice planes of the direct lattice.

(d) If g_1, g_2 and g_3 have no common factor then we can find a vector l'' of the direct lattice such that

$$gl'' = 2\pi(N + 1)$$

This means that the lattice plane with l'' is the distance $2\pi/|g|$ away from the plane with l. Thus, if the components of g have no common factor, then g is inversely proportional to the spacing of the lattice planes normal to g.

(e) It can be shown with the help of the relations [equation (1.19)] that

$$\mathbf{b}_1 \cdot \mathbf{b}_2 \times \mathbf{b}_3 = \frac{1}{\mathbf{a}_1 \cdot \mathbf{a}_2 \times \mathbf{a}_3}$$

which shows that the volume of a unit cell of the reciprocal lattice is inversely proportional to the volume of a unit cell of the direct lattice.

As an example, we find the reciprocal lattice of the face-centred cubic structure (F.C.C., see Fig. 1.3). Important lattice planes are along the a_x, a_y and a_z edges,

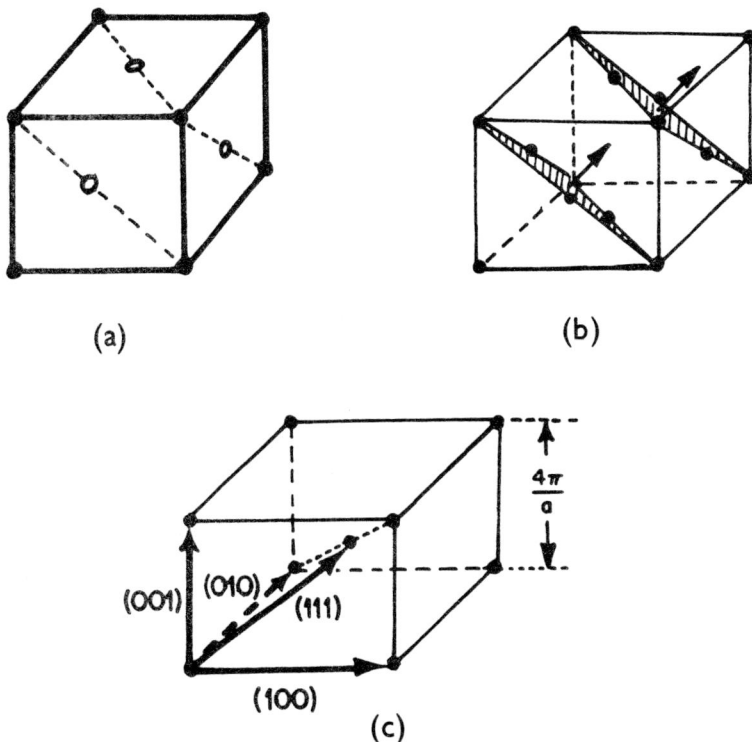

Fig. 1.3   The face-centred cubic structure and its reciprocal lattice: (*a*) the F.C.C. structure; (*b*) the densely populated diagonal {111} planes and their surface vectors; (*c*) the B.C.C. structure—the reciprocal of the F.C.C. structure.

given by the Miller indices {100}. They are spaced a distance $\frac{1}{2}a$ apart. Thus, the reciprocal lattice vector has the length $|g| = 2\pi/\frac{1}{2}a$. Another set of important planes are normal to the diagonal, as indicated in Fig. 1.3*b*; they have the indices {111} and are spaced $a/\sqrt{3}$ apart. This gives a reciprocal lattice vector

$$g = \frac{2\pi}{a}(1, 1, 1)$$

This shows that the reciprocal of the F.C.C. lattice is the B.C.C. one (Fig. 1.3*c*).

An important concept is that of the Brillouin zones. The first one is given by the Wigner-Seitz cell of the reciprocal lattice for any crystal. Therefore, the first Brillouin

zone of the F.C.C. lattice is given by Fig. 1.2d. There exists also a physical inter-
pretation of the Brillouin zones. According to Bragg's law of diffraction total
reflection of the electrons occurs, when the electronic wave number† satisfies the
condition

$$k = \pi/d \tag{1.20}$$

where d is the interplanar spacing of the planes which are normal to the propagating
wave. This condition gives the discontinuities in the allowed-energy ranges of the
electrons in a crystal, which will be described later on. The planes that reflect electron waves most strongly, form the first Brillouin zone of the crystal. Other planes
reflect electrons of larger energies (and, therefore, larger wave numbers), if their
spacing is increased, so that equation (1.20) is fulfilled. The polyhedra, formed by
these planes are called the second, third, etc. Brillouin zones of the crystal.

It is convenient to use the wave numbers k_x, k_y and k_z as coordinate axes for
the Brillouin zones, and the space defined thus, is often called the k-space. As the
kinetic energy of an electron can be related to its momentum, and as the vector of
the reciprocal space is proportional to the momentum of an electron, one often calls
the k-space the momentum space. The contours of equal energy inside a Brillouin
zone are called the energy contours. The energy contour enclosing all the energy
states which are occupied by electrons, is called the Fermi surface, since it denotes
the maximum energy of an electron, i.e. the Fermi energy.

Vibrations of a lattice are quantized. Energy transitions are involved which are
multiples of the quantum $h.f$ (f = frequency of vibration). By analogy to optical
transitions, in which quanta of electromagnetic energy, called photons, are given,
the term phonon has been adopted for the quanta of vibrational energy. It can be
shown that the following relation must be satisfied:

$$E(\mathbf{k}) - E(\mathbf{k}') \pm \hbar f_q = 0 \tag{1.21}$$

where $E(\mathbf{k})$ and $E(\mathbf{k}^1)$ are the electron energies before and after the transition respectively and $\hbar f_q$ is the absorbed or emitted phonon quantum. (f_q is the frequency
of the emitted phonon with wave vector q.) This equation means that the electron
has gained or lost one quantum of energy from the lattice mode with which it interacts; one says, the electron has interacted with the lattice to destroy (or create)
a phonon of wave vector q. Equation (1.21) expresses the conservation of energy. A
similar equation is the following:

$$\hbar\mathbf{k}' = \hbar\mathbf{k} + \hbar\mathbf{q} \tag{1.22}$$

which expresses the conservation of momentum. This justifies considering the phonon
to have particle-like properties.

† The electronic wave number is the propagation constant for the electronic waves.

1.3. Energy Bands and Carrier Statistics

The probability that a particle has energy E_i, is proportional to $\exp(-E_i/kT)$, where T is the absolute temperature of a gas of particles. The ratio of particles with energy E_i to the total number of particles is called the Maxwell-Boltzmann distribution law. It can be used for the calculation of the properties of gases. For example the energy distribution of a gas can be calculated, i.e.

$$\frac{dN}{dE} = 2N \sqrt{\left(\frac{E}{\pi(kT)^3}\right)} \exp(-E/kT) \qquad (1.23)$$

N = number of particles, E = energy of particles (see Fig. 1.4). This treatment is only permissible if an infinite number of energy states is available which an electron is permitted to occupy. This is not the case in quantum mechanics. Here each available state is specified by the quantum numbers and its occupation is controlled by

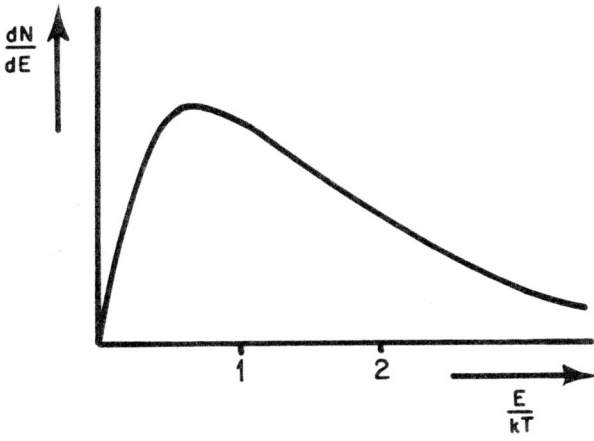

Fig. 1.4   Maxwell distribution of kinetic energies.

the Pauli exclusion principle, which states that only two electrons are allowed to occupy the same energy state in a system. The observation of the actual occupation is governed by Heisenberg's uncertainty principle.

The Pauli exclusion principle means that an electron can only be transferred to a new state, if this is empty. This means, that the distribution function will be different from that of a gas, and it can be shown with the above assumption that

$$f(E_i) = \frac{1}{\exp[(E_i - E_0)/kT] + 1} \qquad (1.24)$$

which is the Fermi-Dirac distribution function $f(E_i)$ (E_0 = the well-known Fermi energy, below which all states are filled at $T = 0$). It is shown in Fig. 1.5 for $kT = 0$ and for $kT = E_0$.

With most semiconductors, one is only interested in cases where $E_i - E_0 \gg kT$, so that

$$f(E_i) \approx \exp\left[(E_i - E_0)/kT\right]$$

The occupation of available states in a Brillouin zone by the valence electrons in a solid, depends on the states contained in the zones. Each Brillouin zone contains one energy level per lattice point of the whole crystal if one considers one atom per

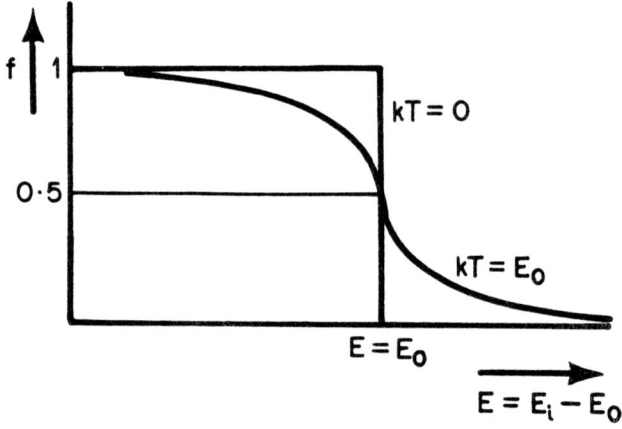

Fig. 1.5   Fermi distribution at temperatures $T = 0$ and $T = E_0/k$.

unit cell, and each energy level represents two quantum states, differing in their spin quantum numbers only. The density of states is zero within the forbidden-energy gap and is given inside an energy band by the following expression, where here E has to be taken zero at the band edge:

$$N_s = 8\pi m \frac{\sqrt{(2mE)}}{h^3} \mathscr{V} = S.\mathscr{V} \tag{1.25}$$

(m = mass of electron, $\mathscr{V}$ = volume of crystal, S = density of states per m^3) if one assumes a free-electron model. In reality, the function is different near the boundaries of the Brillouin zones, where no electrons are permitted.

The density of the occupied states is obtained by multiplying the available density of states with the Fermi-Dirac function.

The solution of Schrödinger's equation shows that the electrons surrounding the nucleus of an isolated atom can only occupy certain permitted energy values. When several atoms are brought together, the permissible energy states are split up, so that the Pauli exclusion principle is also obeyed for the new multiatomic system. Similarly the energy levels of the atoms are broadened to energy bands in solids (see Fig. 1.6). If the energy bands do not overlap inside a crystal, we have separate energy bands. The bands which correspond to the valence electrons of the atoms, are called the valence bands. If the top valence band is only partially filled, its electrons can easily be transferred to higher energy levels inside this almost continuous band, and

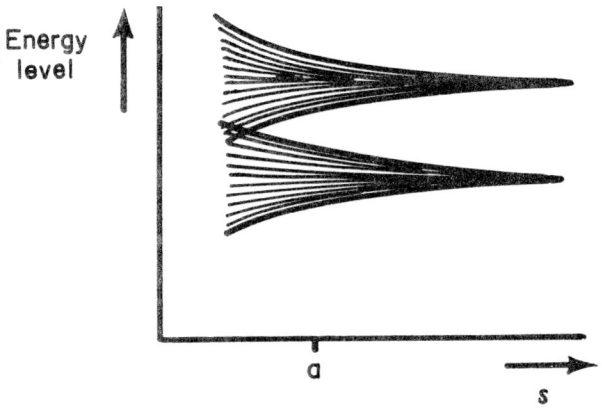

Fig. 1.6 Atomic levels spreading into bands as interatomic separation s decreases.

we have a conductor as it means that the electrons can move freely. On the other hand, if the top valence band is completely filled, its electrons can only be transferred to higher energy values, if they are lifted across a forbidden energy gap into another completely empty band, the so-called conduction band. This is only possible for a reasonable number of electrons, if the forbidden energy gap E_G is small. Therefore, one has then an insulating crystal for a large E_G and a semiconductor for a small one. Table 1.1 gives E_G for a selection of semiconductors.

The introduction of foreign atoms or irregularities into the crystal causes different allowed-energy levels to appear. This is of particular interest if they are situated in E_G, because these levels (if empty) can either receive electrons from the valence band or, if they are filled, deliver electrons to the conduction band with a much reduced energy requirement. This means, more holes or electrons are freely moveable and the conductivity of the material has been increased. However, the product of the electron and hole densities n and p remains independent of impurity concentration and is equal to the square of the electron density in an intrinsic semiconductor where $n_i = p_i$; i.e.

$$np = n_i^2$$

as can be seen from equations (1.37) and (1.38), as given below.

TABLE 1.1

Group	Element	E_G/eV	typical values $\mu_e(m^2/Vsec)$	$\mu_h(m^2/Vsec)$
IV	Diamond	5.3	0.18	0.12
	Silicon	1.1	0.14	0.048
	Germanium	0.72	0.39	0.19
	Grey tin	0.08	0.20	0.1
III-V	AlP	3		
	GaAs	1.34	0.075	0.002
	InSb	0.16	70 (at 77°K)	0.07
	AlAs	2.3		
	GaP	2.25		
	AlSb	1.52	0.040	0.020
	InP	1.27	0.60	0.016
	GaSb	0.7	0.50	0.085
	InAs	0.33	2.3	0.010
II-VI	CdS	2.45	0.02	5.10^{-4} ‖ C
	CdSe	1.74	0.06	$>1.10^{-4}$ ‖ C
	CdTe	1.45	0.10	$0.3 . 10^{-4}$
	ZnS	3.6	0.014	$0.6 . 10^{-4}$ ⊥C
	ZnSe	2.7	0.05	$0.6 . 10^{-4}$
	ZnTe	2.26	0.03	$0.6 . 10^{-4}$
IV-VI	PbS	0.37 ⎫	0.1	0.1
	PbSe	0.27 ⎭		
	PbTe	0.33	100 (at 4°K)	
Other Compounds	Bi_2Te_3	0.16	0.11	0.049
	ZnO	3.3	0.02	
	MgO	7.3		2.10^{-4}
	$C_6H_4:(CH_2):C_6H_2$	3.1	10^{-4}	10^{-4}
	$BaTiO_3$ $(Ba, Pb)TiO_3$ $(Ba, Sr)TiO_3$		change of resistivity by up to 6 orders of magnitude by changing the temperature by less than 50°C (see (2))	
	(Hg,Cd)Te (Hg,Mn)Te	From very small values up to 1.5		
	$Hg_{85}Mn_{15}Te$	0.05	25 at 80°K	0.05 at 77°K

Table 1.1, Continued

Group	Element	E_G/eV	typical values μ_e(m²/Vsec)	μ_h(m²/Vsec)
	GaSe ⎫ MoS₂ ⎬ MoSe₂ ⎭	see (1)		
	WSe₂	see (1)		
	p-type MnSb		0.02 (6)	
	SrTiO₃		0.3 at 4°K (6)	

The positions of the valence and conduction bands vary with crystallographic direction in the crystal. A complete description of the bands has therefore to be three dimensional. Unfortunately, it is not easy to compute the correct energy contours, nor is it easy to obtain them experimentally. However, most is known about Si and Ge, for which Fig. 1.7 (a and b) shows the energy contours along representative lines of the relevant Brillouin zone, as shown in Fig. 1.7c. In order to use the space of the first Brillouin zone also for the energy contours of the higher Brillouin zones, these are folded back into the first one, as demonstrated by Fig. 1.8. Therefore, one finds the energy contours of the top valence band and of the bottom conduction band in the same Brillouin zone. The semiconductors Ge and Si and many others crystallize with the so-called diamond structure (see Fig. 1.9) for which the Wigner-Seitz cell of the reciprocal lattice is given in Fig. 1.7c. It is sufficient for an understanding of most semiconductor properties, to simplify the energy contours to simple bands, where the energy minima and maxima form the lower and upper limits of the bands (see Fig. 1.10). This simplification means that one does not know any more, where the minima and maxima occur in the Brillouin zone.

Early computations of the energy contours did not consider spin orbit interactions between electrons. Figure 1.7 (a and b) shows how much spin orbit interactions cause the energy contours to change.

Calculations show that the electrons occupying states near the band edges behave like free electrons, except for a term which is inversely proportional to d^2E/dk^2. It is therefore justified to treat the electrons as if they had a different mass.

The external acceleration force $\mathbf{F}$ can be taken, in equivalence to classical dynamics, as

$$\hbar \frac{d\mathbf{k}}{dt} = \mathbf{F} \tag{1.26}$$

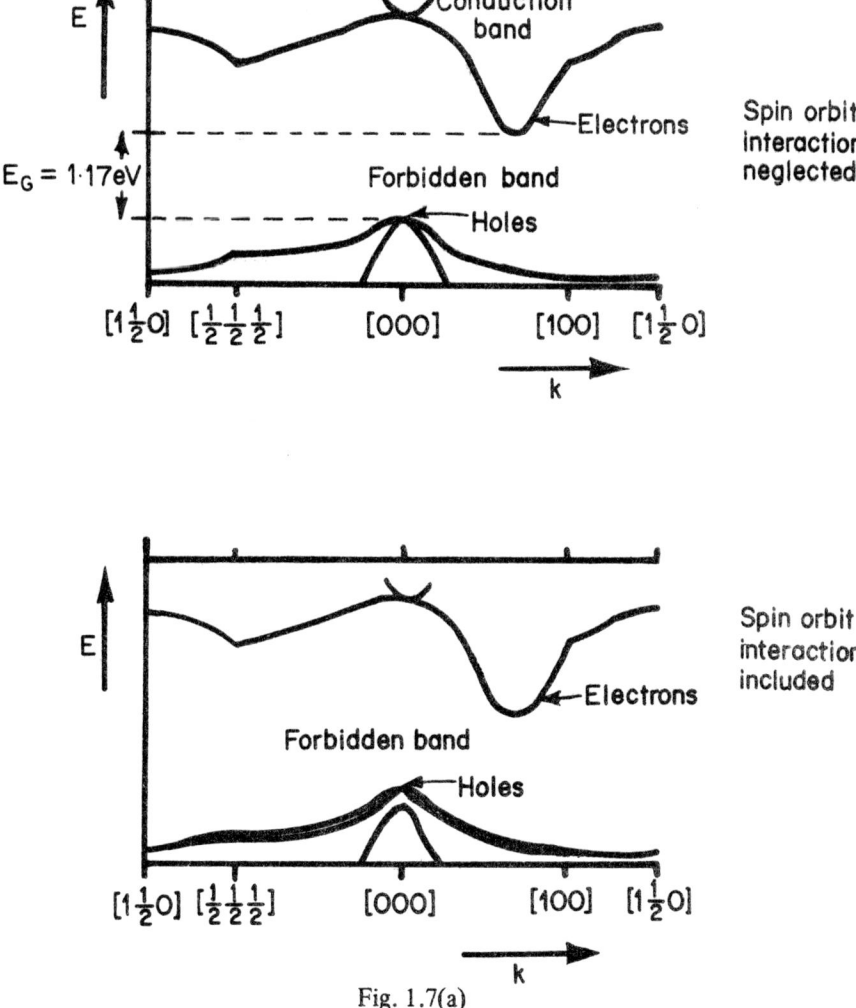

Fig. 1.7(a)

Fig. 1.7 Energy band structures at ~ 0°K: (a) for Si; and (b) for Ge; (c) reduced zone for Si and Ge having the shape of the first Brillouin zone of the diamond structure.

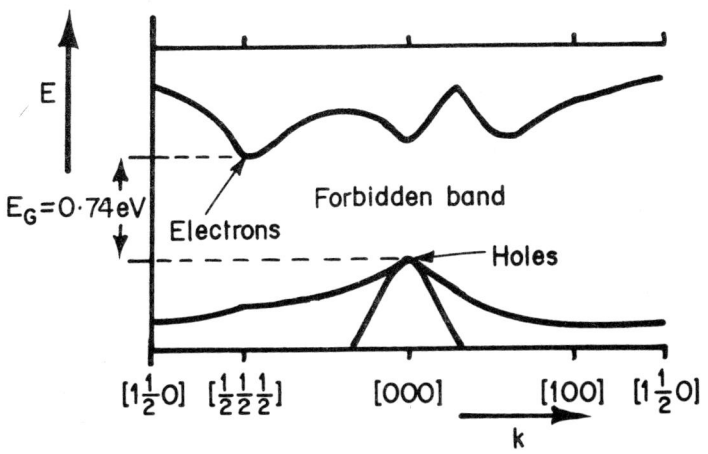

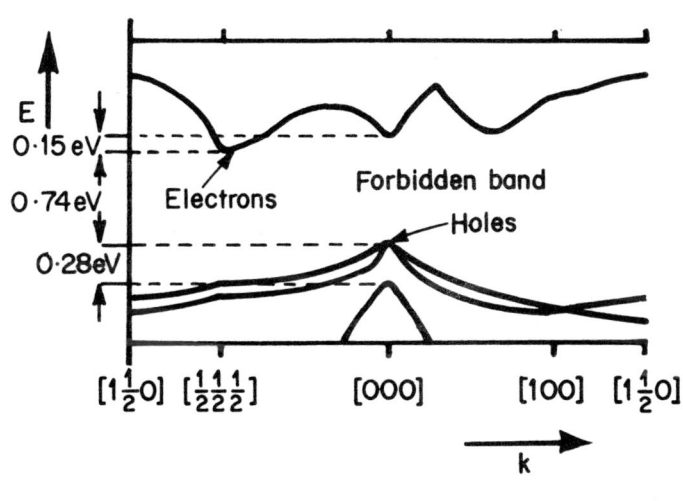

Fig. 1.7(b)

The applied electric field $\mathscr{E}$ is related to $\mathbf{k}$ by

$$\mathscr{E}e = \hbar \frac{d\mathbf{k}}{dt} = \mathbf{F} \tag{1.27}$$

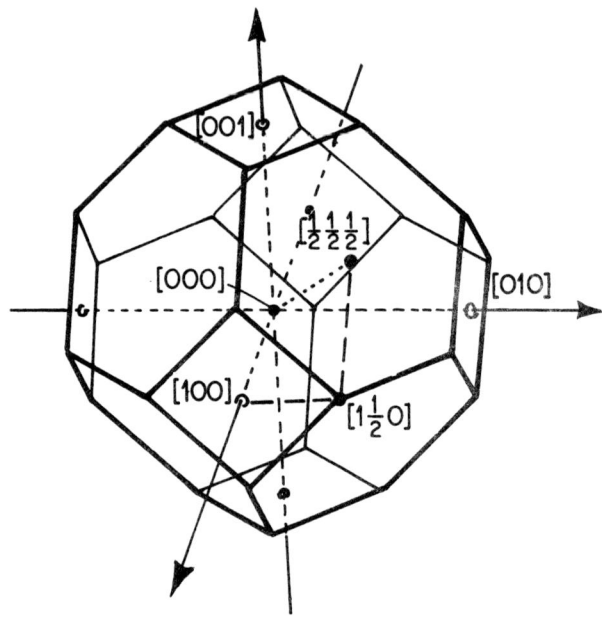

Fig. 1.7(c)

and the group velocity is given by

$$\mathbf{v}_k = \frac{1}{\hbar} \frac{\partial E(\mathbf{k})}{\partial \mathbf{k}} \tag{1.28}$$

i.e., the velocity of an electron in state $|k\rangle$ is the gradient of $E(\mathbf{k})$ in k-space. Differentiating equation (1.28) with respect to time gives the acceleration:

$$\frac{d\mathbf{v}_k}{dt} = \frac{d}{dt} \left(\frac{1}{\hbar} \frac{dE(\mathbf{k})}{\partial \mathbf{k}} \right)$$

which can be transformed by using equations (1.26) and (1.27):

$$\frac{d\mathbf{v}_k}{dt} = \frac{1}{\hbar} \frac{\partial^2 E(\mathbf{k})}{\partial \mathbf{k} \partial \mathbf{k}} . e \mathscr{E} \tag{1.29}$$

Comparing this with Newton's equation $m(\mathrm{d}v/\mathrm{d}t) = e\,\mathscr{E}$, we find the equivalent mass

$$\left[\frac{1}{\hbar^2}\frac{\partial^2 E(\mathbf{k})}{\partial\mathbf{k}\,\partial\mathbf{k}}\right]^{-1}$$

which is a tensor, whose elements are

$$\left\|\frac{1}{m}\right\| = \frac{1}{\hbar^2}\left\|\frac{\partial^2 E}{\partial k_i\,\partial k_j}\right\| \tag{1.30}$$

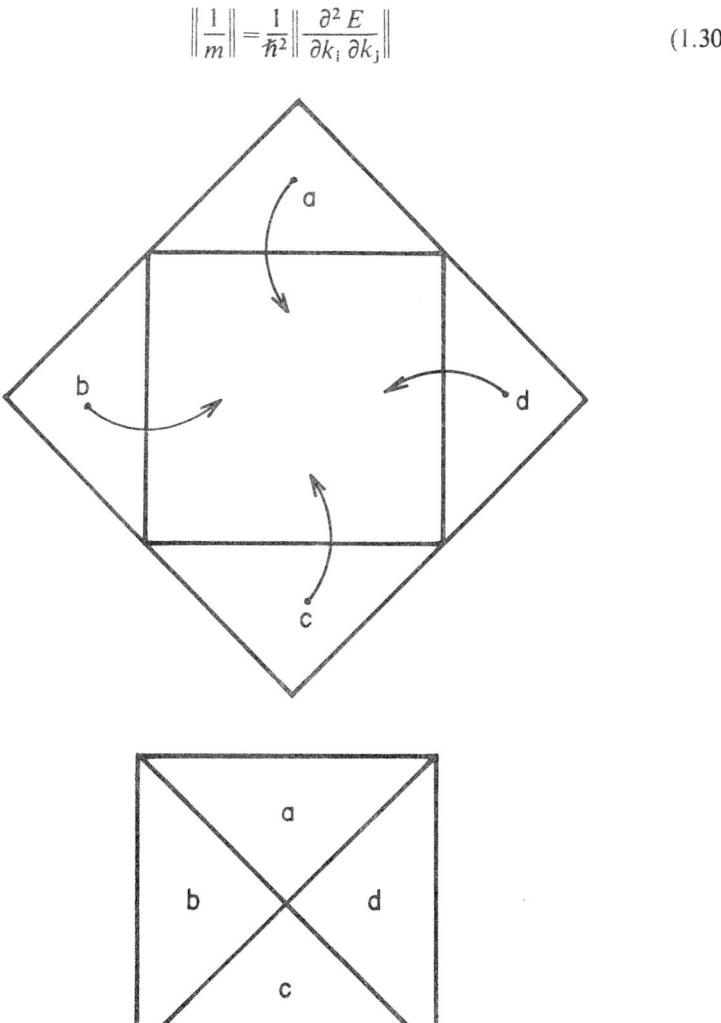

Fig. 1.8 Higher-order Brillouin zone folded back into lower-order zone, thus forming a reduced zone.

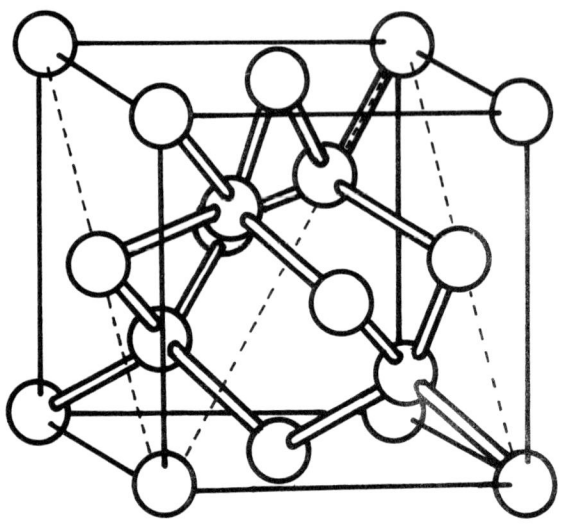

Fig. 1.9   Atomic arrangement in diamond-type crystals.

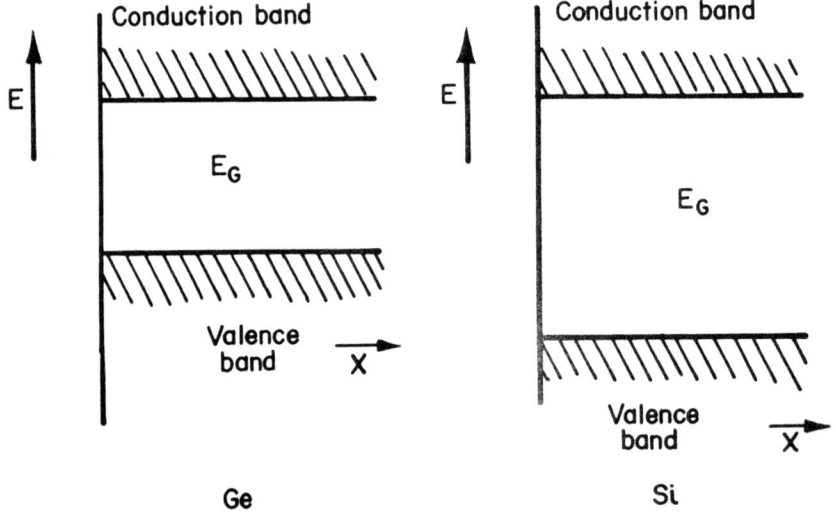

Fig. 1.10   Energy bands for Ge and Si.

By a suitable rotation of coordinate axes, this tensor can always be simplified:

$$\left\|\frac{1}{m}\right\| = \left\|\begin{matrix} 1/m_1 & 0 & 0 \\ 0 & 1/m_2 & 0 \\ 0 & 0 & 1/m_3 \end{matrix}\right\| = \frac{1}{\hbar^2} \left\|\begin{matrix} \dfrac{\partial^2 E}{\partial k_1{}^2} & 0 & 0 \\ 0 & \dfrac{\partial^2 E}{\partial k_2{}^2} & 0 \\ 0 & 0 & \dfrac{\partial^2 E}{\partial k_3{}^2} \end{matrix}\right\| \tag{1.31}$$

The mass tensor has been determined experimentally for a variety of semiconductors, as shown in Table 1.2.

TABLE 1.2 *Effective masses of electrons in conduction band*

	$m_3{}^*$	$m_1{}^* = m_2{}^*$
Ge	1.64 m	0.0819 m
Si	0.98 m	0.19 m

($m_3{}^*$ is the effective mass along the principal axes of the ellipsoids of minimum conduction band energy, $m_1{}^* = m_2{}^*$ is perpendicular to these principal axes; m is the free-space electronic mass).

For certain conditions it is even possible that m is negative. If the band edge is nearly parabolic, the mass does not depend on the energy and remains constant. In very narrow energy valleys, the lower energy states can be filled up entirely and conduction will take place only by electrons of higher energies. One obtains then a charge-carrier mass, which is dependent on carrier density. Very strong changes of mass occur for InSb where one can take this into account by a theory developed by Kane (3), whose results are shown in Fig. 1.11, together with those of some other authors (4, 5).

If the constant energy contour as a function of **k** is a sphere, one talks about spherical energy contours. It means that the mass tensor is reduced to a scalar for the relevant energy values. Often it is possible to find an approximate mass scalar by suitably averaging over the mass components. Then the effective mass is given by

$$m^* = \frac{\hbar^2}{\dfrac{d^2 E}{dk^2}} \tag{1.32}$$

The total density of electrons is given by the integral

$$n = \int_0^\infty f S \, dE \tag{1.33}$$

where f and S are given by equations (1.24) and (1.25), and where the lower boundary of integration is well below the energy levels for holes. The Fermi level E_0 can be obtained by taking

$$n = \int_0^{E_0} S \, dE \qquad (1.34)$$

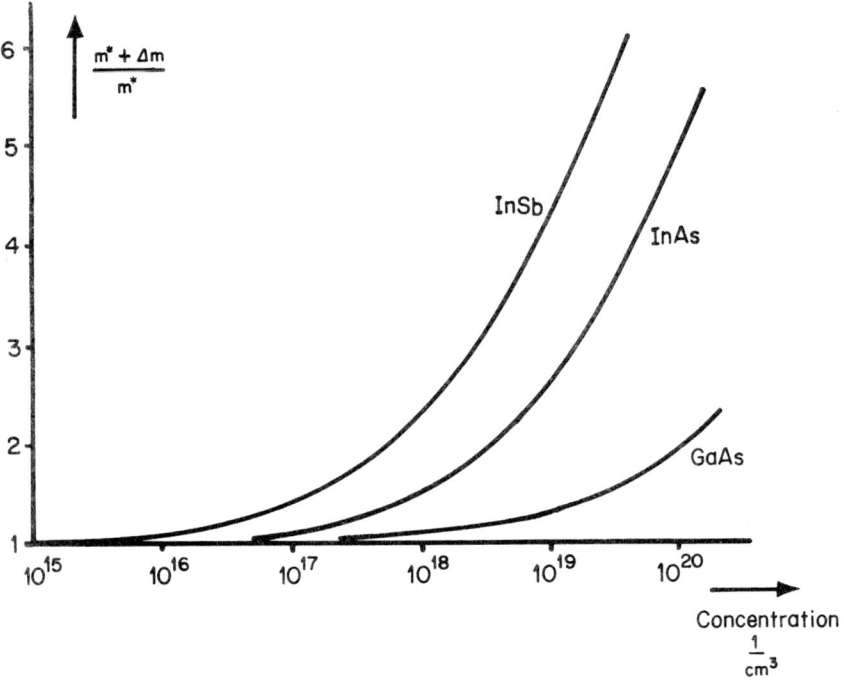

Fig. 1.11 Increase in effective electron mass as a function of carrier density.

In a semiconductor, we have E_G between the bottom level of the conduction band, E_c, and the top level of the valence band, E_v. Therefore, equations (1.33) and (1.34) can be transformed:

$$\int_0^{E_0} S \, dE = \int_0^{E_v} f S_v \, dE + \int_{E_c}^{\infty} f S_c \, dE \qquad (1.35)$$

where the subscripts v and c denote valence and conduction band respectively. Rewriting equation (1.35) gives

$$\int_0^{E_v} [1 - f] S_v \, dE = \int_{E_c}^{\infty} f S_c \, dE \tag{1.36}$$

which states that the number of electrons in the conduction band is equal to the number of holes produced by missing electrons in the valence band. In fact, one can treat the holes as positive charge carriers, which are freely mobile in a similar way as the conduction-band electrons. The hole mass is also given by the second derivative of the energy contour in k-space, in the same way as equations (1.30) and (1.31) for electrons, i.e., the mass of the holes is given by the hypothetical mass of the missing electrons.

If we rewrite $1 - f$ in equation (1.36) as follows:

$$1 - f = 1 - \frac{1}{\exp\left(\dfrac{E - E_0}{kT}\right) + 1} = \frac{1}{\exp\left(-\dfrac{E - E_0}{kT}\right) + 1} = \frac{1}{\exp\left(\dfrac{E_h + E_0}{kT}\right) + 1}$$

we see that the Fermi-Dirac statistics can be applied to holes by introducing a new energy coordinate E_h, which is taken from E_v downwards. For semiconductors we replace E by $E-E_c$ in equation (1.25) and obtain together with equation (1.33) and the approximation of $E_0 \ll E_c$ (which means, $\exp\left[(E_c - E_0)/kT\right] \gg 1$):

$$n = 2\left(\frac{2\pi m_e^* kT}{h^2}\right)^{3/2} \exp\left[-(E_c - E_0)/kT\right] \tag{1.37}$$
$$= N_c \exp\left[-(E_c - E_0)/kT\right]$$

(m_e^* = electronic effective mass) where N_c is called the 'effective density of states' in the conduction band. If we assume, $m^* = m$ and room temperature, $N_c \simeq 2.5 \times 10^{25} \ m^{-3}$.

Similarly, one can obtain an expression for the hole density

$$p = N_v \exp\left[-(E_0 - E_v)/kT\right] \tag{1.38}$$

where

$$N_v = 2\left(\frac{2\pi m_h^* kT}{h^2}\right)^{3/2}$$

(m_h^* = effective hole mass), the effective density of states in the valence band.

One has an 'intrinsic' semiconductor, if $n = p$; this yields

$$N_v/N_c = \exp\left[-(E_c + E_v - 2E_0)/kT\right]$$

which can be used for the solution of the Fermi energy, namely:

$$E_0 = \frac{E_c + E_v}{2} + \frac{3kT}{4} \ln \frac{m_h^*}{m_e^*} \tag{1.39}$$

If $m_e^* = m_h^*$, the Fermi level lies midway between E_v and E_c.

If impurity atoms are present in the structure, the semiconductor is 'extrinsic'. For example, Ge has four valence electrons forming four electron-pair bonds with the valence electrons of neighbouring atoms. If a pentavalent atom replaces a Si atom (P, As, Sb, etc.), only four of its electrons are required for the covalent bonding system of this crystal. The extra electron can be removed by a small thermal

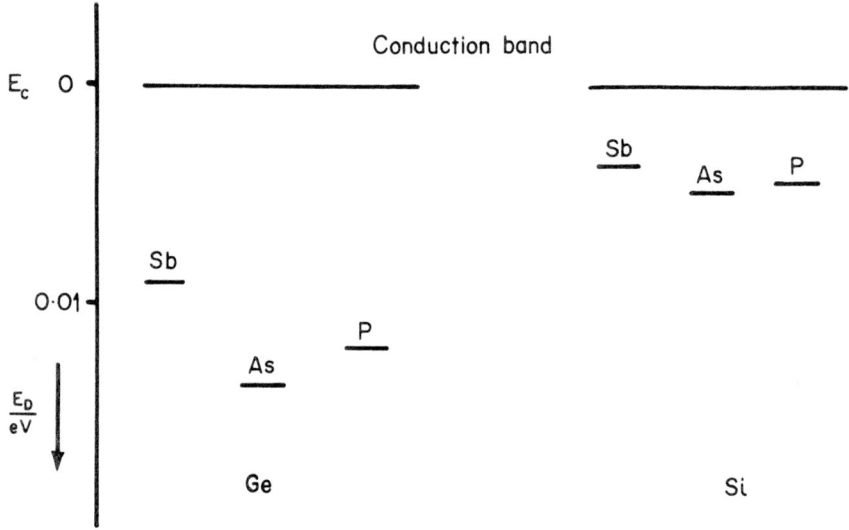

Fig. 1.12   Energy levels of some group V substitutional impurities.

energy, i.e. it is 'donated' to the conduction band. Therefore this type of atom is called 'donor' impurity. A semiconductor with a predominance of these impurities is n-type extrinsic. The energy level of the fifth electron, when attached to its atom, is the 'donor' level, which is somewhere situated below E_c. Figure 1.12 gives the distance of the various donor energy levels E_d from E_c for several semiconductors ($E_{DO} = E_c - E_d$).

On the other hand, if a trivalent atom (B, Al, Ga, In, etc.) substitutes for a silicon atom, one of the covalent bonds cannot be formed. It can be formed, if another valence electron from a nearby Si atom is accepted. These impurities are therefore called 'acceptors'. The loss of a valence electron by a Si atom is represented in the band model by the appearance of a hole in the valence band. This crystal is now called a p-type semiconductor.

Generally in any extrinsic semiconductor, 'majority' carriers are the predominant ones and the other types are called 'minority' carriers. The ionization energy E_A of various acceptors in some semiconductor materials is shown in Fig. 1.13.

Other types of impurities give different impurity levels, depending either on their structure of valence electrons or on the way they are incorporated in the semiconductor. These levels are often far removed from the band edges and are called 'deep' levels. Some impurities produce several discrete levels (see Fig. 1.14). Some types of crystal imperfections, e.g. the vacancy-interstitial pair of the so-called Frenkel effect, produce acceptor levels.

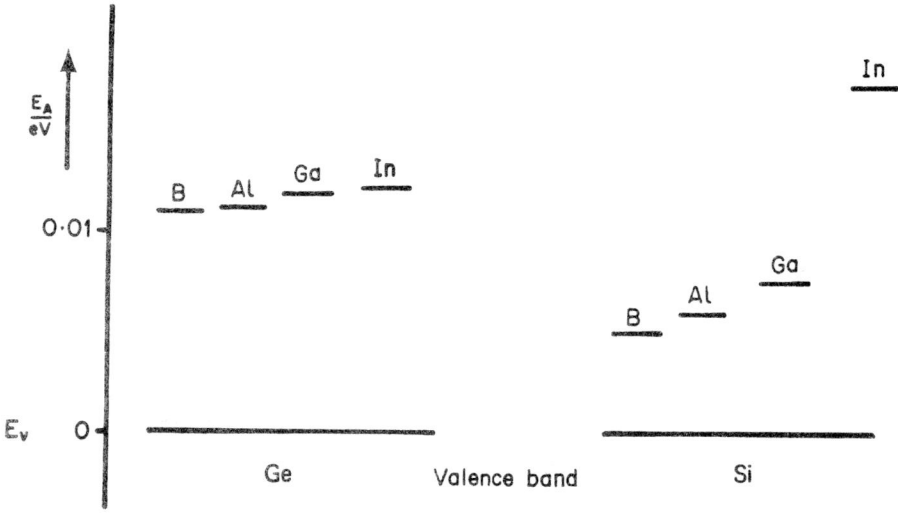

Fig. 1.13   Energy levels of some group III substitutional impurities.

It is difficult to compute the Fermi level E_0 for extrinsic semiconductors, which is required for the calculation of the mobile-carrier density, as given by equations (1.37 and 1.38). Charge neutrality must govern everywhere inside the crystal, which is fulfilled if

$$n + N_a^- = p + N_d^+ \tag{1.40}$$

where N_a^- and N_d^+ are the ionized acceptor and donor densities respectively. Inserting the Fermi-Dirac distribution function f in equation (1.40) yields

$$N_c f(E_c) + N_a f(E_a) = N_v[1 - f(E_v)] + N_d[1 - f(E_d)] \tag{1.41}$$

where N_a and N_d are the acceptor and donor concentrations respectively, and E_a and E_d are the energy values of the acceptor and donor levels. It is often convenient to take $E_v = 0$ as the reference point for all the four energy levels involved, so that

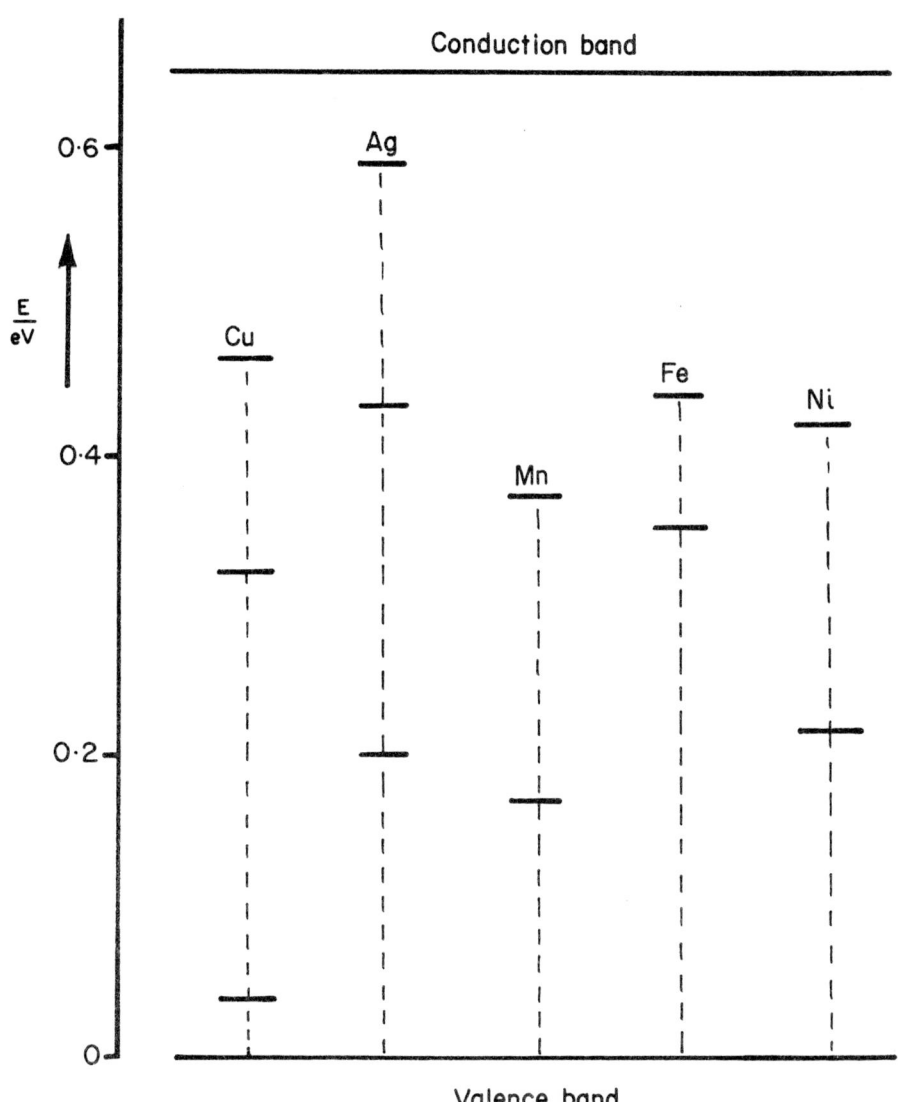

Fig. 1.14   Location of deep levels by substitutional impurities in Ge.

$E_c = E_G$, $E_a = E_A$, and $E_d = E_G - E_{DO}$. Equation (1.41) enables one to compute E_0.

The exact position of the Fermi level E_0 depends on the temperature; in fact, it shifts towards the centre of E_G for increasing T. However, E_G also narrows with growing temperature, owing to increased lattice vibrations.

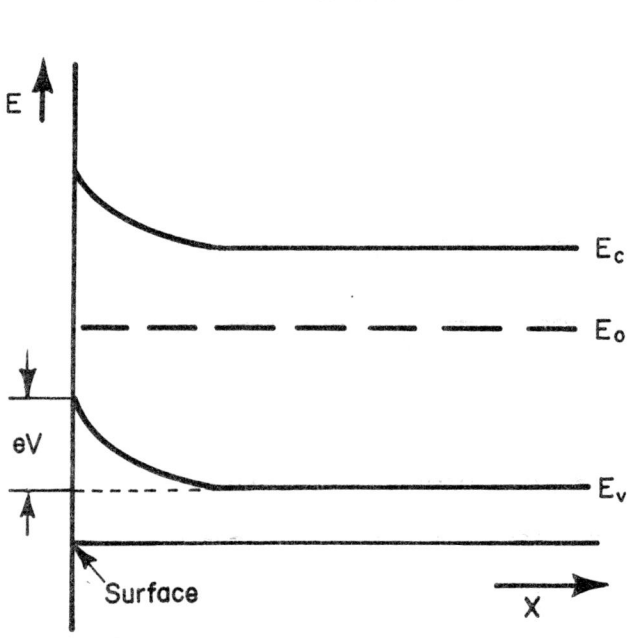

Fig. 1.15   Energy-level diagram for negative surface charge on n-type semiconductor.

Charge neutrality has also to be maintained near surfaces, where extra energy levels are available. These surface levels can be positioned inside the forbidden-energy gap E_G and act as donors or acceptors which can be charged. They are caused either by the abrupt termination of the crystal, or by foreign atoms and by an oxide layer on the crystal surface.

The presence of these immobile surface charges can drive any mobile carriers away, thus forming a depletion layer; they can attract mobile majority carriers, if they have an opposite sign, and cause an accumulation layer, or they attract only minority carriers producing an inversion layer.

The presence of these surface states will alter the relative position of the Fermi level E_0. This can be expressed in energy diagrams as shown in Fig. 1.15. The solution of Poisson's equation enables one to calculate the depth, down to which the surface charge will cause the conductivity to change considerably. As a rough estimate, this is about the same as the Debye length

$$L_D = \sqrt{\left(\frac{\epsilon kT}{(n+p)e^2}\right)}$$

The region of resistance change is usually termed 'space-charge layer'.

To enable a current to pass through the semiconductor crystal, the latter must be fitted with electrical contacts. A suitable contact material has to be found. This

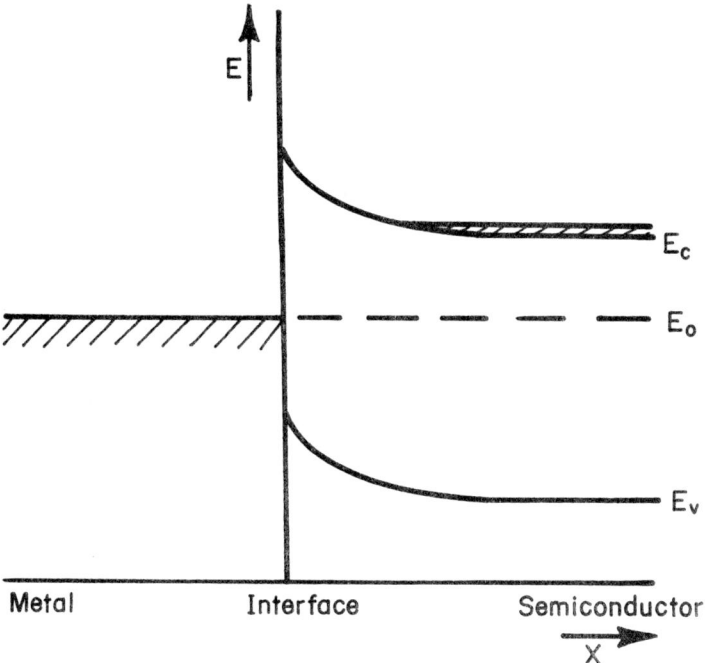

Fig. 1.16 Energy-level diagram of the junction between a metal and an n-type semiconductor, when the work function of the metal is larger than that of the semiconductor.

problem should be seen in the following context. When two types of crystal are brought together, electrons flow across the boundary until the Fermi level of both crystals lines up.

Before two crystals (e.g. a metal and a semiconductor) are brought together, the energy band model involves the workfunction E_W for each solid. This is the energy which an electron has to acquire in order to be able to leave the solid, taken from E_0. If E_W of the metal is larger than that of an n-type semiconductor, electrons flow from the semiconductor to the metal upon contact, until the negative charge on the metal reduces the flow and makes the Fermi level continuous, as shown in Fig. 1.16. This means, a space charge layer is produced in the semiconductor.

The same effect occurs, if the metallic workfunction is smaller than that of a p-type semiconductor. Here electrons flow into the semiconductor.

The space-charge layer means a potential barrier formed at the junction. As the current flow is easier in one direction, we have 'rectifying' contacts, which are usually undesirable. Ohmic contacts can be obtained if the metal is correctly chosen, such that the metallic work function is smaller than that of an n-type semiconductor and larger than that of a p-type one.

Often, non-ohmic contacts occur even with suitable metals. This is caused by a space-charge layer due to surface states. Therefore, it is important to remove as many surface states as possible before applying the metal contact.

1.4. Transport Theory

The fundamental relation in the theory of transport is the Boltzmann equation, which describes the effects of external fields, temperature gradients, impurity scattering, lattice waves, etc. on the charge carriers inside a semiconductor. It deals with the function f_t, the concentration of carriers, which is given by the effect of the following three phenomena.

(a) The change of the distribution owing to diffusion is given by:

$$\frac{\partial f_t}{\partial t}\bigg]_{diff.} = -\mathbf{v_k}\frac{\partial f_t}{\partial \mathbf{r}},\tag{1.42}$$

(b) the changes caused by external fields are

$$\frac{\partial f_t}{\partial t}\bigg]_{field} = -\frac{e}{\hbar}\left(\mathcal{E} + \mu_m \mathbf{v_k} \times \mathbf{H}\right)\frac{\partial f_t}{\partial \mathbf{k}}\tag{1.43}$$

and

(c) scattering can be expressed approximately as

$$\frac{\partial f_t}{\partial t}\bigg]_{scatt.} = -\frac{1}{\tau}g\tag{1.44}$$

where $\mathbf{v_k}$ is the velocity vector, $\mathcal{E}$ and $\mathbf{H}$ the electric and magnetic fields respectively, τ the so-called relaxation time, during which a disturbance of g decreases by the factor e^{-1}, and g is the small-signal deviation of f_t from equilibrium. The sum of all three effects must be zero, i.e.

$$\sum_n \frac{\partial f_t}{\partial t}\bigg]_n = 0\tag{1.45}$$

which is the Boltzmann equation. As we want to discuss here only steady-state conditions, we have neglected the temporal changes in f_t, i.e. $\partial f_t / \partial t = 0$.

We can write

$$f_t = f + g \tag{1.46}$$

where f is the equilibrium distribution function, if no external fields are present (see equation (1.24)). We consider that the term $\partial f_t / \partial r$ is only due to thermal changes and approximate that $\mathscr{E}(\partial g / \partial k) \simeq 0$ which means, a term of order $\mathscr{E}^2$ has been neglected as a deviation from Ohm's law. Then, for $H = 0$ and the temperature $T = $ constant, one obtains:

$$g = \left(-\frac{\partial f}{\partial E} \right) \tau \, (\mathbf{v_k} . \mathscr{E}) \, e \tag{1.47}$$

On the other hand, the current density is given by

$$\mathbf{J} = \int e \mathbf{v_k} f_t \, \mathbf{dk} \tag{1.48}$$

As no current flows if only the equilibrium function is involved, i.e. $\int e \mathbf{v_k} f \, dk = 0$, one can obtain with equations (1.47) and (1.48):

$$\mathbf{J} = \int e^2 \, \tau \mathbf{v_k} (\mathbf{v_k} . \mathscr{E}) \, \left(-\frac{\partial f}{\partial E} \right) \mathbf{dk} \tag{1.49}$$

As Ohm's law is given by

$$\mathbf{J} = \|\sigma\| \, \mathscr{E}$$

(σ = electrical conductivity), we see that the conductivity is here a tensor, with the elements, in dyadic notation:

$$\|\sigma\| = \|e^2 \, \tau \int \mathbf{v_k} . \mathbf{v_k} \left(-\frac{\partial f}{\partial E} \right) \mathbf{dk} \| \tag{1.50}$$

This is a similar case to that of the mass tensor of equation (1.30). Again, one can find a conductivity scalar by a suitable averaging process. Similarly, if the constant energy contour as a function of $\mathbf{k}$ is a circle, the conductivity tensor is reduced to a scalar.

It is possible to treat the question of conductivity more approximately by the kinetic theory. If an electric field is applied, the particles gain extra energy between collisions with impurities. This can be expressed by a drift velocity v_d, which is proportional to the applied electric field $\mathscr{E}$,

$$\mathbf{v_d} = \mu \, \mathscr{E} \tag{1.51}$$

where μ is the mobility of the carriers. This relation is the solution of the equation of motion, i.e.

$$m^*\left(\frac{dv_d}{dt} + \frac{1}{\tau}v_d\right) = e\,\mathscr{E} \tag{1.52}$$

where τ is the average time it takes a carrier to return to its previous drift velocity value $v_d(0)$ after a short disturbance, as given by the relation

$$v_d(t) = v_d(0)\ \exp(-t/\tau)$$

Equations (1.51) and (1.52) give

$$\mu = \frac{e\tau}{m^*} \tag{1.53}$$

The electric current density is given then by

$$J = nev_d = \frac{ne^2\,\tau}{m^*}\,\mathscr{E} \tag{1.54}$$

which gives the conductivity only as a scalar

$$\sigma = \frac{ne^2\,\tau}{m^*} \tag{1.55}$$

If both electrons and holes contribute to the conduction process, this relation has to be changed to

$$\sigma = ne\mu_e + pe\mu_h \tag{1.56}$$

where μ_e and μ_h are the electron and hole mobilities respectively.

The so-called 'Hall-effect' represents a convenient method for the measurement of majority carriers. It is observed when a magnetic field is applied at right angles to the current inside a crystal. The magnetic field H acts on the carriers moving with the drift velocity v_d by the force $\mu_m e \cdot v_d \times H$, which is perpendicular to v_d and H, and which deflects the carriers to the crystal surfaces. (μ_m is the permeability of the material.) There, an electrical charge is built up, which produces an additional electric field, the transverse Hall field $\mathscr{E}_H$. Under equilibrium, $e\mathscr{E}_H = ev_d B$, which leads to $\mathscr{E}_H = R_H J B$ with equation (1.54) where $B\ (=\mu_m H)$ is the magnetic induction and $R_H = 1/ne$ the Hall constant. The measurement of R_H can be performed by measuring the Hall voltage $V_H = \mathscr{E}_H \cdot w$ and the current density J. The sign of R_H indicates if holes or electrons are the majority carriers, and the amplitude gives the carrier density. Using equations (1.53) and (1.55) one finds the mobility, which can be obtained by a measurement of R_H : $\mu = R_H \cdot \sigma$. The mobility values thus obtained are called the 'Hall mobility'. The treatment presented here approximates that the carriers of one type all have the same velocity and collision time. In reality, this is incorrect, and an additional coefficient is involved, which depends on the type of scattering and energy surfaces.

If one considers both holes and electrons, i.e. the Hall effect in a nearly intrinsic material, one has to consider the total current formed by both types of carriers. The Hall coefficient is then, using the approximation described above:

$$R_H = \frac{\sigma_p|\mu_h| - \sigma_n|\mu_e|}{(\sigma_n + \sigma_p)^2}$$

which is generally smaller than the one for extrinsic semiconductors. Similarly, one can show that the resistivity ρ in J-direction is changed to ρ_H if a perpendicular magnetic field is applied to a nearly intrinsic semiconductor with two types of carriers of unequal mobility.

One often uses the 'transverse magneto-resistivity', M_t, which is defined by the relation

$$M_t = \frac{\rho_H - \rho}{\rho}$$

The same result is also given for the case of an extrinsic semiconductor where the carriers have different masses or relaxation times. In this case we have to replace the hole and electron conductivities and mobilities σ_p, σ_n, μ_h and μ_e by the corresponding conductivities and mobilities pertaining to each type of carrier denoted by subscript 1 and 2, i.e., σ_1, σ_2, μ_1 and μ_2. One defines a magneto-resistance mobility

$$\mu_M = \frac{\sqrt{M_t}}{B}$$

The terms R_H and M_t are called 'galvanomagnetic coefficients'.

One can also observe longitudinal magneto-resistance, when B is parallel to J.

For the scattering expression of equation (1.44) we introduced the relaxation time, which we have to discuss further.

One can distinguish between energy relaxation and momentum relaxation. The first term means that energy-changing collisions are involved, whereas the second expression relates to momentum-transfer collisions. The latter one is used in the relation for the mobility

$$\mu = \frac{e\tau_m}{m^*} \tag{1.57}$$

with τ_m the momentum relaxation time.

There are collisions which influence either τ_m or τ_e, or both relaxation times, together (τ_e = energy relaxation time).

At high crystal temperatures, collisions between charge carriers and thermally-excited phonons dominate, whereas collisions with impurities and irregularities are most important at low crystal temperatures. Phonon scattering can either occur by the so-called acoustical phonons, or by the optical ones. The latter are important at high carrier temperatures, which are given by the average carrier velocity fluctuations raised by a high applied electric field. Acoustic phonons are to be considered for low carrier temperatures. The interaction between carriers and acoustical phonons is performed by deformation potential coupling. In some semiconductors, which have piezoelectric properties (such as CdS, ZnO, and GaAs), this interaction can also take place via the piezoelectric coupling.

Many semiconductors have energy contours, which form valleys at various positions in momentum space. If the energy levels at the bottom of these valleys are near E_c, the lowest level of the conduction band, electrons can be scattered, so that they are either moved to another position in the same valley—which is called 'intravalley scattering'—or to a position in a neighbouring valley—this is termed 'intervalley scattering'.

When collisions occur with impurities, no energy is transferred, whereas acoustical and optical phonon collisions relax energy almost as efficiently as momentum. The relaxation time for ionized-impurity scattering is almost independent of the lattice temperature T_l and is related to the carrier temperature T_c by:

$$\tau_m \propto T_c^{3/2} \qquad (1.57a)$$

The ratio of energy and momentum relaxation for acoustical phonon scattering is given by the following relation if the applied voltage is not too large.

$$\frac{\tau_e}{\tau_m} \approx \frac{kT_l}{m^* v_s^2}$$

(v_s = sound velocity). This is independent of T_c and in general very large.

When the carrier temperature approaches the so-called Debye temperature, which is a material constant, optical phonon scattering becomes important, in particular in polar crystals, which are semiconductors with some of their binding forces given by ionic bonding. Ionic bonding is stronger, the larger the number difference of the valence electrons for the constituent elements, i.e. no ionicity for the group IV semiconductors and large ionicity for those formed by II-VI compounds.

Finally, intercarrier collisions are of importance for high carrier densities. They have no direct influence on τ_m or τ_e. However, they influence the velocity distribution, and have a secondary effect on τ_m and τ_e, which depend on the shape of the carrier distribution function. It is only possible to treat the distribution function as being a Maxwellian one, if the carrier density is large enough, so that intercarrier collisions are predominant.

Owing to the many collisions, the carriers experience a diffusive motion if a density gradient is present, in analogy to the motion of gas particles for a pressure gradient. This diffusion causes an electric current density J_D to flow:

$$J_D = -eD\frac{dn}{dx}. \tag{1.58}$$

D is the diffusion constant, which is given by the Einstein relation

$$D = \frac{kT}{e}\mu \tag{1.59}$$

A density gradient can be set up for example, if light photons can shift electrons across the forbidden gap, i.e. if $h.f > E_G$ (f being the photon frequency). This process is called carrier 'generation'. When electrons fall back into a hole of the valence band, one talks about 'recombination' transitions. They can either be direct transitions across the whole forbidden gap, or they can occur by a transition to a localized level within E_G, where the electrons will stay for a limited time before they 'recombine' with a hole. The temporal change of carrier density is equal to the generation rate g_c minus the rate of carrier recombination, i.e.

$$\frac{dn}{dt} = g_c - \frac{n}{\tau_1} \tag{1.60}$$

where τ_1 is the carrier life-time.

Recombination is often aided by 'recombination centres' which lie near the centre of the forbidden energy gap. They capture an electron and subsequently a hole. They are effective, because the dissipated energy is smaller for each individual transition than for a direct recombination, and because the momentum of the carriers can be transmitted more easily to the crystal structure. The probability of capturing a carrier is expressed by the 'capture cross-section'. If the capture cross-section is larger for one type of carrier than for the other, one talks about a trap.

The surface of a crystal contains many imperfections. This causes a large concentration of surface levels, which produce an increased amount of recombination transitions on the surface. One often speaks, therefore, about 'bulk life-time' τ_b and 'surface life-time' τ_s. Together they give the observed life-time τ_1 where approximately,

$$\frac{1}{\tau_1} = \frac{1}{\tau_b} + \frac{1}{\tau_s} \tag{1.61}$$

Surface recombination becomes most effective if the carriers can diffuse to the surfaces. L, the average distance a carrier diffuses before recombination, is given by

$$L = \sqrt{(D.\tau_1)} \tag{1.62}$$

and is often called the diffusion length.

1.5. Semiconducting Materials

Group IV. Carbon, silicon, germanium and grey tin belong to this group (see Table 1); they crystallize with the diamond structure (Figure 1.9). The bonding is covalent.

The most important semiconductors are silicon and germanium. Whereas it is difficult to produce intrinsic Si (the highest resistivities obtained so far are of the order of 100 Ωcm) intrinsic Ge is readily available, because its E_G is smaller.

By introducing suitable impurities into the crystal (which is termed 'doping') one can obtain a desired conductivity, as long as it is higher than the intrinsic conductivity (Figs. 1.12 and 1.13).

III-V Compounds. These compounds are formed by elements of the third and and fifth columns of the periodic table. They crystallize also in the diamond struc-ture, where each group III atom is tetrahedrally surrounded by group V atoms and vice versa. The bonding is covalent together with a small amount of ionic bonding (5 to 10%), owing to the different sizes of the atoms of the two different groups (electronegativity of group V elements). The aluminium compounds are chemically unstable, as they disintegrate with time.

GaAs is a semiconductor with very widespread technical applications. One of its main disadvantages is that the thermal conductivity is lower than in other semi-conductors such as silicon. This makes it often less acceptable for high-power appli-cations if another suitable semiconductor can replace it.

The mobility of InSb is limited by phonon scattering at room temperature and can be increased to values of 100 (m^2/Vsec) if the crystal is cooled below 80°K, so that usually impurity scattering predominates. The valley of the conduction band is very narrow, which causes a small effective electron mass and a low density of states. The latter effect means, together with the small value of E_G, that the crystal will quickly be degenerate at higher carrier densities. This means, all the lower states of the conduction band are completely filled. In fact, as the Fermi level E_0 is always very near to the bottom of the conduction band, intrinsic InSb is only on the verge of being degenerate at temperatures as low as 80°K. Owing to its small electron-hole mass ratio, intrinsic InSb is strongly *n*-type.

On account of the identical crystal structures and similar interatomic distances, a whole range of isomorphous systems can be produced, in which the semiconductor properties can be made to vary in proportion to their relative composition. Some examples are In(As, Sb), In(P, As), Ga(P, As), (In, Al)Sb, (Ga, Al)Sb, Ga(As, Sb), (Ga, In)As. By producing a crystal with a concentration gradient of, say Ga and In in (Ga, In)As, one can obtain a single crystal with E_G = 0.33 eV at one end and E_G = 1.34 eV at the other end.

II-VI Compounds. Again, the average valence electrons are four for the semicon-ductors formed by atoms of the second and sixth column of the periodic table, and covalent bonding is present. However, the increased electronegativity of the group VI elements introduces considerable ionicity, which causes E_G to widen.

CdS and CdSe crystallize normally in a wurtzite structure (hexagonal) (see Fig.

1.17), however they can also form the diamond structure, and sometimes both types occur in one single crystal. CdTe can be found only as a diamond type crystal (see Fig. 1.9). Intrinsic CdS is an insulator in darkness with resistivities of about 10^8 Ωcm. Illumination with light of a suitably high frequency $f(hf > E_G)$ decreases the resistivity considerably. CdSe behaves similarly. CdTe can be doped with In and

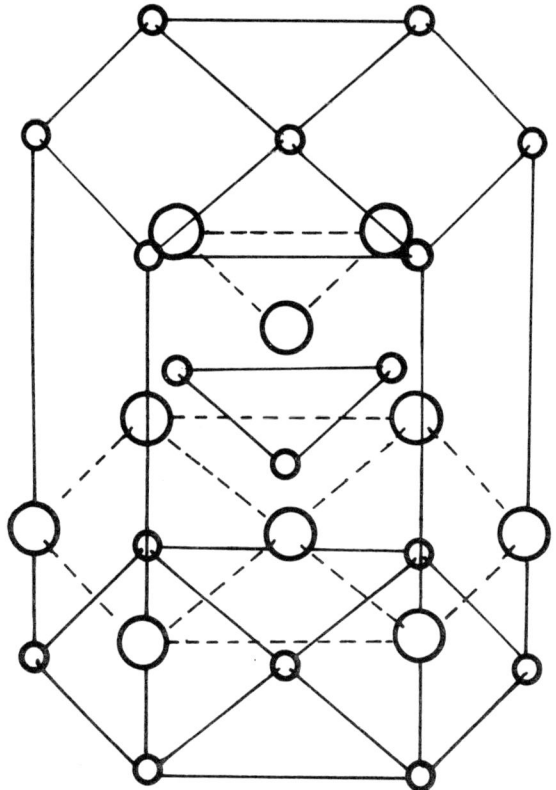

Fig. 1.17   Wurtzite structure (hexagonal), which is adopted by CdS and CdSe.

Ga (donors) or Ag and Sb (acceptors). The donor levels are usually very shallow, i.e. they are only 0.003 eV away from E_c. The acceptor levels lie much deeper.

I-VII Compounds. The alkaline halides are usually insulators, with $E_G > 5$ eV.

IV-VI Compounds. The crystal structure is that of sodium chloride (Fig. 1.18). As the bonding is partly ionic, the mobility varies with $T_c^{-5/2}$ instead of with $T_c^{-3/2}$, as could be expected from equation (1.57a), ($T_c \approx T_l$ for small applied fields). The mobility is predominantly given by phonon scattering even with large impurity concentrations. The most important materials are here PbS, PbSe and PbTe. In addition to impurity doping, excess lead will also produce p-type material and lead deficiency leads to n-type crystals.

V-VI Compounds. Bi_2Te_3, Sb_2Te_3 and Bi_2Se_3 belong to this group. They have a low thermal conductivity owing to their complicated hexagonal crystal structure. (The thermal conductivity of Bi_2Te_3 is only 2 W/°Cm).

Metal-Oxides. As ionic bonds do not involve any electron sharing by neighbouring atoms, intrinsic electronic conductivity in ionic compounds is usually negligibly small. The bonding of oxides is predominantly ionic. Extrinsic crystals can be obtained by excess oxygen or excess metal. Some very common oxide semiconductors are ZnO and MgO. The first one crystallizes in the wurtzite structure (see Fig. 1.17), whereas MgO has a halite structure (see Fig. 1.18).

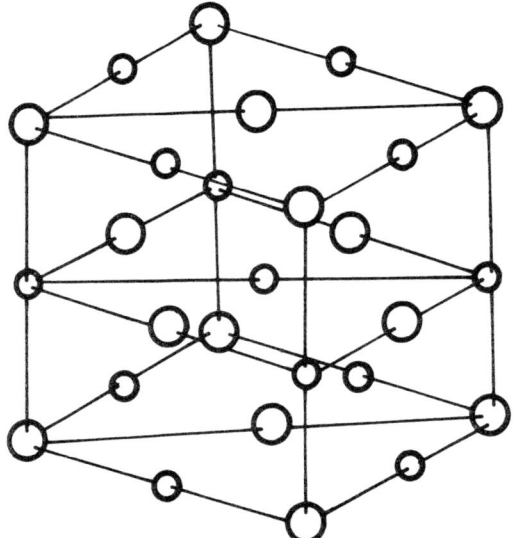

Fig. 1.18 Halite structure.

Of interest are the transition-metal oxides, as the energy bands important for semi-conductivity are related to inner electronic levels of the atoms instead of to the outermost valence-electron levels. These oxides have partly metallic properties (e.g. Ti_2O_3) partly insulating if intrinsic and semiconducting if extrinsic (e.g. TiO_2). Often, bands are very narrow (e.g. TiO_2, V_2O_3); or electrons are localized on individual ions and can only move across the crystal by a so-called hopping process (Fe_2O_3, NiO). This produces very small mobilities. On the other hand, holes can be produced by thermal excitation in NiO in a slightly deeper-lying band. As this band is very wide, the corresponding hole mobility is large (about 0.01 to 0.1 m^2/V sec). This means that NiO is then a *p*-type semiconductor. A similar effect takes place in Fe_2O_3, when excess oxygen is present which produces a *p*-type crystal. Oxygen deficiency in Fe_2O_3, on the other hand, can enable thermal transitions of electrons to an empty wide band, which is situated here slightly above the localized levels of the hopping process. This produces *n*-type semiconduction in Fe_2O_3.

Finally, the oxides with the formula AB_2O_4 should be mentioned briefly. They crystallize in a so-called spinel structure and exhibit interesting electrical and magnetic properties. So far, they have only been utilized for their magnetic properties. However, it could be possible that in future, advantage will be taken of their often simultaneous electrical and magnetic properties.

Organic Semiconductors. One does not yet know very much about these materials, but it is to be expected that they will show a multiplicity of various semiconducting properties owing to the wide range of possible crystal structures. Anthracene ($C_6H_4 : (CH_2): C_6H_2$) has been studied extensively, showing hole and electron mobilities of about 10^{-4} m^2/Vsec. The conductivity is strongly anisotropic, due to the anisotropy of the crystal structure.

Some polymers exhibit semiconductivity and, although a hopping mechanism may take place, the conduction mechanism is not yet at all clear. The mobilities are always very small ($\leqslant 10^{-7}$ m^2/Vsec) and the materials are p-type.

TABLE 1.3 Ternary-Compound Semiconductors

$AgSbS_2$	$CuInSe_2$	$AgCrTe_2$
$AgSbSe_2$	$CuInTe_2$	$CuFeSe_2$
$AgSbTe_2$	$AgGaSe_2$	$AgFeTe_2$
$AgBiS_2$	$AgGaTe_2$	$CuAsSe_2$
$AgBiSe_2$	$AgInSe_2$	$CuSbS_2$
$CuGaSe_2$	$AgInTe_2$	$CuBiS_2$
$CuGaTe_2$	$AgCrSe_2$	$AgAsSe_2$

A very extensive review of the knowledge available in early 1966 about organic semiconductors has been published by Gutmann and Lyons (9). One can, in fact, find there also a detailed discussion of the importance of organic-semiconductor plasmas and their instabilities (pp. 621 *et seq.*), and a speculative chapter (pp. 632 *et seq.*), deals with possible devices based on organic semiconducting materials.

On the whole, one can say that the conductivity ranges are about the same for organic and inorganic semiconductors (namely, from about 10^3 to 10^{-14} Ωcm), whereas the carrier concentrations and the mobilities are usually smaller for the first type. The most important rôle of these materials has been in the field of research into biological phenomena associated with charge or energy transfer over long distances, in particular in connection with the transmission of nerve impulses. One can, however, envisage that they will soon find also numerous technical applications (10).

3d-Transition Metal Compounds. These metal compounds often show semiconducting and ferromagnetic properties simultaneously, and could possibly lead to interesting future applications. Several ternary chromium compounds such as $CuCr_2Se_4$ and $FeCr_2S_4$, and the compound MnSb, show high Hall mobilities of 25, 10 and 200 cm^2/Vsec respectively at 300°K, and $SrTiO_3$ has a mobility of

3000 cm^2/Vsec at $4°K$ (6). Similarly, the antiferromagnetic semiconductor MnTe has been found to have mobilities up to 250 cm^2/Vsec at $77°$ K (7).

Other Compounds. A whole range of further semiconductors has been made, such as GeTe. A list of representative ternary compounds, which consist of three kinds of atoms, is given in Table 1.3.

REFERENCES

1. Fivaz, R., Mooser, E., 'Mobility of Charge Carriers in Semiconducting Layer Structures', *Phys. Rev.,* **163**, pp. 743-755, 1967.
2. Andrich, E., Härdtl, K. H., 'Investigations on Ba Ti O_3 Semiconductors', *Phil. Techn. Rev.,* **26**, pp. 119-127, 1965.
3. Kane, E. O., 'Band Structure of Indium Antimonide', *J. Phys. Chem. Solids,* **1**, p. 249, 1957.
4. Sosnowski, L., 'Transport Phenomena in Semiconductors with Non-Standard Energy Bands', *Proc. 7th Internat. Conf. on Phys. Semicond., Paris, 1964,* Academic Press, New York and London, Dunod, Paris, p. 341, 1964.
5. Okada, K., Oku, T., 'Measurements of Electron Concentration in GaAs Using Plasma Reflection Edge', *Jap. J. Appl. Phys.,* **6**, p. 276, 1967.
6. Lehmann, H. W., 'Semiconducting Properties of Ferromagnetic $CdCr_2 Se_4$', *Phys. Rev.,* **163**, pp. 488-496, 1967.
7. Zanmarchi, G., 'Optical Measurements on the Antiferromagnetic Semiconductor MnTe', *J. Phys. Chem. Solids,* **28**, pp. 2123-2130, 1967.
8. Schiff, L. I., *Quantum Mechanics,* McGraw-Hill, Internat. Student Ed., Tokyo, 1955, pp. 19, etc.
9. Gutmann, F., Lyons, L. E., *Organic Semiconductors,* J. Wiley, New York, 1967.
10. Eley, D. D., 'Organic Semiconductors', *Science Journal,* **3**, No. 12, pp. 61-65, 1967.

ADDITIONAL REFERENCES *(For Further Study)*

1. Adler, R. B., Smith, A. C., Longini, R. L., *Introduction to Semiconductor Physics,* J. Wiley, New York, 1964.
2. Aven, M., Prener, J. S., (editors), *Physics and Chemistry of II-VI Compounds,* North-Holland Publ. Co., Amsterdam, 1967.
3. Azaroff, L. V., Brophy, J. J., *Electronic Processes in Materials,* International Student Edition, McGraw-Hill, 1963; Kogakusha Co., Tokyo.
4. Dirac, P. A. M., *Quantum Mechanics,* Oxford University Press, Oxford, 1947.
5. Goudet, G., Meuleau, C., *Semiconductors,* McDonald and Evans, London, 1967.
6. Green, H. S., *Matrix Mechanics,* Nordhoff Ltd., Groningen, The Netherlands, 1965.
7. Hilsum, C., Rose-Innes, A. C., *Semiconducting III-V Compounds,* Pergamon Press, London, 1961.

8. Jonscher, A. K., *Principles of Semiconductor Device Operation,* Bell & Sons Ltd., London, 1960.
9. Kittel, C., *Introduction to Solid-State Physics,* J. Wiley, New York, (2nd Edition), 1956.
9a. Kittel, C., *Quantum Theory of Solids,* J. Wiley, New York, 1963.
10. Lindmayer, J., Wrigley, C. Y., *Fundamentals of Semiconductor Devices,* v. Nostrand Co., Inc., Canada, 1965.
11. Madelung, O., *Physics of III-V Compounds,* J. Wiley, New York, 1964.
12. Many, A., Goldstein, Y., Grover, N. B., *Semiconductor Surfaces,* North-Holland, Publ. Co., Amsterdam, 1965.
13. McKelvey, J. P., *Solid-State and Semiconductor Physics,* Harper & Row, New York; Weatherhill, Tokyo, 1966.
14. Moss, T.,S., *Optical Properties of Semiconductors,* Academic Press Inc., New York, 1959.
15. Nergaard, L. S., Glicksman, M., (editors), *Microwave Solid-State Engineering,* v. Nostrand, New York, 1964.
16. Nussbaum, A., *Semiconductor Device Physics,* Prentice-Hall, London, 1962.
17. Shive, J. N., *The Properties, Physics and Design of Semiconductor Devices,* v. Nostrand, Princeton, New Jersey, 1959.
18. Smith, R. A., *Semiconductors,* Cambridge University Press, London, 1959.
19. Spenke, E., *Electronic Semiconductors,* McGraw-Hill, New York, 1958.
20. Wang, S., *Solid-State Electronics,* McGraw-Hill, New York, 1966.
21. Ziman, J. M., *Principles of the Theory of Solids,* Cambridge University Press, London, 1965.

CHAPTER II

The Relevant Equations for Plasma Instabilities

The aim of this book is to study instabilities occurring in the bulk of semiconductor crystals. As these instabilities always involve one or both types of electric-charge carriers, forming a semiconductor plasma, the phenomena are very similar to those of gaseous plasmas consisting of electrons and ions. Therefore basically the same equations are relevant for the problems of gaseous plasmas and those of solid-state plasmas.

In this chapter we discuss the equations of importance for the treatment of the instabilities described in Chapter IV.

2.1 Maxwell's equations

Disturbances of a plasma can propagate by electromagnetic waves, whose basic quantities are the electric and magnetic field vectors $\mathscr{E}$ and $\mathbf{H}$. The waves are generated by the current density $\mathbf{J}$, which involves also the space-charge density ρ_c. All these terms are related to each other in space (position vector $\mathbf{r}$) and time t by the Maxwell's equations:

$$\nabla \times \mathscr{E} = -\mu_m \frac{\partial \mathbf{H}}{\partial t} \tag{2.1}$$

$$\nabla \times \mathbf{H} = \epsilon \frac{\partial \mathscr{E}}{\partial t} + \mathbf{J} \tag{2.2}$$

$$\nabla \cdot \mathscr{E} = \frac{\rho_c}{\epsilon} \tag{2.3}$$

$$\nabla \cdot \mathbf{B} = 0 \tag{2.4}$$

where ϵ and μ_m are the permittivity and permeability of the medium respectively.

It is often useful to eliminate either the electric field or the magnetic one. As an example we eliminate $\mathbf{H}$. By multiplying equation (2.1) vectorially with ∇, we obtain, by using equation (2.2), Maxwell's wave equation:

$$\nabla \times (\nabla \times \mathscr{E}) = -\mu_m \frac{\partial}{\partial t}(\nabla \times \mathbf{H}) = -\mu_m \epsilon \frac{\partial^2 \mathscr{E}}{\partial t^2} - \mu_m \frac{\partial \mathbf{J}}{\partial t} \tag{2.5}$$

One can rewrite this relation as follows

$$\mathbf{J} = -\|M\| \mathscr{E} \tag{2.6}$$

where $\|M\|$ is a tensor. Together with Ohm's law

$$\mathbf{J} = \|\sigma\|\mathscr{E} \tag{2.7}$$

one finds the eigenvalue equation

$$(\|\sigma\| + \|M\|).\ \mathscr{E} = 0 \tag{2.8}$$

This equation has non-trivial solutions, if the determinant of this homogeneous system of equations disappears. This means, one has a general dispersion relation.

$$D(\omega, \beta) = 0 \tag{2.9}$$

Assuming a field variation of the form exp $j(\omega t - kr)$ we can rewrite equation (2.2):

$$\nabla \times \mathbf{H} = \mathbf{J} + j\omega\epsilon\,\mathscr{E} \tag{2.10}$$

The total current density $\mathbf{J}_t$ is given by the right-hand side of this equation, which can be written together with equation (2.7):

$$\mathbf{J}_t = \mathbf{J} + j\omega\epsilon\,\mathscr{E} = j\omega\epsilon\left[\|1\| + \frac{\|\sigma\|}{j\omega\epsilon}\right]\mathscr{E} \tag{2.11}$$

where $\|1\|$ is the unity matrix. It is then possible to introduce a so-called dielectric tensor:

$$\|\epsilon\| = \|1\| + \frac{\|\sigma\|}{j\omega\epsilon} = \begin{Vmatrix} \epsilon_{xx} & \epsilon_{xy} & \epsilon_{xz} \\ \epsilon_{yx} & \epsilon_{yy} & \epsilon_{yz} \\ \epsilon_{zx} & \epsilon_{zy} & \epsilon_{zz} \end{Vmatrix} \tag{2.12}$$

which enables one to rewrite equation (2.5):

$$\mathbf{k} \times (\mathbf{k} \times \mathscr{E}) = \|\epsilon\|\frac{\omega^2}{c^2}\mathscr{E} \tag{2.13}$$

$(c = 1/\sqrt{(\mu_m \epsilon)}$ is the velocity of light).

By a suitable transformation of coordinates, one can always arrange that the wave travels in z-direction, without any loss of generality, i.e. $\mathbf{k} = (0, 0, k_z)$. Then:

$$n_r^2(\mathscr{E}_x \mathbf{x} + \mathscr{E}_y \mathbf{y}) = \|\epsilon\|\,\mathscr{E} \tag{2.14}$$

(x and y are unit vectors in x and y direction respectively, and $n_r = \sqrt{(k_z^2 c^2/\omega^2)}$ is the index of refraction), or:

$$\begin{Vmatrix} \epsilon_{xx} - n_r^2 & \epsilon_{xy} & \epsilon_{xz} \\ \epsilon_{yz} & \epsilon_{yy} - n_r^2 & \epsilon_{yz} \\ \epsilon_{zx} & \epsilon_{zy} & \epsilon_{zz} \end{Vmatrix} \mathscr{E} = 0 \qquad (2.15)$$

This implies the vanishing of the determinant, which yields the dispersion relation of equation (2.9) in a different form:

$$\begin{vmatrix} \epsilon_{xx} - n_r^2 & \epsilon_{xy} & \epsilon_{xz} \\ \epsilon_{yx} & \epsilon_{yy} - n_r^2 & \epsilon_{yz} \\ \epsilon_{zx} & \epsilon_{zy} & \epsilon_{zz} \end{vmatrix} = 0 \qquad (2.16)$$

Let us assume as an example that ϵ, σ and c are isotropic and that the charge carriers are approximately stationary if no externally-applied field $\mathscr{E}$ is acting on them (which is called the cold-plasma approximation). Then one obtains a scalar for $\| \epsilon \|$, namely

$$\left| \|\epsilon\| \right| = 1 - \frac{\omega_p^2}{\omega^2}$$

where

$$\omega_p = \sqrt{\left(\frac{ne^2}{m^* \epsilon} \right)}$$

is the plasma frequency, the natural resonant frequency of the plasma. This gives two possible solutions of the dispersion equation, namely (a) for transverse electromagnetic waves:

$$k^2 c^2 = \omega^2 \left| \|\epsilon\| \right|$$

$$\mathbf{k} \cdot \mathscr{E} = 0$$

and (b) for longitudinal plasma oscillations at ω_p:

$$\left| \|\epsilon\| \right| = 0$$

$$\mathbf{k} \times \mathscr{E} = 0$$

Let us finally discuss the case of $J = 0$ and $\rho_c = 0$. With the relation $\nabla \times \nabla \times \mathscr{E} = \nabla(\nabla \cdot \mathscr{E}) - \nabla^2 \mathscr{E}$ and equation (2.3), one finds

$$\nabla^2 \mathscr{E} - \mu_m \epsilon \frac{\partial^2 \mathscr{E}}{\partial t^2} = 0 \qquad (2.17)$$

We consider, by way of an example, a polarized plane wave travelling in z-direction with only the x-component of $\mathscr{E}$ present, i.e. $\mathscr{E}_x \neq 0$. One finds the equation

$$\frac{\partial^2 \mathscr{E}_x}{\partial z^2} - \mu_m \epsilon \frac{\partial^2 \mathscr{E}_x}{\partial t^2} = 0 \qquad (2.18)$$

Two solutions have the form

$$\mathscr{E}_x = F\left(z \mp \frac{t}{\sqrt{(\mu_m \epsilon)}}\right)$$

where the $-$ sign refers to a wave propagating in the $+z$ direction and the $+$ sign denotes one travelling in the opposite direction. We assume again the fields to vary with $\exp j(\omega t - kz)$, where ω is the angular frequency and k the propagation constant, which can be expressed as

$$k = \alpha + j\beta$$

α is the attenuation constant and β the phase constant. Inserting these exponential functions into equation (2.18) yields

$$\beta = \omega\sqrt{(\mu_m \epsilon)} \qquad (2.19)$$

for $\alpha = 0$.

There are two different types of velocities involved. The phase velocity v_{ph} gives the speed of points of constant phase on a wave, and can be obtained by taking

$$v_{ph} = \frac{\omega}{\beta} \qquad (2.20)$$

On the other hand, when signals are transmitted via electromagnetic waves, this can only be achieved by the transmission of a wave change (of amplitude, frequency or phase). This signal velocity is called the group velocity v_g and is given by the relation

$$v_g = \frac{d\omega}{d\beta} \qquad (2.21)$$

A convenient way of describing the propagation characteristics of a transmission system is to use the ω-β diagrams. If v_{ph} varies with ω, the system is called dispersive. One classifies the transmission media as follows: (a) no dispersion, $v_{ph} = $ const., e.g. wave through free space; (b) normal dispersion, $(\partial v_{ph}/\partial \omega) < 0$, e.g. wave guides and (c) anomalous dispersion, $(\partial v_{ph}/\partial \omega) > 0$, e.g. resonance phenomena and backward-wave structures.

The electromagnetic properties of the plasma are determined through the source terms $\mathbf{J}$ and ρ_c in Maxwell's equations. These, in turn, are determined by the microscopic motions of the particles under the action of internal and external forces. The response to the acting forces is given by a set of kinetic equations, which are derived from Boltzmann's equation.

2.2 Boltzmann's equation

In the first chapter we introduced the Boltzmann equation [see equation (1.45)] in order to derive the conductivity tensor $\|\sigma\|$ for semiconductors. We have given there the basic relation, which is described by Boltzmann's equation. Let us quote this equation now again under a slightly different form by including the term which relates to the time dependence of the distribution function f_t:

$$\frac{\partial f_t}{\partial t} + \mathbf{v}\nabla_r f_t + \dot{\mathbf{p}}_e\nabla_p f_t = \left(\frac{\partial f_t}{\partial t}\right)_{\text{collisions}} \tag{2.22}$$

where

$$\nabla_r = \left(\frac{\partial}{\partial x}, \frac{\partial}{\partial y}, \frac{\partial}{\partial z}\right)$$

and

$$\nabla_p = \left(\frac{\partial}{\partial p_x}, \frac{\partial}{\partial p_y}, \frac{\partial}{\partial p_z}\right)$$

In semiconductors, one will have to include the effect of generation–recombination, so that the right-hand side of equation (2.22) has to be enlarged by the term $(\partial f/\partial t)_{\text{g+r}}$. The distribution function $f_t(\mathbf{r},\mathbf{p}_e,t)$ is defined in such a manner that at time t the quantity

$$f_t dp_x dp_y dp_z dx dy dx \equiv f_t d^3 p_e d^3 r$$

is the weighted probability of finding a particle with a momentum lying within $dp_x . dp_y . dp_z$ at p_x, p_y and p_z and with a position in the volume element $dx . dy . dz$ at x, y and z. f_t is normalized by the relation

$$n = \int f_t d^3 v \tag{2.23}$$

where n is the local density of particles at time t, and $v = p_e/m^*$ is the velocity.

A traditional convention is that collective effects, owing to many-particle interactions and external fields, are considered by the left-hand side of equation (2.22), whereas the short-range, binary-type of collisions are treated by its right-hand term.

The electric field $\mathcal{E}$ can be composed of any outside field and any field arising from the distribution of particles and determined by Poisson's equation. This treatment is possible when the average potential energy of an electron is small compared with the average kinetic energy. This is fulfilled if

$$L_D \geqslant \frac{e^2}{\epsilon k T_e}$$

with T_c the carrier temperature and with L_D, the Debye length. For most cases of semiconductor plasmas with their high carrier densities this condition is fulfilled.

Current density **J** and charge density ρ_c are given by the following relations:

$$J = e \int v f_t d^3 v \qquad (2.24)$$

(notice that this expression, which will be employed in the following, is different from equation (1.48)), and

$$\rho_c = e \int f_t d^3 v \qquad (2.25)$$

If different species of charge carriers are available such as electrons and holes, two different distribution functions will be given and the corresponding current densities and charges will have to be added up.

The transport equation (2.22) can also be derived by considering another distribution function, namely Liouville's function $F_l(r_1, r_2, \ldots r_N, v_1, v_2, \ldots v_N; t)$ which gives the probability of finding particle 1 at r_1 with velocity v_1, while all the other particles are at their positions r_i with their velocity v_i. The one-particle distribution function f_t may be obtained by integrating F_l over all but the individual particle in question, i.e.

$$f_t(x_1, v_1, t) = \int F_l \, d^3 r_2 \ldots d^3 r_N \, d^3 v_2 \ldots d^3 v_N$$

Liouville's equation is given by

$$\frac{\partial F_l}{\partial t} + (F_l, H) = 0 \qquad (2.26)$$

where (F_l, H) is the Poisson bracket of F_l with the Hamiltonian H, i.e.

$$(F_l, H) = \sum_{i=1}^{N} v_i \frac{\partial F_l}{\partial r_i} + a_i \frac{\partial F_l}{\partial v_i}$$

with a_i being the acceleration experienced by the ith particle.

In order to obtain equation (2.22), one has to integrate equation (2.26) over all but one of the coordinates.

Usually collisions introduce wave damping. For certain conditions, waves can also be strongly damped by an interparticle process, which does not involve any collisions directly. This phenomenon is called Landau damping.

For its study (1) one has to use Laplace's transformation in order to solve the collisionless Boltzmann equation, which is often also referred to as the Vlasov equation. It is difficult to give any physical meaning to the quantities which arise in this computation, however there are important advantages in this technique.

Let us assume that $\mathbf{v_k} \times \mathbf{H} = 0$ in equation (2.22) [or equation (1.43)], and that $\mathscr{E}$ is pointing in the z-direction. Then we can integrate equation (2.22) over v_x and v_y. For the small-signal field quantity $\mathscr{E}_1$ ($\mathscr{E} = \mathscr{E}_0 + \mathscr{E}_1$), we introduce a Fourier transformation in space and a Laplace transformation in time, i.e.:

$$\mathscr{E}(\omega, k) = \int_0^\infty dt \int_{-\infty}^{+\infty} \frac{dz}{\sqrt{(2\pi)}} \exp\left[-j(kz - \omega t)\right] \mathscr{E}_1(z, t) \qquad (2.27)$$

The inverse transformation is

$$\mathscr{E}_1(z, t) = \int_{-\infty + j\sigma}^{\infty + j\sigma} \frac{d\omega}{2\pi} \int_{-\infty}^{+\infty} \frac{dk}{\sqrt{2\pi}} \exp\left[j(kz - \omega t)\right] \mathscr{E}(\omega, k) \qquad (2.28)$$

where the integral is carried out in the ω plane above the singularities of $\mathscr{E}(\omega, k)$. One can actually carry out the integration along a line which is far above any singularity, such that $\text{Im}(\omega) > |\gamma|$ where $\mathscr{E}_1(z, t) < |M e^{\gamma t}|$ for some value of M and γ. However, it is easier to evaluate the integral along a different line, which is possible if no singularities of $\mathscr{E}(\omega, k)$ are contained in the area described by the line. Landau therefore proposed to carry out the inverse transformation along the contour in Fig. 2.1. This does not enclose the singularity denoted by a cross or a branch cut. The contribution from the horizontal legs of this contour evanesce as $\exp(\text{Im } \omega t)$ and can be made small by pushing the contour lower and letting t become large. The integral is then given by the integrals round the branch cuts and by the sum of the residues of $\exp(-j\omega t)\mathscr{E}(\omega, k)$. Let us neglect here the branch cuts and consider only isolated singularities. The most important contribution comes from the uppermost pole in the ω-plane. Then the solution is given by:

$$\lim_{t \to \infty} \mathscr{E}_1(k, t) \approx \exp(-j\omega_m t)[(\omega - \omega_m)\mathscr{E}(\omega, k)]_{\omega - \omega_m} \qquad (2.29)$$

with ω_m the uppermost pole of $\mathscr{E}(\omega, k)$.

For the solution of equation (2.29), one requires the relation of equation (2.27). This has to be obtained by using the Boltzmann equation with

$$\left.\frac{\partial f}{\partial t}\right]_{\text{coll.}} \equiv 0$$

and one of Maxwell's equations. If the wavelength of the frequency of $\mathscr{E}_1$ is larger than L_D, the Debye length, one can approximate the problem by a quasi-static treatment, i.e. only equation (2.3) is required, which is Poisson's equation.

One approximates

$$f_t = f + g \tag{2.30}$$

as used in equation (1.46) and performs similar integrations with these distribution functions as for equations (2.27) and (2.28), i.e. one uses the Laplace transformation in time and the Fourier transformation in x. The transformed functions are

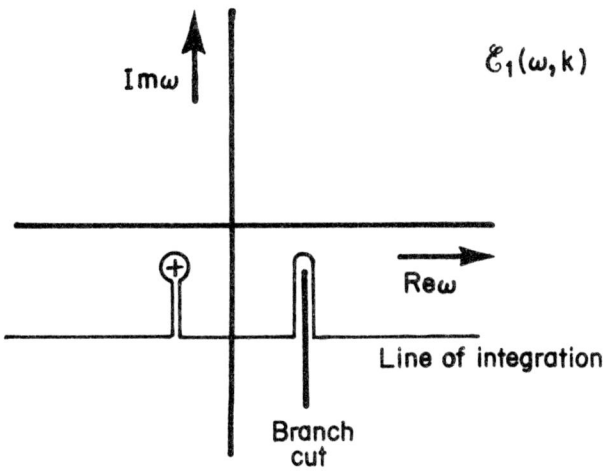

Fig. 2.1   Landau's contour for the inverse Laplace transformation (+ is a singular point in $\mathscr{E}_1$; l is a branch cut).

then used to obtain the transformed collisionless Boltzmann equation where the initial disturbance $g_j(v, z) = g(v, z, t = 0)$ has been introduced by the term $g_j(v, k)$. Using Poisson's equations (2.3) and (2.25), one obtains finally

$$\mathscr{E}(\omega, k) = \frac{\dfrac{e}{\epsilon k} \displaystyle\int_{-\infty}^{+\infty} \dfrac{g_j(v, k)}{\omega - kv}\, dv}{1 + \dfrac{e^2}{km\epsilon} \displaystyle\int_{-\infty}^{+\infty} \dfrac{\partial f(v)/\partial v}{\omega - kv}\, dv} \tag{2.31}$$

which describes the transformed field correctly as long as Im $\omega > 0$. Landau used an analytic continuation, in order to make this also valid for Im $\omega < 0$.

Landau found the following: If f is the Maxwell distribution and if the initial distribution $g_j(z, v)$ fulfils the condition that its Fourier transform $g_j(k, v)$ is an entire function of the complex variable v, then $\lim_{t \to \infty} \mathscr{E}_1(k, t) = 0$. This means the electric field is damped. This phenomenon has been subsequently called 'Landau damping'. If the above conditions for f and g_j are not fulfilled, oscillations may be undamped.

An alternative method for the solution of Vlasov's equation was used by van Kampen. The steady-state solution to the Boltzmann equation for longitudinal oscillations is

$$g = \frac{e\epsilon\mathscr{E}_1}{jm} \frac{1}{j(\omega - kv)} \frac{\partial f}{\partial v}$$

which shows a singularity at $v = \omega/k$, making this expression meaningless, except if one introduces the δ-function of Dirac (5), i.e.

$$g = \frac{e\epsilon\mathscr{E}_1}{jm} \frac{\partial f}{\partial v} \left[P \frac{1}{\omega - kv} + \lambda\delta\left(\frac{\omega}{k} - v\right) \right]$$

Here we have used the principle value (P) notation. The principle value of an integral through an isolated singular point is the average of the two integrals which pass just above and just below the point. In the above expression the singular point is $v = \omega/k$.

Van Kampen showed that an arbitrary initial disturbance excites a band of modes such that the gross perturbation decays in the same way as in Landau's analysis.

Since then, many papers have been published on the controversy of the physical significance of Landau damping (see for example (3)).

The same type of calculation, which reveals Landau damping, shows an instability for a different zero-order distribution function f. Let us consider a stable function f which is slowly distorted into an unstable one. Then, the roots of the denominator of equation (2.31) start first in the lower half of the complex plane of Fig. 2.1, showing attenuation, and move upwards. When they pass the real axis, the attenuation is changed into an instability. Each new root in the upper half plane corresponds to a new unstable mode.

One can explain these phenomena in the following way: If the phase velocity of a disturbance field is faster than the majority of charge carriers, then energy is transferred from the disturbance to the carriers, which are heated up, and we have attenuation. If, on the other hand, the majority of carriers is travelling slightly faster than the wave, the disturbance will grow. The phenomena are therefore the same as in a Travelling Wave Tube, where the electrons have to travel faster than the phase velocity of a wave in order to obtain amplification.

The question of Landau damping has been considered by Pines and Schrieffer (4), when they computed two-stream instabilities in semiconductor plasmas. They neglected collisions, which is difficult to justify for semiconductors, however they argue, that they consider the question of growing waves in the following way: An oscillation will only be unstable, if the wave grows between collisions to such an extent that $\omega_i \tau > 1$, where τ is the time between collisions.

The Boltzmann equation describes the same relation as Ohm's law, equation (2.7). Therefore, it can also lead to a dispersion relation by employing Maxwell's equations (2.1) to (2.4). Again, one can either use the full set of Maxwell's relations or one approximates by a quasi-static treatment, which considers only Poisson's equation. One is able to derive a similar relation to that given generally by equations (2.9) and (2.16).

Of interest is the Landau dispersion relation, which can be obtained from equation (2.31) for longitudinal plasma oscillations. Setting the denominator equal to zero, we obtain:

$$1 + \frac{e^2}{km\epsilon} \int\limits_{-\infty}^{+\infty} \frac{\partial f(v)}{\partial v} \frac{dv}{\omega - kv} = 0 \qquad (2.32a)$$

which is valid for $\mathrm{Im}\,\omega > 0$.

We use Landau's analytic continuation in order to obtain the dispersion relation for $\mathrm{Im}\,\omega < 0$, and find by employing the principle value (P) notation again:

$$1 + \frac{e^2}{km\epsilon} P \int\limits_{-\infty}^{+\infty} \frac{f'(v)\,dv}{\omega - kv} - \frac{j\pi e^2}{k|k|m\epsilon} f'\left(\frac{\omega}{k}\right) = 0 \qquad (2.32b)$$

where f' has to be an entire function. The solution of this dispersion equation again gives ω_i, which is positive for the case of carrier velocities larger than wave velocities, giving wave growth, and which is negative for the reverse situation, showing attenuation.

2.3 Kinetic Energy Approach

The Boltzmann equation (2.22) is a fundamental relation from which the other relevant transport equations can be derived, as reviewed by Jonscher (6).

Let us multiply equation (2.22) by a function $\phi(\mathbf{r}, \mathbf{p}, t)$ and integrate throughout velocity space. With equation (2.23) to (2.25), we obtain then:

$$\frac{\partial}{\partial t}(n\bar{\bar{\phi}}) - n\frac{\overline{\overline{\partial\phi}}}{\partial t} + \mathbf{V}_r.(n\bar{\bar{\phi}}\mathbf{v}) - n\overline{\mathbf{v}.\mathbf{V}_r\,\phi} - n\overline{\dot{\mathbf{p}}_e.\mathbf{V}_p\phi} = (\Delta n\bar{\bar{\phi}})_c + (\Delta n\bar{\bar{\phi}})_{g+r} \quad (2.33)$$

where the terms on the right-hand side are the abbreviated symbols for collision and generation-recombination and where a double bar denotes an average value, defined in the way shown in the example below:

$$\bar{\bar{\phi}} = \frac{1}{n}\int \phi f d^3\mathbf{v} \quad (2.34)$$

The velocity vector can be split into the average drift component $\mathbf{v}_d$ and the remaining random velocity $\mathbf{v}_1$ (which is often termed 'Peculiar Velocity'), such that

$$\mathbf{v} = \mathbf{v}_d + \mathbf{v}_1, \quad \bar{\bar{\mathbf{v}}} = \mathbf{v}_d, \quad \bar{\bar{\mathbf{v}}}_1 = 0 \quad (2.35)$$

First we set $\phi = 1$ and obtain the continuity equation:

$$\frac{\partial n}{\partial t} + \mathbf{V}_r.(n\mathbf{v}_d) = g_c - r \quad (2.36)$$

where we have taken account of the fact that $(\Delta n\bar{\bar{\phi}})_c$ can usually be zero here and that $(\Delta n\bar{\bar{\phi}})_{g+r}$ is conveniently approximated by the difference $g_c - r$ of the two corresponding constants g_c and r.

Taking $\phi = m^*\mathbf{v}$, with $\mathbf{v}$ and m^* independent of t and $\mathbf{r}$, one finds the momentum transport equation:

$$\frac{\partial}{\partial t}(n\mathbf{v}_d) + \frac{1}{m^*}\mathbf{V}_r.(m^*\,n\overline{\overline{\mathbf{v}_1\,\mathbf{v}_1}}) + \mathbf{V}_r.(n\mathbf{v}_d\,\mathbf{v}_d) - n\dot{\mathbf{p}}_e = (\Delta n\bar{\bar{\phi}})_c + (\Delta n\bar{\bar{\phi}})_{g+r} \quad (2.37)$$

where $m^*n\,\overline{\overline{\mathbf{v}_1\mathbf{v}_1}}$ is the pressure tensor. Finally, with $\phi = \frac{1}{2}m^*\mathbf{v}^2$, one has

$$\bar{\bar{\phi}} = \tfrac{1}{2}m^*\overline{\overline{v_1}}^2 + \tfrac{1}{2}mv_d^2,$$

where

$$\tfrac{1}{2}m^*\overline{\overline{v_1}}^2 = \tfrac{3}{2}kT_c \quad (2.38)$$

gives the temperature of the carriers in terms of the mean square of the random velocity. This yields the energy transport equation:

$$\frac{\partial}{\partial t}(\tfrac{3}{2}nkT_c + \tfrac{1}{2}m^* v_d^2 n) + \nabla_r . \mathbf{Q} + \nabla_r . (m^* n\overline{\mathbf{v}_1 \mathbf{v}_1}) . \mathbf{v}_d$$

$$+ \nabla_r . \{(\tfrac{3}{2}nkT_c + \tfrac{1}{2}m^* nv_d^2)\mathbf{v}_d\} - n\dot{\mathbf{p}}_e m^* . \mathbf{v}_d$$

$$= \tfrac{1}{2}m^*[(\Delta nv^2)_c + (\Delta nv^2)_{g+r}] \tag{2.39}$$

where $\mathbf{Q}$ is the heat flow vector.

$$(\mathbf{Q} = \tfrac{1}{2}m^* \overline{nv_1^2 \mathbf{v}_1})$$

Equation (2.39) is most commonly used for the analysis of plasma instabilities and can often be found in a slightly different form, namely:

$$\frac{\partial \mathbf{v}_d}{\partial t} + \frac{1}{n} \operatorname{grad}(v_1^2 n) + \mathbf{v}_d \operatorname{grad} \mathbf{v}_d$$

$$+ \frac{e}{m}(\mathscr{E} + \mathbf{v}_d \times \mu_m \mathbf{H}) = \frac{\mathbf{v}_d}{\tau} \tag{2.40}$$

where the corresponding terms are here in the same positions in both equations.

Equation (2.40) has been used for many analyses together with Maxwell's or Poisson's equation. These treatments give correct results except for two phenomena which are not considered by the energy transport equation, namely: (a) the problem of Landau damping, and (b) the effect of different shapes of the velocity distribution. The thermal velocities are in fact only taken as an average by which the carrier temperature is defined in accordance with equation (2.38).

On the other hand, equation (2.40) considers the effects of diffusion, collisions and recombination–generation by introducing some suitable approximation term. If one wants to discuss any instability, one will actually have to choose between equation (2.7), (2.22) or (2.40), depending on how important various effects are for the instability to be considered. For example, the magnetic-field-free longi-tudinal two-stream instability of Pines and Schrieffer (4) can only be treated properly by Boltzmann's equation, as Landau damping is certainly very strong, and has to be overcome by the instability proper. However, the treatment will then be too difficult and other approximations have to be introduced which are not easy to justify. Pines and Schrieffer have not considered collisions in an appropriate way. Therefore, Köchner (7) used the hydrodynamic approach of equation (2.40) in order to compute two-stream instabilities in InSb. Both treatments are therefore complementary, as long as the total Boltzmann equation has not yet been solved for this problem.

2.4 Other Relevant Relations

It is useful to discuss the remaining most common relations often employed for the study of plasma instabilities in semiconductors.

As shown in the previous section, the continuity equation (2.36) can be obtained from the Boltzmann equation. It can be expressed most generally in words as the spatial current change plus the ionization and injection current change being equal to the time change and recombination change of charge, i.e.

$$\text{div } \mathbf{J} - g_c = \frac{-\partial \rho_c}{\partial t} - \frac{n}{\tau_1} \qquad (2.41)$$

where τ_1 is the carrier life-time, and where the current density $\mathbf{J}$ is given by the well-known relation $\mathbf{J} = \rho_c . \mathbf{v_d} = ne\, \mathbf{v_d}$. For different types of carriers, the equation has to be enlarged correspondingly. For example, instabilities based on the transferred electron effect (see Chapter IV) require (taking now only a one-dimensional approach):

$$J = ev_d(n_L + n_u) \qquad (2.42)$$

where n_L and n_u are the lower and upper-valley electrons respectively. The avalanche instabilities need an expression for g_c, namely

$$g_c = \alpha_n |v_e| \, n + \beta_h |v_h| p \qquad (2.43)$$

with α_n and β_h the ionization rates of electrons and holes respectively and v_e and v_h the electron and hole drift velocities. For many applications, one or the other term of equation (2.41) can be neglected.

It is important to know also the full equation for the current density:

$$\mathbf{J_e} = en\mathbf{v_d} - e.\text{grad}\,(nD) \qquad (2.44)$$

with D the diffusion constant [see equation (1.59)].

Often, it is important to take into account the total current density $\mathbf{J_t}$ of a device, which is given by

$$\mathbf{J_t} = \mathbf{J_e} + \frac{\partial \mathbf{D_d}}{\partial t} \qquad (2.45)$$

where $\mathbf{D_d}$ is the electric displacement.

The current conservation means that Kirchhoff's equation has to be satisfied, i.e.

$$\text{div } \mathbf{J_t} = 0 \qquad (2.45a)$$

for a closed system.

In piezoelectric materials, one has the two piezoelectric equations:

$$\mathscr{T} = c_e \mathscr{S} - e_p \mathscr{E} \tag{2.45b}$$

and

$$D_d = e_p \mathscr{S} + \epsilon \mathscr{E} \tag{2.45c}$$

where c_e is the elastic constant for constant $\mathscr{E}$, e_p is the piezoelectric constant, $\mathscr{T}$ is the stress and $\mathscr{S}$ is the strain. The strain is related to the lattice displacement u by

$$\mathscr{S} = \frac{\partial u}{\partial z} \tag{2.45d}$$

and Newton's second law states

$$\rho_m \frac{\partial^2 u}{\partial t^2} = \frac{\partial \mathscr{T}}{\partial z} \tag{2.45e}$$

with ρ_m the mass density.

A basic set of equations (2.45b to e) would treat this in vector notation, where the constants c_e, e_p and ϵ have to be considered as tensors.

2.5 Power Flow

Maxwell's equations give the relation between the fields, and the current and space-charge densities in time and space. It does not show, however, the direction and the amplitude of the electromagnetic power flow. This we obtain by the Poynting vector $\mathscr{E} \times \mathbf{H}$, the instantaneous electromagnetic flux density.

The equation expressing the conservation of energy is obtained by multiplying equation (2.1) by $\mathbf{H}$ and equation (2.2) by $-\mathscr{E}$ and adding:

$$\nabla . (\mathscr{E} \times \mathbf{H}) + \frac{\partial}{\partial t} (\tfrac{1}{2}\mu_m H^2 + \tfrac{1}{2}\epsilon \mathscr{E}^2) = - \mathbf{J} . \mathscr{E} \tag{2.46}$$

The first term incorporates the Poynting vector, the second term contains in brackets the instantaneous magnetic and electric energy densities respectively, and the term on the right hand side expresses the specific power dissipation or gain of the medium.

It is often convenient to transform the two fields into $\mathscr{E}$ (ω, k) and $\mathbf{H}$ (ω, k) and it is, for many problems permissible to approximate a plane wave as done for equation (2.10), such that the fields show the space-time behaviour given by

$$\exp(j\omega t - j\mathbf{k}.\mathbf{r}) \tag{2.47}$$

Depending on the medium, one can have either growing or evanescent waves, so that ω and k are usually complex quantities.

An important question concerns the velocity at which energy in the wave propagates.

We take the case of plane waves as given by expression (2.47) and introduce this into equations (2.1) to (2.4) by using equations (2.11) and (2.12). Then we scalar-multiply the first equation by H^* and the second one by $\mathscr{E}^*$, where a star indicates the complex conjugate value. We introduce small changes δk, $\delta \omega$, $\delta \mathscr{E}$, etc., neglect all products of the small quantities and obtain:

$$\delta k . (\mathscr{E} \times H^* + \mathscr{E}^* \times H) = (\delta \omega)\mu_m H . H^* + \epsilon \mathscr{E}^* . [\delta(\omega \| \epsilon \|)] . \mathscr{E} \qquad (2.48)$$

where we have approximated $\| \epsilon \| \cong \| \epsilon \|^*$, which means we treat the case of an almost loss-free medium. We can write

$$\delta(\omega \| \epsilon \|) = \frac{\partial \omega \| \epsilon \|}{\partial \omega} \delta \omega + \frac{\partial \omega \| \epsilon \|}{\partial k} \delta k$$

which yields the group velocity vectors (v_g) [see equation (2.21)], when introduced into equation (2.48):

$$v_g = \frac{\partial \omega}{\partial k} = \frac{\frac{1}{2}\mathrm{Re}(\mathscr{E} \times H^*) - \frac{1}{4}\epsilon \mathscr{E}^* . \dfrac{\partial \omega \| \epsilon \|}{\partial k} . \mathscr{E}}{\frac{1}{4}\mu_m |H|^2 + \frac{1}{4}\epsilon \mathscr{E}^* . \dfrac{\partial \omega \| \epsilon \|}{\partial \omega} \mathscr{E}} \qquad (2.49)$$

The first term in the numerator on the right-hand side is the Poynting vector, representing the flow of electromagnetic energy, whereas the second term denotes the non-electromagnetic energy flux owing to the particles flowing coherently with the wave (8). The first term in the denominator on the right-hand side in equation (2.49) is the time-averaged magnetic energy density and the second term is the sum of the electrical energy density plus that part of the kinetic energy of the charge carriers which is coherent with the wave. If the medium is not time dispersive, this last expression can be written in its familiar form:

$$\frac{1}{4}\epsilon \mathscr{E}^* . \frac{\partial \omega \| \epsilon \|}{\partial \omega} . \mathscr{E} \simeq \frac{1}{4}\epsilon \mathscr{E}^* \| \epsilon \| \mathscr{E}$$

Erroneous use of this approximation for many semiconductor problems can lead to wrong results, and one has to be careful in applying it.

The total energy density in a transverse electromagnetic wave propagating in an isotropic medium is given by the denominator of equation (2.49), which can be rewritten as

$$\frac{1}{2}\epsilon |\mathscr{E}|^2 n_r \left(\frac{c}{v_g}\right)$$

where n_r is the refractive index [see equation (2.14)] and v_g is the magnitude of the group velocity, i.e.

$$v_g = \frac{d\omega}{dk}$$

The above definitions of the group velocity vector $\mathbf{v}_g$ given by equation (2.49) show that it is equal to the velocity of energy propagation, if we use its usual definition, namely being the time-averaged flux divided by the time-averaged energy density. We see also that the group velocity is in the direction of the total flux, composed of Poynting and particle fluxes.

REFERENCES

1. Landau, L. D., 'On the Vibrations of the Electronic Plasma', *J. Phys. (USSR)*, **10**, 25, 1946.
2. Van Kampen, N. G. 'On the theory of Stationary Waves in Plasmas', *Physica*, **21**, p. 949, 1955.
3. Hayes, N., 'Damping of Plasma Oscillations in the Linear Theory', *Phys. Fluids*, **4**, p. 1387, 1961.
4. Pines, D., Schrieffer, J. R., 'Collective Behaviour in Solid-State Plasmas', *Phys. Rev.*, **124**, p. 1387, 1961.
5. Dirac, P. A. M., *'The principles of Quantum Mechanics'*, Oxford Univ. Press, New York, 1947.
6. Jonscher, A. K., 'Transport of hot injected plasmas in semiconductors', *Proc. Phys. Soc.*, **84**, p. 767, 1964.
7. Köchner, W., 'Untersuchung der Zweistrom-Instabilität in driftenden Halbleiterplasmen' *Archiv Der Elektrischen Übertragung*, **19**, p. 445-452, 1965.
8. Stix, T. H., *The Theory of Plasma Waves*, McGraw-Hill, New York, 1962. (section 3.3., pp. 49-52).

ADDITIONAL REFERENCES *(for Further Study)*

1. Akhiezer, A. I., Akhiezer, I. A., Polovin, R. V., Sitenko, A. G., Stepanov, K. N., *Collective Oscillations in a Plasma*, Pergamon Press, Oxford, 1967.
2. Allis, W. P., Buchsbaum, S. J., Bers, A., *Waves in Anisotropic Plasmas*, M.I.T. Press, Cambridge, Mass., 1963.
3. Brandstatter, J. J., *An Introduction to Waves, Rays and Radiation in Plasma Media*, McGraw-Hill, New York, 1963.
4. Brown, S. C., *Basic Data of Plasma Physics*, J. Wiley, New York, 1959.
5. Drummond, J. E., *Plasma Physics*, McGraw-Hill, New York, 1961.
6. Gartenhaus, S., *Elements of Plasma Physics*, Holt, Rinehart, Winston, New York, 1964.

7. Holt, E. H., Haskell, R. E., *Foundations of Plasma Dynamics,* Macmillan, New York, 1965.

8. Longmire, C. L., *Elementary Plasma Physics,* J. Wiley, New York, 1963.

9. Papas, C. H., *Theory of Electromagnetic Wave Propagation,* McGraw-Hill, New York, 1965.

10. Stix, T. H., *The Theory of Plasma Waves,* McGraw-Hill, New York, 1962.

11. Thompson, W. B., *An Introduction to Plasma Physics,* Pergamon Press, London, 1962.

12. de Witt, C., Detoeuf, J. F. (editors), *La théorie des gaz neutres et ionisés,* Herman, Paris; Wiley, New York, 1960.

CHAPTER III

Methods for the Analysis of Instabilities

An important task has to be carried out after the relevant equations have been established. Namely, one has to find under which conditions wave damping will be transformed into wave growth, representing either an absolute instability or an amplification phenomenon. A threshold computation is often still relatively easy because one can use small signal approximations, which means that the wave fields are small compared with any constant-value terms, so that their higher-order terms can be neglected. However, as soon as the wave has grown, one can no longer employ the small-signal equations. Therefore, the further problems of wave growth rate, etc. are usually very difficult to solve.

3.1 Small-Signal Analysis

We have shown in the last chapter, how one can obtain the dispersion equation. This equation contains valuable information about the type and threshold criteria of instabilities.

A first approach has been to introduce real values of the wave number k into the dispersion equation and to see, when positive or negative imaginary parts of the angular frequency ω ($= \omega_r + j\omega_i$) occur. Positive values of ω_i show wave attenuation and negative values indicate growth, as the fields vary with $\exp j(\omega t - kr)$. Twiss (1,2), Landau and Lifshitz (3) and Sturrock (4,5) pointed out that there are two different types of instabilities. A convective instability occurs, if a disturbance at some point in space on a uniform system travels along the system and grows while in transit. At a particular constant point, in space, the disturbance will in fact decrease in time. This is the instability occurring in travelling wave tubes. A nonconvective or absolute instability occurs, if a disturbance increases with time at every point in space. One can usually distinguish between the two types of instability by investigating if the introduction of frequencies ω into the dispersion equation yields complex wave numbers. Negative imaginary parts of k indicate decreasing, dying waves, whereas positive values demonstrate spatially growing waves. However, this type of analysis can lead to wrong results and it is advisable to use the method of treatment developed by Briggs (6). It involves essentially a complete mapping of the complex ω-plane into the complex k plane. One can then determine from the shape of the contours how the system behaves.

Firstly, let us consider the question of convective instabilities. If one has obtained a complex $k = k_r + jk_i$ for a real ω, a wave is only a growing one if k_i has a different sign when the frequency takes on a large negative imaginary part. One can produce a simple argument demonstrating the validity of this rule. A source may be localized in space and may produce the waves which grow while travelling away from it. Now we assume that the source grows very quickly. If its growth rate is large enough, then the waves travelling away from it will now decay away from it. This means, k_i changes sign. As one wants to know how the system behaves for a whole range of frequencies one usually draws the line of varying

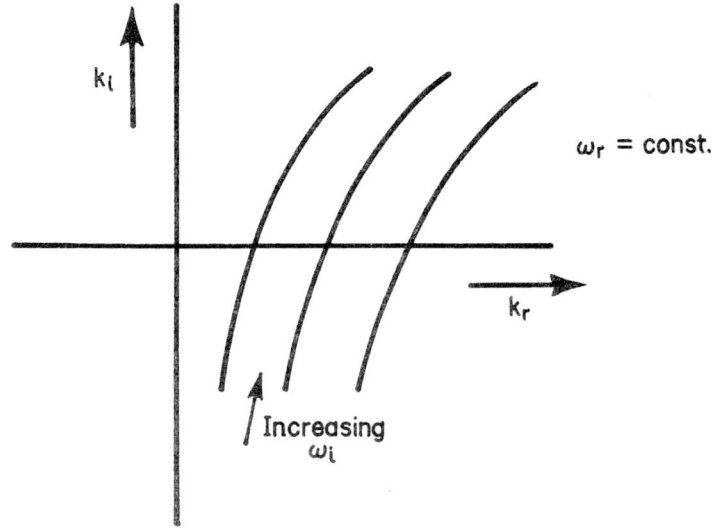

Fig. 3.1 Mapping on ω into the k plane.

ω_i for constant ω_r into the k-plane, which means a mapping of the lines of constant ω_r into the k-plane (Fig. 3.1). For a dispersion equation of higher order in ω and k, there will be as many mapped figures required as there are roots.

After having performed the mapping, one is also able to find out where absolute instabilities occur. At certain places one might find a double root of k for some complex ω with some negative ω_i, where the two merging roots originate from different upper and lower halves of the complex k-plane for a large negative ω_i. The basic mathematical analysis of such problems involves the integration along certain contour lines in order to obtain the direct functions in time and space coordinates again, in the same way as shown in Chapter 2, equations (2.28) and (2.29). Integrating along a line in the k-plane, yields the spatial dependence of any quantity F of the wave (e.g. the electric field $\mathscr{E}_1 (\omega, z)$). A saddle point in the k-plane for $\omega = \omega_s$, given by a double root as mentioned above, means that the function $F(\omega, z)$ tends to infinity as one approaches the point ω_s, since the integration path cannot be deformed around the two merging poles. This means, we have a non-convective or absolute instability (see Fig. 3.2).

The appearance of such a saddle point can be determined easily even for a low line density if one investigates the problem carefully. One has to find the curves for constant ω_r in the k-plane, which represent the steepest ascent and descent; if a cross-over occurs, as shown in Fig. 3.2, one has found already one criterion for absolute instabilities fulfilled.

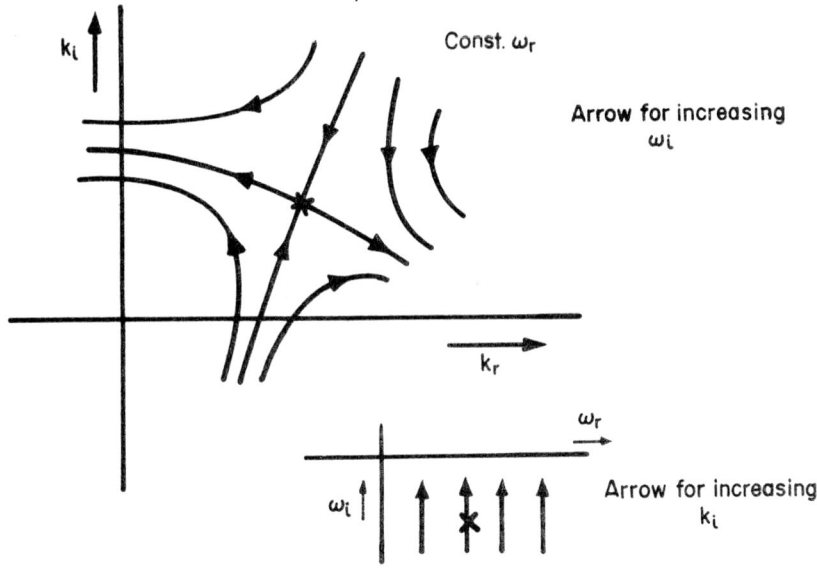

Fig. 3.2   A saddle point (x) indicating an absolute instability (the arrows in the k plane indicate increasing ω_i, as shown in the ω plane).

The important second requirement is that the two roots come from different halves of the complex k-plane, as indicated by Fig. 3.2. One can explain this required property roughly as follows: If a fast enough growing impulse is produced at $z = 0$, the waves must decay away from $z = 0$. One can conclude that one root of k has to be related to $z > 0$ (let us say k_+), and the other one belongs to $z < 0$ (i.e. k_-). Now we assume a decrease of the pulse applied at $z = 0$ and at one particular decaying rate, k_+ could become equal to k_-. This would mean that there is no discontinuity of F at $z = 0$. We have the same case as a wave travelling across $z = 0$. However, any applied impulse would surely produce an instability. The case of $k_+ = k_-$ means therefore that the oscillation of the system is not affected by the applied impulse, as the whole system 'resonates' at the particular frequency ω_s, and does not require a source any more. This argument indicates that the two roots have to come from different halves of the k-plane. A full

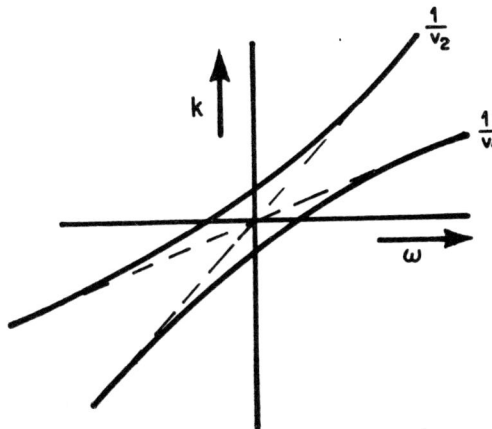

Fig. 3.3 Weak coupling between two propagating waves; no instabilities (v_1 and v_2 are the velocities of the waves).

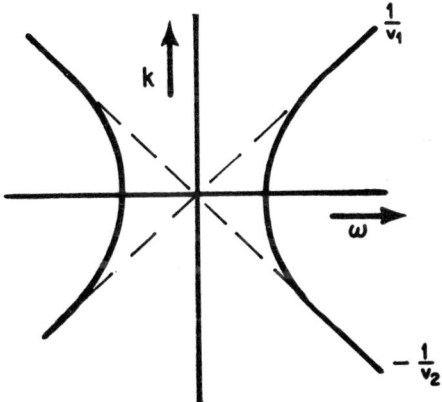

Fig. 3.4 Two coupled waves giving evanescence.

mathematical justification of this requirement has to make use of reciprocal Fourier (or Laplace) transformations as indicated by equation (2.28).

Sometimes the tedious task of mapping ω into k completely, can be avoided by studying the dispersion equation intelligently. For example, if no values are obtained in the lower half of the ω-plane for real k, then neither convective, nor absolute instabilities can occur. It is often possible to obtain some information about an explicit solution for all possible k's, if one analyses the dispersion equation for complex ω with $\omega_i \to -\infty$.

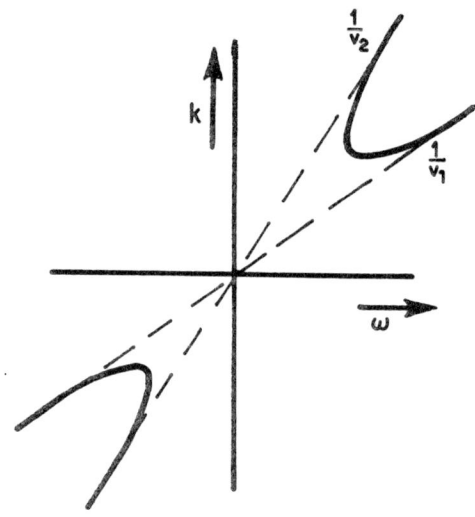

Fig. 3.5   Coupling of two waves resulting in one wave being amplifying and the other one evanescent.

It is instructive to discuss a few examples. We take the cases of weak coupling between two propagating waves in a lossless system.

(a) $[k - (\omega/v_1)] \, [k - (\omega/v_2)] = k_L^2$ (Fig. 3.3).
 k is real for all real ω and ω is real for all real k.
 This indicates that we do not have any instabilities, but only propagating waves.

(b) $[k - (\omega/v_1)] \, [k + (\omega/v_2)] = -k_L^2$ (Fig. 3.4).
 There are complex roots of k for real ω, but ω is real for all real k. Therefore, there are only evanescent waves.

(c) $[k - (\omega/v_1)] \, [k - (\omega/v_2)] = -k_L^2$ (Fig. 3.5).
 One has complex roots of k for real ω and complex roots of ω for real k. It can be shown easily that one has one amplifying and one evanescent wave.

(d) $[k - (\omega/v_1)] \; [k + (\omega/v_2)] = k_L^2$ (Fig. 3.6).

k is real for all real ω, whereas ω is complex for real k. A double root of k occurs when

$$\omega = \omega_s = -2 \, jk_L\left(\frac{1}{v_1} + \frac{1}{v_2}\right)^{-1}$$

It can be found that for $\omega_i \rightarrow -\infty$, one root is in the half of the plane with positive k_i and the other one is in the half with negative k_i. One sees that this is an absolute instability at ω_s.

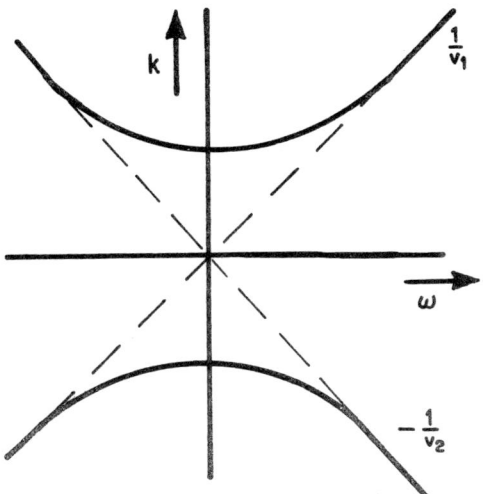

Fig. 3.6   The case of an absolute instability.

We can produce simple descriptions for the four cases treated so far. A useful concept is the distinction between waves carrying positive small-signal energy and waves with negative energy, as developed by the theory of energy transfer between waves, and as described in detail below, with the help of the classical example of an electron beam in a microwave tube.

Cases (a) and (b) show a coupling between two waves with equal energy signs and the remaining two dispersion equations concern the interaction between one wave with negative energy and another one with positive energy. In (c) the group velocities of the uncoupled waves are in the same direction, whereas they are of opposite direction for (d).

The analytical technique described so far is not the only one which has been developed for the treatment of the dispersion equation. There are entirely different methods (11-14) as well as improvements of Briggs's criteria. For example, Hall and Heckrotte enlarged the theory by introducing an arbitrary velocity frame, so that results obtained for one velocity frame can easily be related to answers for adjacent frames. (15)

––––––––––––––––––

There are many different ways of expressing the dispersion relation between k and ω. The most commonly used is the diagrammatic representation which we employed in Figs. 3.3 to 3.6 and which was used first by Brillouin systematically (7). Since then it has commonly been referred to as the $\omega - \beta$ diagram, where $\beta = k_r$ is the real part of k. A straight line through the origin of such a plot is the line of the phase velocity v_{ph} and the tangent to the curve represents the group velocity v_g. If there are two waves with different dispersion relations in one system, then an interaction can occur for a large enough coupling between them, where the dispersion characteristics have cross-overs.

The interaction phenomena can only be properly understood if one understands the concept of negative and positive energy which we use above in connection with Figs. 3.3 to 3.6. A very instructive example is given by the waves on an electron beam flowing in z direction and of infinite extent in x and y direction.

We use Maxwell's equations [see equations (2.1) to (2.4)] and introduce the small-signal approximations $\mathcal{E} = \mathcal{E}_0 + \mathcal{E}_1$, etc. again. We require the small-signal part of the force equation

$$m \frac{dv}{dt} = e\mathcal{E},$$

i.e.

$$\frac{dv_1}{dt} = \frac{\partial v_1}{\partial t} + v_0 \frac{\partial v_1}{\partial z} = -\frac{e}{m^*} \mathcal{E}_z$$

giving:

$$j(\omega - kv_0)v_1 = -\frac{e}{m}\mathcal{E}_z \tag{3.1}$$

by using the plane-wave approximation of equation (2.47).

The continuity equation [equations (2.36) and (2.41)] yields with $g_c = r = 0$:

$$J_1 = \frac{\omega \rho_1}{k} \tag{3.2}$$

and the products of two or more small-signal terms are neglected, so that

$$J_1 = -\rho_{0c} v_1 + v_0 \rho_1 \tag{3.3}$$

The wave equation as given by equation (2.5) leads to

$$\frac{\partial^2 \mathcal{E}_z}{\partial x^2} + \frac{\partial^2 \mathcal{E}_z}{\partial y^2} - \left(k^2 - \left(\frac{\omega}{c}\right)^2\right)\mathcal{E}_z = \frac{jk\rho_1}{\epsilon} + j\omega\mu_m J_1 \tag{3.4}$$

where we consider only the z-component of $\mathcal{E}$
Equations (3.1) to (3.3) give

$$J_1 = -j\omega\epsilon \frac{\omega_p^2}{(\omega - kv_0)^2}\mathcal{E}_z \tag{3.5}$$

with

$$\omega_p = \sqrt{\frac{e}{m}\frac{\rho_{0c}}{\epsilon}}$$

the plasma frequency. Using equations (3.2) and (3.5), we can rewrite equation (3.4):

$$\frac{\partial^2 \mathcal{E}_z}{\partial x^2} + \frac{\partial^2 \mathcal{E}_z}{\partial y^2} - \left(k^2 - \left(\frac{\omega}{c}\right)^2\right)\left(1 - \frac{\omega_p^2}{(\omega - kv_0)^2}\right)\mathcal{E}_z = 0$$

In order to simplify the equation further, we consider the case, where the electron beam is focused by a strong axial magnetic field H. This means, we can say approximately, that the electrons are only able to move in z-direction, so that

$$\frac{\partial^2 \mathcal{E}_z}{\partial x^2} \simeq 0 \simeq \frac{\partial^2 \mathcal{E}_z}{\partial y^2}$$

and

$$\left(k^2 - \left(\frac{\omega}{c}\right)^2\right)\left(1 - \frac{\omega_p^2}{(\omega - kv_0)^2}\right)\mathcal{E}_z = 0 \tag{3.6}$$

The roots of equation (3.6) are

$$k_{1,2} = \pm\frac{\omega}{c}$$

$$k_{3,4} = \left(\frac{\omega \pm \omega_p}{v_0}\right)$$

The first two waves propagate with the velocity of light and do not depend on the electron beam. The remaining ones have phase velocities just above and below the beam velocity, i.e.

$$v_{p3,4} = \frac{v_0}{1 \pm \dfrac{\omega_p}{\omega}} \tag{3.7}$$

The corresponding dispersion diagram is given in Fig. 3.7. The phase velocities of equation (3.7) are those of the beam-space-charge waves. It is important to realize that they are produced by displacement electrons. Once an initial displacement has occurred for a short time, the rearrangement of electrons carries on

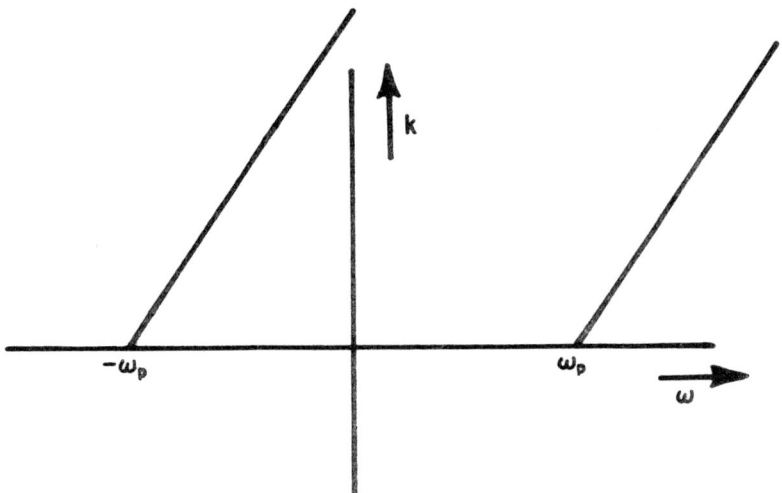

Fig. 3.7   Dispersion diagram of two space-charge waves on an electron beam.

without any extra power requirements. There exists an analogy between a transmission line and an electron beam, as pointed out by Bloom and Peter (8) if one introduces the kinetic voltage V_1 by equating

$$(v_0 + v_1)^2 = \frac{2e}{m}(V_0 + V_1) \tag{3.8}$$

(V_0 is the cathode-anode voltage of the electron-beam gun). This leads to the approximate expression

$$V_1 \simeq \frac{v_1 v_0 m}{e} \tag{3.9}$$

The power flow of space charge waves in electron beams can therefore be described by power densities $\mathscr{P}$ and the characteristic impedance Z, defined by the ratio of kinetic voltage V_1 to small-signal current I_1.

We have:
$$\mathscr{P}_1 = \tfrac{1}{4}(V_1 J_1{}^* + V_1{}^* J_1)$$
$$\mathscr{P}_2 = \tfrac{1}{4}(V_2 J_2{}^* + V_2{}^* J_2) \tag{3.10}$$

where $\mathscr{P}_1$ and $\mathscr{P}_2$ are the power densities of two different waves; V_1 and J_1 refer to the input conditions, and V_2 and J_2 relate to output conditions. The corresponding characteristic impedances Z are then given by

$$Z_{01} = -\frac{V_1}{F_b J_1} = \frac{-2\omega_p V_0}{I_0 \omega} \tag{3.11}$$

and

$$Z_{02} = -\frac{V_2}{F_b J_2} = \frac{2\omega_p V_0}{I_0 \omega} \tag{3.12}$$

where F_b is the cross-sectional surface of the whole beam and I_0 is the beam current. The first wave has the slow phase velocity of equation (3.7) and the other one the fast velocity. The first wave has a negative characteristic impedance (equation 3.11), so that the power flow becomes

$$\mathscr{P}_1 = -\frac{|Z_{01}|}{2}(J_1 J_1{}^*)$$

As this has a negative value, one says that this wave carries negative power, as the power flow will always be in the $+z$ direction along with the electron beam.

This concept can be illustrated by the following deliberation: A coupling structure near the beginning of the beam excites the slow space charge wave only. It will then in fact remove power from the unmodulated beam. Negative power will then flow along the beam in $+z$ direction. A second coupler near the beam end must feed power into the beam in order to restore it to the original state.

If the slow wave loses power, the signal amplitude on the beam increases. This is, for example, the case for the resistive-wall amplifier (19), which dissipates the energy it has taken away from the slow wave. The resistive wall amplifier has been built as an electron-beam tube and operates very well. Many convective instabilities suggested in semiconductor plasmas rely on the resistive-wall-amplification phenomenon, as will be described in the next chapter. This amplification occurs with slow waves of a carrier stream, where the negative energy is taken away by dissipation through collisions.

When the fast wave loses power to some dissipative medium around the electron beam, then the signal amplitude decreases.

3.2 Nyquist's Instability Criterion

In the previous chapter, we derived an expression for the transformed small-signal field $\mathscr{E}(\omega, k)$ [equation (2.31)] and found a solution $\lim_{t \to \infty} \mathscr{E}(k,t)$ by integrating along a conveniently chosen line in the complex ω plane, so that

the residues of the singularities form the main contribution to the solution
(see equation 2.29). Depending on whether the solution goes to infinity or not
for any k-value, we can decide about the presence of an instability. This is also
a frequently-employed technique for the study of instabilities. We have described
this method already in the previous chapter in order to introduce Landau damping.
It remains, however, to discuss here an extension of this type of treatment.

Fried and Jackson (9) applied the electric-circuit instability criterion of Nyquist
(10) to plasma instabilities. The roots of the denominator of equation (2.31),
start in the lower half of the complex plane indicating damping. They move
upwards and cross finally the real axis, which means, the plasma can exhibit
wave growth. Each new root in the upper half plane corresponds to a new unstable
mode. If we transform the complex function into another plane, we can possibly
make the analysis simpler.

We denote the denominator of equation (2.31) by $H(\omega/k, k)$, for $\text{Im } \omega > 0$
If $\partial f(v)/\partial v$ is absolutely integrable, the nth derivative of H with respect to ω/k
is bounded by

$$|H^{(n)}| < 1 + \left| \frac{e^2}{k^2 m \epsilon} \frac{n! \int\limits_{-\infty}^{+\infty} |\partial f/\partial v| \, dv}{(\text{Im } \omega/k)^{n+1}} \right|$$

The above condition for $\partial f/\partial v$ is sufficient for H to be analytic.

The number of poles will be equal to the number of zeros of H within the
upper half plane. As H is analytic there, the number of zeros within the upper
half of the ω plane is given in accordance with the residue theorem.

$$N_0 = \frac{1}{2\pi j} \int\limits_C d\omega \frac{H'}{H} \tag{3.13}$$

where the integral is carried along the contour C, as shown by Fig. 3.8.
The contour is a half circle with infinite radius. Along the circular line, H
is equal to unity. Along the line immediately next to the real axis H is given by
equation (2.32b). Now we consider H as a complex variable forming the complex
H plane. We map the contour C into the H plane and obtain the contour D
(Fig. 3.9). The entire half-circle in contour C maps into the single point at
$H = 1$. The remainder of the contour originates from the real axis in the ω
plane. Values of H along the real ω-axis are easy to compute as no analytic
continuation of f is required, as needed for Landau's method.

The transformation can be expressed mathematically by rewriting equation
(3.13) as

$$N_0 = \frac{1}{2\pi j} \int\limits_D \frac{dH}{H}$$

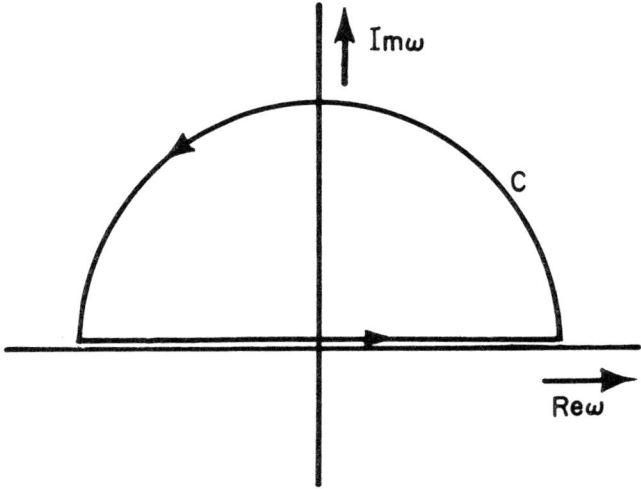

Fig. 3.8   Contour C of integration for equation 3.13.

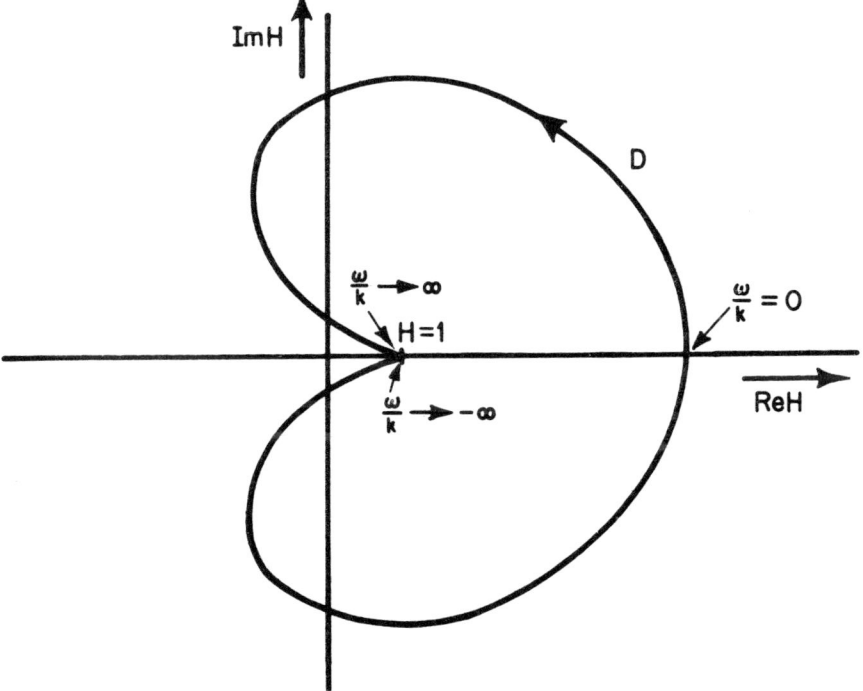

Fig. 3.9   Nyquist diagram, obtained by mapping the contour C of Fig. 3.8 onto the H plane.

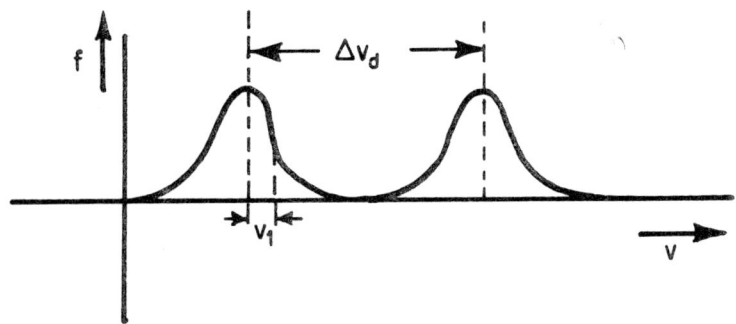

Fig. 3.10 The shifted Maxwellian distribution functions of two electron beams (v_1 is the thermal velocity of a beam; Δv_d is the difference in average velocities for both beams).

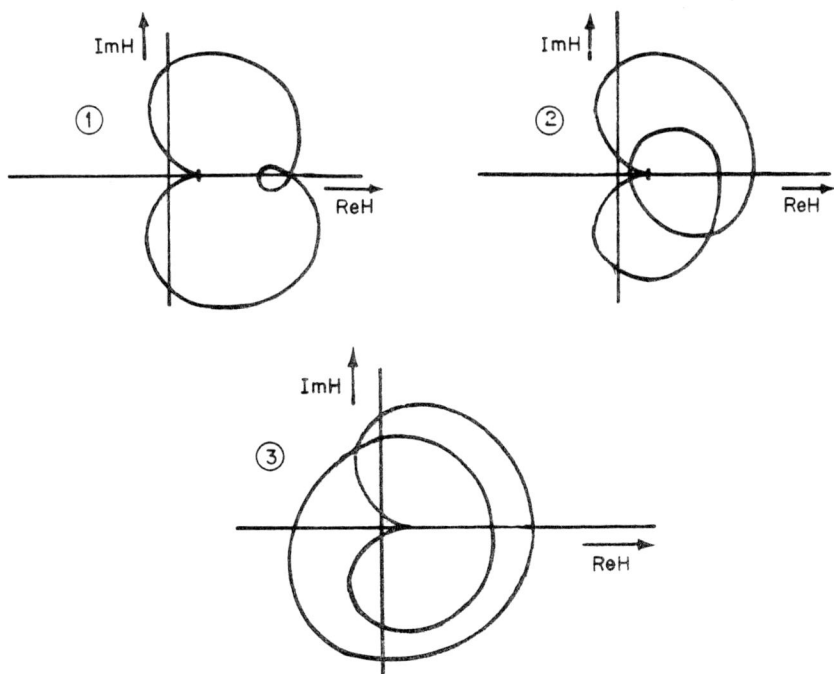

Fig. 3.11 Nyquist diagrams for velocity distributions of Fig. 3.10: (1) $\Delta v_d < 2v_1$; (2) $\Delta v_d \cong 2v_1$; (3) $\Delta v_d > 2v_1$, giving instability.

The number of unstable modes is now simply equal to the number of times the origin of the H plane is enclosed by contour D.

It is instructive to present an example. We take two electron beams, both with Maxwellian velocity distributions and with an average-velocity difference Δv_d (Fig. 3.10). The Nyquist diagrams for this system can be obtained as a function of Δv_d and one finds, from which value of Δv_d onwards the origin is enclosed by the contour (see Fig. 3.11).

3.3 Large-Signal Analysis

The preceding two sections show how instabilities can be analysed if the amplitudes involved can be considered small as compared with the d.c. terms. As any instability has to start first as a small-signal one, it is a permissible approximation to take products of two or more small-signal terms as negligible. Such an analysis shows the onset conditions and the initial growth rate of an instability. However, it cannot be used for the study of phenomena, where a wave has grown to full size. This means then, not only can the products of small-signal terms no more be neglected but also the nonlinear behaviour of any function involved has to be considered. This makes the analysis very difficult and in most cases impossible.

An important task is therefore to study any nonlinearity of the functions involved. For example, one has to find out how the electromechanical coupling constant or the drift velocity and carrier density change for large electric fields in the case of the electroacoustic oscillator. Only a treatment which incorporates this information can yield the correct information about frequency of operation, power output etc.

However, it is possible to classify large-signal instabilities roughly into two groups. One is based on an effect incorporating the whole device possibly together with an external circuit. Examples are the lsa-mode (see p. 96), the p-n avalanche diode oscillator and the piezoelectric photoconductive oscillator. The other group produces domains of localized high or low fields which travel across the crystal. These are observed in the Read diode, the Gunn-effect domain, the semiconductive electroacoustic device and the field-dependent trapping and recombination oscillation. The domains of the field-dependent permittivity instability are outside the subject of this book, but they can be treated in a similar way. The details of all these effects are given in Chapter IV. Here we want to discuss only a few general principles.

The instabilities based on travelling domains are treated quite extensively now because they can usually be subjected to good approximations. This is not the case for the other group of instabilities, though some cases have been analyzed by computer techniques. Therefore, we want to discuss some of the principles of domain-instabilities.

A necessary (but generally not sufficient) condition for domain formation

is usually the negative slope of the conductivity, as shown by Fig. 3.12.
This is not the conductivity of a total crystal, but it is the conductivity for a
given electric field. It is not possible to measure the negative slope by conventional
techniques, as the crystal normally breaks into oscillations immediately after
a large voltage has been applied. The techniques which usually enable one to
determine σ, rely on very fast measurement methods such as the use of microwave
fields, so that σ has been determined before the crystal begins to oscillate.

In the presence of some initial inhomogeneities, static domains of high field
are formed first near the inhomogeneities, if the applied voltage is raised.

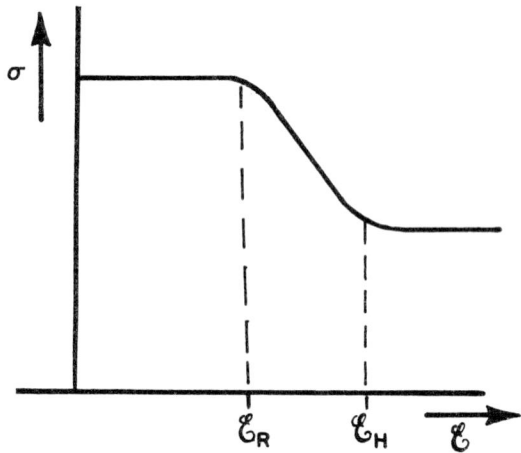

Fig. 3.12 Negative dynamic conductivity.

This localized inhomogeneity has then a lower σ than the remainder of the crystal,
whose higher σ can be in series or in parallel. If both conductivity areas are in
series, the field across the low conductivity part will be higher. This in turn
increases the electric field again and this phenomenon continues until a saturation
point is reached. This would be a stable situation then, unless the negative differential resistance is associated with some moving elements contributing to
the conductivity decrease. These can be movable charge carriers, with different
masses (the Gunn effect) or different trapping times, or different carrier densities
(Read diode) or phonon interactions moving with the sound velocity (electroacoustic device). This moving term causes the low resistivity to travel across
the crystal away from the domain-nucleating inhomogeneity. Arriving at the
positive electrode of the crystal, the domain discharges and a new domain
can now form at the nucleating centre. As the total current through the crystal
is controlled by the amplitude of a domain, the effect causes a current oscillation.

A similar effect must occur if the conductivity is a function of current density and if the regions with different conductivities are in parallel. Effects like this have been observed in phenomena such as current pinching (see Chapter IV), however they have not yet obtained any technical importance.

Several authors (16,17) have studied these domain instabilities. A steady-state domain moves with a uniform velocity c_d, so that $\mathscr{E} = \mathscr{E}(x - c_d t)$. $\partial \mathscr{E}/\partial t$ can therefore be replaced by $-c_d(d\mathscr{E}/dx)$. The treatment of domain dynamics usually considers an infinitely long sample, so that the anode and cathode electrodes do not have to be considered as boundaries. The total current density J_t obeys the current conservation equation $\partial J_t/\partial x = 0$ and was given by equation (2.45), i.e.

$$J_t = nev_d(\mathscr{E}) + \frac{\partial D_d}{\partial t} - e\frac{\partial}{\partial x}(D.n) \tag{3.14}$$

where D_d is the electric displacement, $D = D(\mathscr{E})$ the diffusion constant, and $ne = \rho_c = \rho_c(\mathscr{E})$. If one considers the Gunn effect, then $D_d = \epsilon\mathscr{E}$ and $v_d(\mathscr{E})$ is a function showing the characteristic negative slope for certain ranges of $\mathscr{E}$. Or, for the trapping instability, $D_d = \epsilon\mathscr{E}$ and n has to include the trapping effect. Similarly, for the Read instability, the current density n is dependent on $\mathscr{E}$. For the electroacoustic instability, however, one has to include the strain terms $\mathscr{S}$ in D_d via the piezoelectric equation (2.45c),

$$D_d = e_p\mathscr{S} + \epsilon\mathscr{E}$$

where e_p is the piezoelectric constant. With the relation $\mathscr{S} = (\partial u/\partial x)$ (u is the lattice displacement), one finds the following expression for the total current density:

$$J_t = nev_d + \frac{\partial}{\partial t}\left(e_p\frac{\partial u}{\partial x} + \epsilon\mathscr{E}\right) - e\frac{\partial}{\partial x}(Dn) \tag{3.14a}$$

Taking the other piezoelectric relation [equation (2.45b)],

$$\mathscr{T} = c_e\mathscr{S} - e_p\mathscr{E}$$

(where $\mathscr{T}$ is the stress and c_e is the elastic constant) and the equation in accordance with Newton's second law [equation (2.45e)],

$$\rho_m\frac{\partial^2 u}{\partial t^2} = \frac{\partial\mathscr{T}}{\partial x}$$

(with ρ_m the mass density of the material and u, the lattice displacement), one finds the equation giving the relation between $\mathscr{E}$ and u, namely:

$$\rho_m \frac{\partial^2 u}{\partial t^2} = c_e \frac{\partial^2 u}{\partial x^2} - e_p \frac{\partial \mathscr{E}}{\partial x} \qquad (3.14b)$$

In addition to the expression for the total current density one requires Poisson's equation [equation (2.3)],

$$\frac{d\mathscr{E}}{dx} = \frac{\rho_c - \rho_0}{\epsilon} \qquad (3.15)$$

which enables us to express n as a function of $\mathscr{E}$, where ρ_0 represents the immobile and trapped charge density. The relation for $D(\mathscr{E})$ has to be obtained either by experiment or by a microscopic treatment. The problem is then to find a solution for equations (3.14) and (3.15) which represents a travelling domain, i.e. we have to find values of J, c_d and $\mathscr{E}_R$ ($\mathscr{E}_R$ is the field for the high conductivity value of Figure 3.12) such that a solution exists for which either $\mathscr{E} \to \mathscr{E}_R$ as $x \to \pm \infty$; or $\mathscr{E} \to \mathscr{E}_R$ for $x \to +\infty$ and $\mathscr{E} \to \mathscr{E}_H$ for $x \to -\infty$; or vice versa. ($\mathscr{E}_H$ is the low-conductivity field of Fig. 3.12.)

In principle, one can find four different classes of solution, namely (1) a low-field dipole domain, (2) a high-field dipole domain, (3) an accumulation layer, and (4) a depletion layer, depending on the type of boundary condition one has applied.

The applied voltage V_B is equal to

$$V_B = \int_0^l \mathscr{E}\,dx = \mathscr{E}_R\, l + V_D \qquad (3.16)$$

where V_D is the excess voltage the domain absorbs, namely:

$$V_D = \int [\mathscr{E} - \mathscr{E}_R]\,dx \qquad (3.17)$$

The excess voltage V_D can be obtained from a computer solution of equations (3.14) and (3.15) and is dependent on $\mathscr{E}_R$. It has been computed (16) and measured (18) for Gunn-effect domains. It might also be obtained for many other travelling-domain instabilities and could be of quite general applicability. The typical behaviour of V_D ($\mathscr{E}_R$) is shown in Fig. 3.13 where the straight line is called the device line and is given by equation (3.16). The slope of the device line is given by l and its intercept with the curve V_D ($\mathscr{E}_R$) determines the excess voltage and $\mathscr{E}_R$. The device line can be moved up and down by changing V_B. It is somewhat analogous to a load line for a vacuum tube. If V_B/l is made smaller than $\mathscr{E}_t$, the threshold field for domain nucleation, no new domain can be nucleated; however, a previously nucleated domain can continue along its trajectory, if the device line still crosses the line $V(\mathscr{E}_R)$.

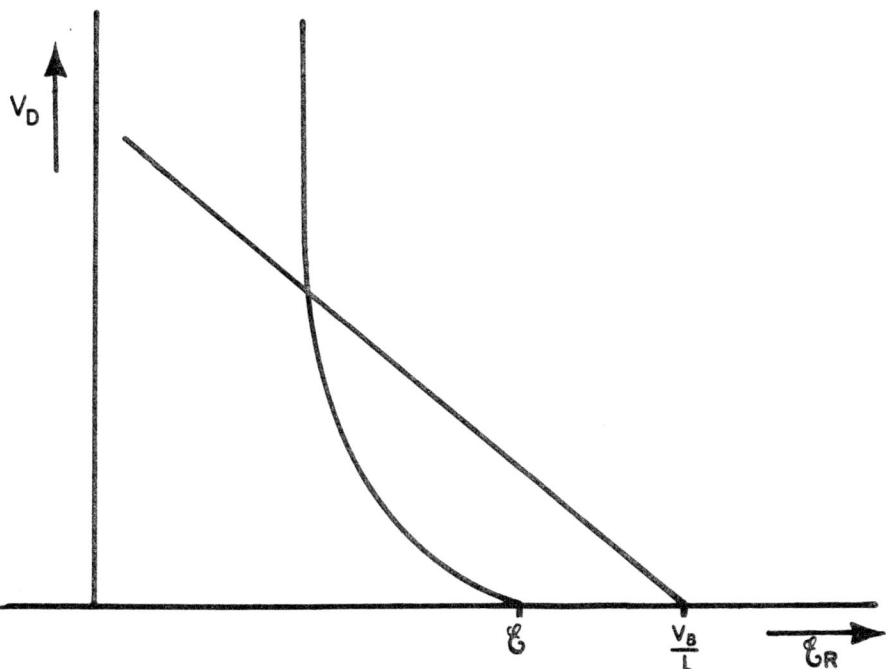

Fig. 3.13 Domain characteristics; excess voltage V_D versus electric field outside the domain, $\mathscr{E}_R$; the straight line through V_B/l is the device line, which yields the values of V_D and $\mathscr{E}_R$ by the cross point with the domain characteristics.

REFERENCES

1. Twiss, R. Q., 'On Oscillations in Electron Streams', *Proc. Phys. Soc. (London)* **B64**, p. 654, 1961.
2. Twiss, R. Q., 'Propagation in Electron-Ion Streams', *Phys. Rev.*, **88**, p. 1392, 1952.
3. Landau, L. D., Lifshitz, E. M., 'Electrodynamics of Continuous Media', *G.I.T.T.L.*, Moscow, 1953; *Fluid Mechanics*, chap. III, Pergamon Press, London, 1959.
4. Sturrock, P. A., 'Kinematics of Growing Waves', *Phys. Rev.*, **112**, p. 1488, 1958.
5. Sturrock, P. A., in *Plasma Physics* ed. Drummond, McGraw-Hill, New York, 1961.

6.   Briggs, R. J., 'Electron-Stream Interactions with Plasmas', Res. Monograph No. 29, M.I.T. Press, Cambridge, Mass., 1964.
7.   Brillouin, L., *Wave Propagation in Periodic Structures*, McGraw-Hill, New York, 1946.
8.   Bloom, S., Peter, R. W., 'Transmission Line Analog of a Modulated Electron Beam.', *R.C.A. Rev.*, **15**, p. 95, 1954.
9.   Jackson, J. D., 'Longitudinal Plasma Oscillations', *J. Nuclear Energy C*, **1**, pp. 171-189, 1960.
10. Nyquist, H. 'Regeneration Theory', *Bell Syst. Tech. J.* **11**, p. 126, 1932..
11. Fainberg, Ya. B., Kurilko, V. I., Shapiro, V. D., 'The Character of Instabilities Caused by Interaction between Beams of Charged Particles and a Plasma', *Zh. Tekh. Fiz.*, **31**, pp. 633-639, 1961, Transl; *Sov. Phys.–Techn. Phys.*, **6**, p. 459, 1961.
12. Polovin, R. V., 'Criteria for Instability and Gain', *Zh. Techn. Fiz.*, **31**, p. 1220 1961, Transl: *Sov. Phys.–Techn Phys.*, **6**, p. 889, 1962.
13. Feix, M., 'Propagation of a Double-Stream Instability in a Plasma', *Il Nuovo Cimento*, **27**, p. 1130, 1963.
14. Sudan, R. N., 'Classification of Instabilities from their Dispersion Relations', *Phys. Fluids*, **8**, p. 1899, 1965.
15. Hall, L. S., Heckrotte, W., 'Instabilities: Convective vs. Absolute', *Phys. Rev.* **166**, p. 120, 1968.
16. Copeland, J. A., 'Stable Space-Charge Layers in Two-Valley Semiconductors', *J. Appl. Phys.*, **37**, p. 3602, 1966.
17. Bonch-Bruevich, V. L., 'On the Theory of Electrical Domains in Hot Electron Semiconductors', *phys. stat. sol.*, **22**, p. 267, 1967.
18. Kuru, I., Robson, P. N., Kino, G. S., 'Some Measurements on the Steady-State and Transient Characteristics of High-Field Dipole Domains in GaAs', *I.E.E.E. Trans. El.Dev.*, **ED-15**, 1968.
19. Birdsall, C. K., Brewer, G. R., Haeff, A. V., 'The Resistive-Wall Amplifier', *Proc. I.R.E.*, **41**, p. 865, 1953.

ADDITIONAL REFERENCES *(For Further Studies)*

1.   Bandler, J. W., 'Comparison of ρ Plane with H-Plane Negative-Resistance Stability Criteria Using the Smith Chart', *I.E.E.E. Trans. Microw. Theory and Techn.*, **MTT-15**, p. 532, 1967.
2.   Beck, A. H. W., *Space Charge Waves*, Pergamon Press, London, 1958.
3.   Bekefi, G., *Radiation Processes in Plasmas*, Wiley & Sons Inc., New York, 1966.
4.   Böer, K. W., Dussel, G. A., 'Uniformly Propagating Solutions of Transport and Poisson Equations for Periodic Field Domains', *Phys. Rev.*, **154**, pp. 292-301, 1967.
5.   Burger, P., 'Energy-Dependent Mobility in the Small-Signal Analysis of Waves in Semiconductors', *Electronics L.*, **3**, p. 416, 1967.

6. Chawla, B. R., Unz, H., 'Poynting Vector in Moving Plasmas', *Proc. I.E.E.E.*, **55**, p. 1741, 1967.

7. Derfler, H., 'Growing Wave and Instability Criteria for Hot Plasmas', *Phys. L.*, **24A**, p. 763, 1967.

8. Dysthe, K. B., 'Convective and Absolute Instability', Int. Atomic Energy Agency, Vienna. *Fusion Nuclear,* **6**, pp. 215-222, 1966.

9. Ginzburg, V. L., *The Propagation of Electromagnetic Waves in Plasmas'*, Pergamon Press, Oxford, 1964.

10. Hall, L. S., Heckrotte, W., 'Instabilities: Convective vs. Absolute', *Phys. Rev.,* **166**, p. 120, 1968.

11. Lyamov, V. E., Sapogin, L. G., 'Trapping of Particles by Waves', *Zh. Tekhn. Fiz.,* **37**, pp. 624-632, 1967. Transl: *Sov. Phys.–Techn. Phys.,* **12**, pp. 449-454, 1967.

12. McCune, J. E., 'Exact Inversion of Dispersion Relations', *Phys. of Fluids,* **9**, pp. 2082-2084, 1966.

13. Pastrnak, J., 'A Thermodynamic Investigation of the Conditions for the Generation of Oscillations of an Electric Current Flowing through a Non-Ohmic Medium', *phys. stat. sol.,* **22**, p. 407, 1967.

14. Repalov, N. S., Khizhnyak, N. A., 'Nonlinear Theory of Longitudinal Waves in a Plasma', *Zh. Tekhn. Fiz.,* **37**, pp. 471-480, 1967, Transl: *Sov. Phys.–Techn. Phys.,* **12**, 339-344, 1967.

15. Sterzer, F., 'Power Output and Efficiency of Voltage-Controlled Negative Resistance Oscillators', *I.E.E.E. Trans. Il.Dev.,* **ED-14**, p. 718, 1967.

16. Stix, T. H., *The Theory of Plasma Waves,* McGraw-Hill, New York, 1962.

17. Vural, B., Bloom, S., 'Small-Signal Power Flow and Energy Density for Streaming Carriers in the Presence of Collisions', *I.E.E.E. Trans. El.Dev.,* **ED-14**, pp. 345-349, 1967.

18. Wilhelm, W. E., 'A Simple Asymptotic Formula for the motion of Simultaneous Electric Field and Conductivity Domains in Semiconductors', *phys. stat. sol.,* **16**, p. K59, 1966.

19. Wohlers, M. R., 'On Electromagnetic Gain Mechanism in Solid-State Plasmas', *Proc. I.E.E.E.,* **55**, p. 1230, 1967.

CHAPTER IV

Instabilities of Semiconductor Plasmas

In the preceding chapters, we have described the basic theory of semiconductors and the methods of studying instabilities. Now, we shall treat the various types of instabilities, which have either been observed experimentally or whose existence has been proposed on very strong theoretical grounds. The main emphasis is on those cases which have important device potentialities.

4.1 Gunn Oscillators and other Transferred-Electron Effects

4.1.1 Basic Principle

J. B. Gunn discovered current instabilities in GaAs in 1963, when he applied electric fields larger than 3000 V/cm (102), however he could not give an explanation for the effect.

Ridley and Watkins (238), and Hilsum (123) had already previously suggested on theoretical grounds that current instabilities could occur in certain many-valley semiconductors. However, it was only in 1964 that it was proposed that this theory could give the explanation for Gunn's instabilities and it took a further year to gather enough experimental evidence which showed conclusively its correctness.

Since then enormous advances have been made. Tunable microwave oscillators (mechanically and electronically tunable, i.e., suitable also for frequency modulation) (291) have been produced, appreciable CW power has been obtained at 88 GHz, and many users are considering their application, ranging from teaching equipment for schools to space craft telecommunication. A new field of application is the use of the Gunn effect for pulse production and processing of digital information.

It is therefore important to understand the principles of its mechanism. Several review papers have been written so far (e.g. 35, 126, 175a).

As described in Chapter I, a wave-mechanical treatment of semiconductors shows that electrons can only occupy special energy levels. These levels can conveniently be expressed as a function of the momentum of the electrons. If this is done for the energy levels of the conduction electrons, the conduction band, we find some structure such as that of Fig. 4.1, which shows the energy contours of the GaAs conduction band. It so happens in GaAs that we find the lowest valley in the centre of the Brillouin zone and three side valleys in the [100] directions.

Detailed knowledge about GaAs has been obtained by various measurement techniques such as those of the Hall coefficient, the conductivity, Faraday rotation etc. A detailed review was given by Hilsum and Rose-Innes (123a). In particular, the energy difference Δ between the central valley and the satellite ones has been obtained by conductivity measurements on crystals under heavy external stress (129a) or by the addition of phosphorus to form $GaAs_x P_{1-x}$ (82), as the energy separation Δ decreases linearly from 0.36 eV to zero as x goes from 1 to 0.5. Upon application of hydrostatic pressure, the energy minimum at the centre of the Brillouin zone moves up in energy, the electrons in this valley

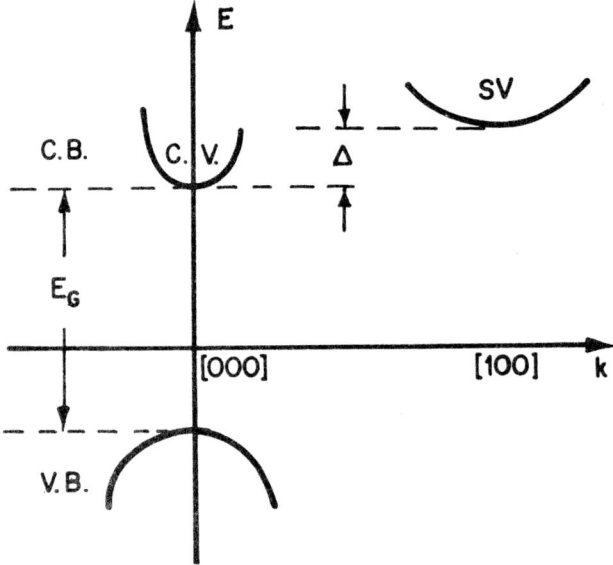

Fig. 4.1   Energy contours of GaAs in reduced zone (E = energy; CB = conduction band; VB = valence band; CV = central valley; SV = satellite valley; E_G = forbidden gap; Δ = energy difference between the lowest levels of CV and SV).

obtain a higher effective mass and electron transfer to the higher-lying satellite valleys occurs for smaller electron temperatures, or, in other words, for smaller applied electric fields. In fact, an increasing pressure results in a decrease of the threshold field for the transferred-electron effect (257) and if the applied pressure is large enough, no Gunn oscillations can occur (292).

The energy difference Δ is 0.36 eV for GaAs and the carrier properties in the two types of valleys are given in Table 4.1. If no drift field is applied at the GaAs crystal, the carriers will be on the bottom of the central valley. For a given drift field, the carriers gain energy and move up to higher energy levels. If they have gained more energy than Δ = 0.36 eV, they will cross over to the satellite valley, caused by inter-valley scattering. Owing to this transfer mechanism, this theory is called 'transferred electron theory'.

According to Table 4.1, the electrons in the satellite valleys will now have a larger mass and subsequently smaller mobility. The drift velocity as a function

TABLE 4.1 (m_0 = free-electron mass)

	effective mass	mobility
centre valley	$m^* = 0.07m_0$	~7500 cm^2/Vsec
satellite valley	$m^* = 0.4m_0$	200 cm^2/Vsec

of field must then have a shape as shown in Fig. 4.2, where the negative slope depends on the efficiency of the transfer to the satellite valley.

If the crystal is long enough, the following will happen: If the carriers in the satellite valley form a lower density at some place, they will cause a local increase in field, which means that further electrons will be lifted and transferred into the satellite valley, which causes the local field to grow further. If the applied voltage is constant, the increased field will finally only occur at one place, thus forming a high-field domain; the field outside the domain will be reduced as the domain has absorbed most of it. The domain will travel across the crystal and produce a current drop while in transit. After it has disappeared at the anode, the field in the whole crystal increases again and a new domain can form at some suitable nucleating centre.

As the domain velocity is typically 10^7 cm/sec, a specimen with a length of 10 microns will produce an oscillation of 10 GHz.

Other materials which exhibited the Gunn effect, are CdTe (82, 176), InP, some alloys of GaAs$_{1-x}$P$_x$ (5, 257), ZnSe (176a), and Ge for low temperatures (76, 78, 148, 188). The conditions are:

(1) a low mobility satellite valley at Δ above a high mobility central one,
(2) $\Delta < E_G$,
(3) $\Delta > kT_1$ (T_1 = lattice temperature) as otherwise transitions are possible due to thermal activation, and
(4) suitable scattering processes.

4.1.2 The Domain

The function $v = f(\mathcal{E})$ was first calculated by Hilsum (123) and Butcher and Fawcett (47, 47a), under the assumption that the distribution function is Maxwellian. Conwell and Vassell (61) have pointed out that these assumptions are difficult to justify for GaAs in the electron concentration ranges for which the

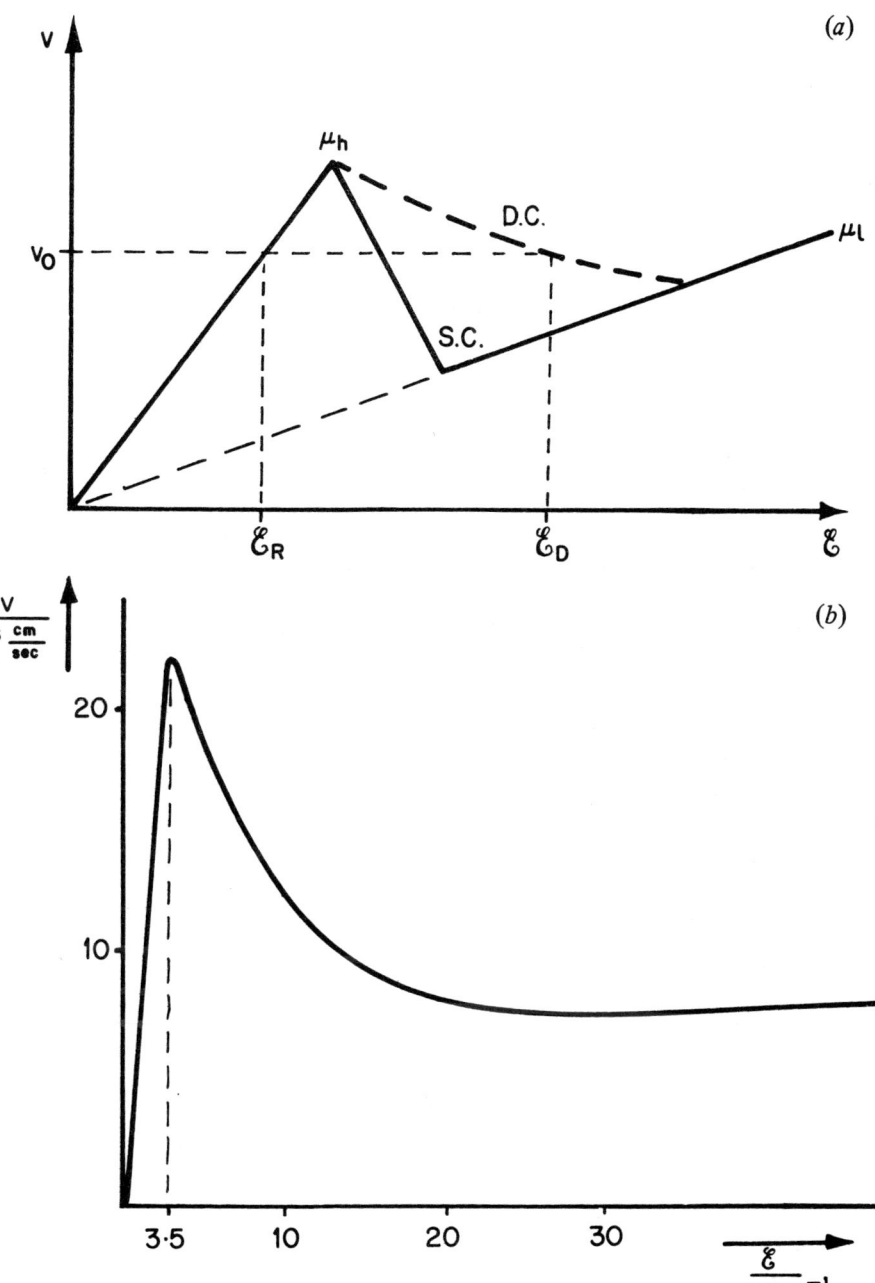

Fig. 4.2. Characteristics of drift velocity vs. Field of transferred-electron effect:
(a) approximate representation; (b) theoretical characteristics (S.C. = static characteristic, D.C. = dynamic characteristic).

Gunn effect is usually observed. Since then, Conwell and Vassell (61a) have
included many effects which affect the velocity-field characteristics, such as
the nonparabolicity of the (100) valley, and found some agreement with most of
the experimental results. Sher and Thornber (254) included two-phonon processes
and argued that these tend to drive the electrons towards a drifted Maxwellian
distribution. This result seems to justify the assumption made by Butcher and
Fawcett (47, 47a), whose results agree in fact very well with experiment.
Unfortunately, it is not easy to measure this relation directly. Measurements are
possible with voltage pulses having a duration smaller than the rise time for
a domain. Therefore, several authors have employed fast pulses (102a) or
microwaves (1, 1a, 40, 105c, 147d) for this purpose. Indirect measurements were
performed by Chang and Moll (54)—(a reverse biased Schottky-barrier $i-n^+$
GaAs photodetector), Thim (277b)—(point contact probes), and by Ruch (243)—
(time of flight experiment in semi-insulating GaAs).

Allen, Shockley and Pearson (5a), Copeland (62), Butcher, Fawcett and Hilsum
(47b), Heinle (117), and several other authors (47c, 123b, 165, 275) have developed
the theory of domain dynamics with the v–$\mathcal{E}$ relation. Advanced theories have
included trapping (238b) and field-dependent diffusion (47d, 261). The amount
of trapping depends very much on the way the crystal was grown, and varies often
from crystal to crystal. The position of various trapping levels in the energy gap
has been measured and it has been suggested that epitaxially-grown GaAs
generally has a lower trap density than bulk material (87, 87a).

The diffusion length of electrons varies appreciably with applied field.
Experimental small-field results are given by Aukerman. *et al.* (12).

The general theory of electrical domains in hot-electron semiconductors has
been developed by Bonch-Bruevich (34, 34a).

We describe here a simplified treatment. The approximation is made that
the specimen is very long, so that no contact effects have to be considered.

Poisson's equation is:

$$\frac{\partial \mathcal{E}}{\partial x} = \frac{e}{\epsilon}(n - n_0) \tag{4.1}$$

and the current conservation equation:

$$\frac{\partial J_t}{\partial x} = 0 \tag{4.2}$$

where $\quad J_t = nev\,(\mathcal{E}) - eD(\partial n/\partial x) + \epsilon\,(\partial \mathcal{E}/\partial t)$

$\qquad \epsilon$ = dielectric constant

$\qquad n$ = electron density

$\qquad n_0$ = donor density

$\qquad \mathcal{E}$ = electric field

$\qquad D$ = diffusion constant and

$\qquad J_t$ = total current density

A solution to equation (4.1) and (4.2) is:

$$\frac{n}{n_0} - \log\left(\frac{n}{n_0}\right) - 1 = \frac{\epsilon}{n_0\,De} \int_{\mathscr{E}_R}^{\mathscr{E}} d\mathscr{E} \left\{ (v(\mathscr{E}) - v_D) - \frac{n_0}{n}\,(v_R - v_D) \right\} \quad (4.3)$$

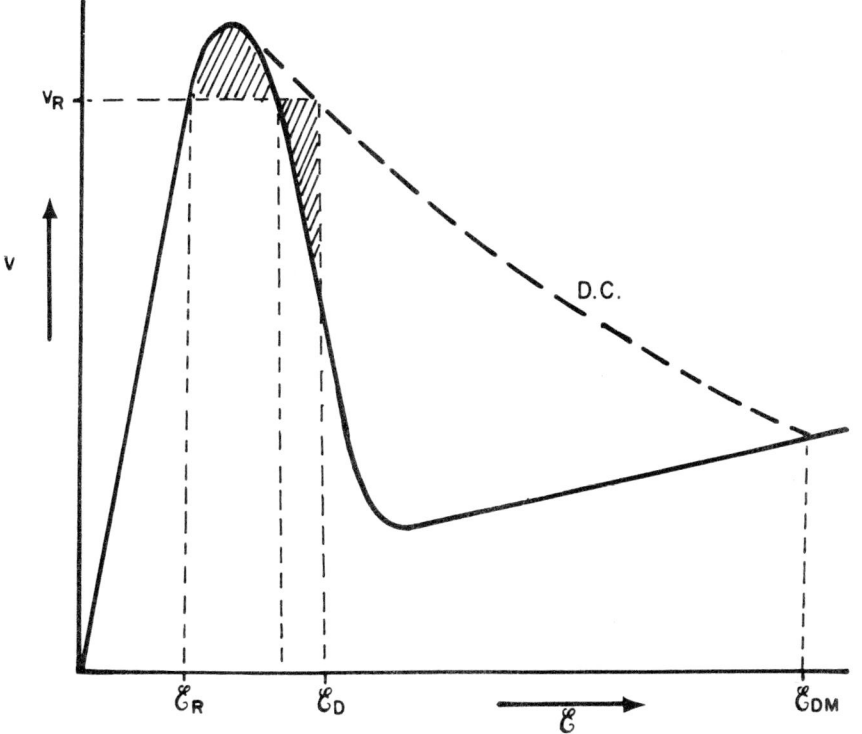

Fig. 4.3   Equal-areas rule indicated by hatched surfaces (D.C. = dynamic characteristics, $\mathscr{E}_{DM}$ = maximum possible domain field).

where the boundary condition $n = n_0$ at $\mathscr{E} = \mathscr{E}_R$ has been imposed, and where the following expression has been used:

$$\frac{\partial \mathscr{E}}{\partial t} = -v_D\,\frac{\partial \mathscr{E}}{\partial x}.$$

[$\mathscr{E}_R$ = field outside the domain, v_D = domain velocity, $v_R = v(\mathscr{E}_R)$].

This solution is simplified on physical grounds if $v_R = v_D$. If we consider cases where $n = n_0$, equation (4.3) reduces to:

$$\int_{\mathscr{E}_R}^{\mathscr{E}_D} d\mathscr{E}[v(\mathscr{E}) - v_D] = 0 \tag{4.4}$$

This is correct if the upper limit of integration is either $\mathscr{E}_R$ or $\mathscr{E}_D$, but not the field of the domain slopes. Equation (4.4) defines an equal-areas rule, as illustrated in Fig. 4.3. The integral over $v(\mathscr{E})$ from $\mathscr{E}_R$ to $\mathscr{E}_D$ must be equal to the domain velocity times $\mathscr{E}_D - \mathscr{E}_R$. This is only fulfilled, if v_D has such a value that the shaded areas in Fig. (4.3) are the same.

The points derived by the equal-areas rule are given by the dashed line, which is called the dynamic characteristic. This gives, therefore, the domain velocity v_D as a function of domain field $\mathscr{E}_D$.

The excess voltage V_D of the domain can be defined by:

$$V_D = \int_{-\infty}^{+\infty} (\mathscr{E} - \mathscr{E}_R) \, dx \tag{4.5}$$

As $v_R = v_D$, the domain velocity v_D is related to $V_R = \mathscr{E}_R \cdot l$ (diffusion neglected). Therefore one can derive the dependence of the excess domain voltage on the field outside the domain, i.e. $V_D = f(\mathscr{E}_R)$ as shown in Fig. 4.4. It is possible to draw a 'load line' into this graph, where the total applied voltage V_B gives the cross point with the voltage axis and the sample length l gives the slope.

For the evaluation of $V_D = f(\mathscr{E}_R)$, one requires $\mathscr{E}_R = f(x)$, which can be obtained from equation (4.1). For $D \neq 0$, this can only be obtained by computer, otherwise an analytic solution is possible, which means that the leading domain edge is a fully depleted layer and the trailing edge is an accumulation layer of zero width and infinite electron density. It has been suggested that for small domain voltages V_D, the field profile is triangular, until $\mu_1 \mathscr{E}_R = \mu_2 \mathscr{E}_D$, at which point $\mathscr{E}_D$ has reached the value $\mathscr{E}_{DM}$ in Fig. (4.3) and the domain forms a flat top. However, no flat-topped domain has ever been observed experimentally. The function of Fig. (4.4) has been determined experimentally by Kuru, Robson and Kino (166a) and agrees quite well with theory.

Figure 4.4 is an important characteristic of a particular diode material. One can find from it: influence of bias voltage and sample length on domain, domain voltage and field $\mathscr{E}_R$ outside domain. And from $\mathscr{E}_R$ and μ_1 (= low-field mobility), we can calculate v_D, as $v_R = v_D$, and obtain finally the transit time and frequency of the current oscillations.

Foyt and McWhorter (47c, 82) have measured the domain potential versus specimen length and found very good agreement with theory (see Fig. 4.5).

As the application of the Gunn-effect as a pulse device has stimulated a wide interest in domain dynamics, it is important to describe the current pulses produced by travelling domains in greater detail. A growth of a domain means a reduction in current through the crystal (102c). The amplitude of the reduction can be obtained from Fig. 4.4. This gives the operating point $\mathscr{E}_{R_0}$ for a given

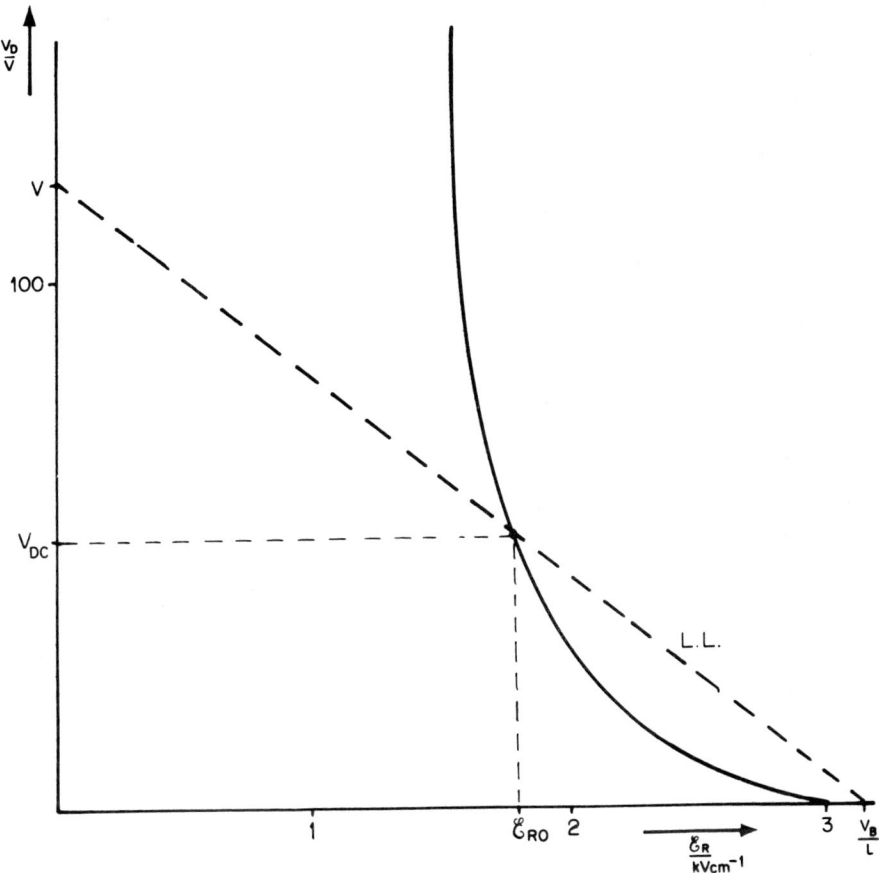

Fig. 4.4 Domain characteristics of typical Gunn diode ($l = 400\mu$, $\rho = 1 \ \Omega$cm). (L.L = device line).

length of the crystal. As the current through the diode is given by $I = A\mathscr{E}_{R_0}/\rho$, the value of $\mathscr{E}_{R_0}$ gives the amount by which the current drops owing to domain formation (ρ is the low-field resistivity and A the diode cross-sectional surface area). The ratio of the current values is therefore $V_B/(l.\mathscr{E}_{R_0})$, where V_B is the bias voltage and l the length of the diode between the two biased ohmic contacts..

The domain with its depletion layer can be treated as a capacitor C_d which has to charge up via the remainder of the diode whose resistance is approximately the small-field value R_0 of the diode. The time T_d of domain growth is the same as the charging time of C_d via R_0. Equally, a domain disappears during T_d, as the

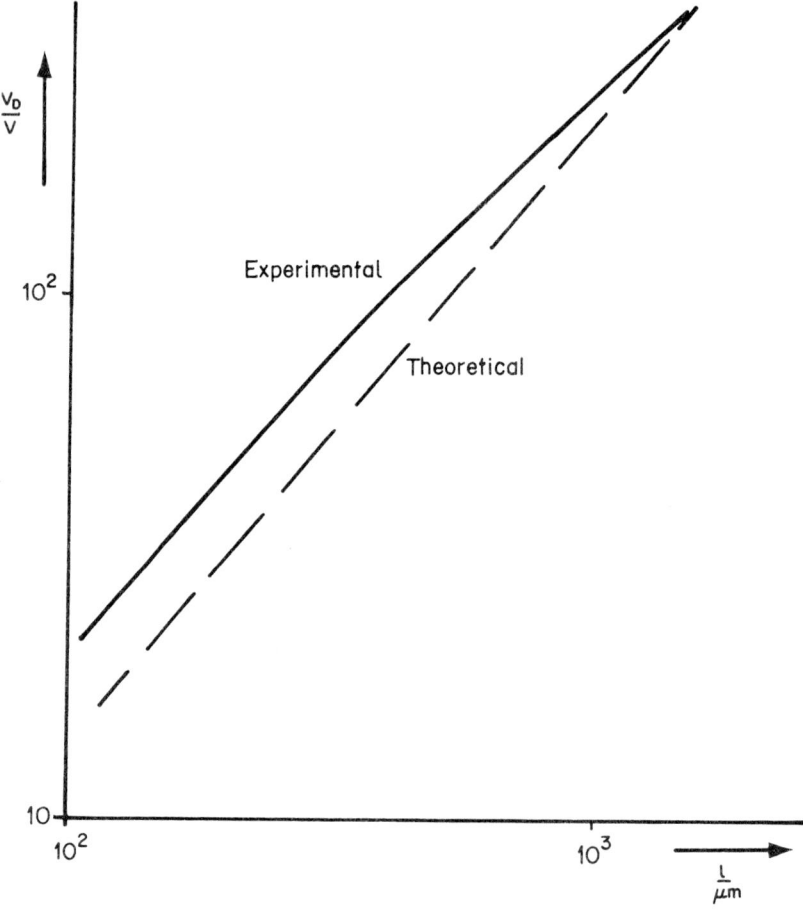

Fig. 4.5   Domain voltage V_D versus sample length l (experimental and theoretical results).

charge on C_d has to be discharged via R_0. With $R_0 = \rho l/A$ and $C_d = \epsilon A/d$ one finds

$$T_d = R_0\,C_d = \frac{\rho l \epsilon}{d} \tag{4.5a}$$

where d is the width of a domain. The excess voltage V_D can be about 50% of the applied voltage V_B if the device is operated with V_B just above the threshold value for domain nucleation as seen from Fig. 4.4. The width d of the depletion layer can be obtained from Poisson's equation by assuming complete depletion in this layer. The accumulation layer can be treated as being much smaller than the depleted region. The ionized donor impurities ρ_D are the only charges in the depletion layer, so that we have

$$\frac{d^2 \phi}{dx^2} = \frac{\rho_D}{\epsilon}$$ (4.5b)

where ϕ is the potential. This gives a relation between the voltage V_D and d, namely

$$V_D = \frac{\rho_D d^2}{2 \epsilon}$$ (4.5c)

If one operates just above threshold, the applied voltage is

$$V_B \simeq \frac{\rho_D d^2}{\epsilon}$$

For complete depletion, ρ_D must be equal to the electron charge density $n \cdot e$ in the low-field case, so that

$$d \simeq \sqrt{\left(\frac{V_B \epsilon}{ne}\right)}$$ (4.5d)

The transit time t_d for a domain is approximately given by the following relation:

$$t_d \simeq 2l(\mu_l \mathscr{E}_{tn})^{-1}$$ (4.5e)

where μ_l is the low-field mobility and $\mathscr{E}_{tn}$ is the field near threshold, and the dielectric relaxation time is

$$\tau_d = \frac{\epsilon}{\mu\rho}$$ (4.5f)

Equations (4.5a), (4.5d), (4.5e) and (4.5f) give now the rise and decay time of a Gunn-effect current pulse,

$$T_d \simeq \sqrt{(t_d \cdot \tau_d)}$$ (4.5g)

This relation indicates a basic condition for the occurrence of domains, namely, that $T_d \leqslant t_d$. However, there exists also another limit, which is basic to the transferred-electron effect and will impose limitations also on all the other instability modes described in the next section. This is the time it takes an electron to be scattered into the satellite valley. It has been shown that the relaxation time τ_1 for electron transfer from the central valley to the satellite one, is field-dependent, in contrast to the field-independence of the relaxation time τ_2 for the reverse process(61b). For frequencies

$$f_g > \frac{1}{2\pi}\left(\frac{1}{\tau_1} + \frac{1}{\tau_2}\right)$$

the imaginary part of the r.f. conductivity becomes larger than the real part. If this is taken as the upper frequency limit, one finds that f_g increases mono-tonically from 85 GHz to 700 GHz with electric field (215).

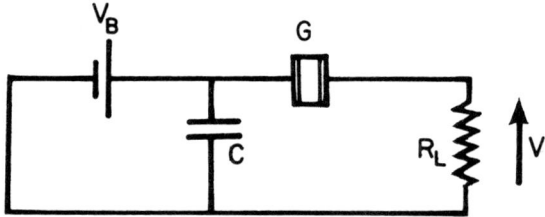

Fig. 4.6   External circuit of Gunn diode G for the 'fundamental transit-time mode' (C=by-pass capacitor, R_L =load resistance).

4.1.3 Modes of Operation

Only in exceptional circumstances, will high-field domains cross from the nucleation point to the anode. This mode of operation will occur if the following two conditions are given:

(a)   The crystal is long enough, so that a domain can form. The theoretical condition has been derived by Ridley (238a), and is given by the relation $t_d > T_d$ which leads to the expression

$$n.l \simeq 10^{12}\,\frac{l}{cm^2} \qquad\qquad (4.5aa)$$

where n = carrier density.

(b)   The external circuit, presented to the diode, is of low ohmic value, as shown in Fig. 4.6.

If R_L is not small, the voltage across R_L must at least be small enough not to interfere with the process of nucleation and extinction of domains. For large load values, the resistance R_L has to be included in the above expression, [see equation (4.5a)], for the growth-time of a domain, i.e.

$$T_d = (R_0 + R_L)\,C_d$$

This shows an increase in T_d, which will finally cause $T_d \gtrsim t_d$ so that no domain can be nucleated any more. For $T_d < t_d$, the output will be non-sinusoidal, as shown in Fig. 4.7. The high-voltage level is given by the diode current in the absence of a domain, whereas the voltage drops when a domain is formed and rises again when the domain is discharged near the anode. The domain causes, therefore, a negative voltage pulse across the load with a pulse duration being that of the domain transit time. The rise and fall time of the pulse is given by the charging and discharging time T_d. Only if $T_d \simeq t_d$, is the output voltage approximately sinusoidal.

If this pulse output is fed into a resonant circuit with a high enough Q-factor, we obtain the '*fundamental transit-time mode*', if the circuit-resonance frequency is the same as the transit-time frequency. The efficiency is low,

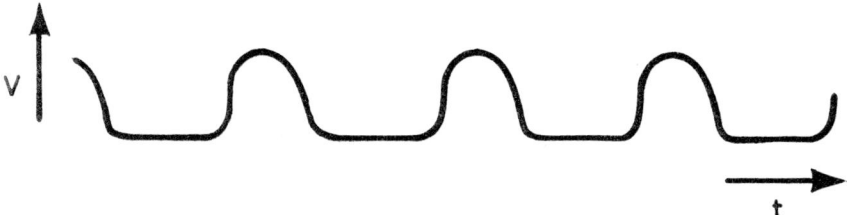

Fig. 4.7 Output voltage V of transit time mode as measured across the load resistance R_L.

as the frequency spectrum of the current contains little energy at the fundamental frequency.

On the other hand, if the circuit-resonance frequency f_0 is tuned to some harmonic of the transit-time pulses, we obtain the '*harmonic transit-time modes*'. One can describe this also as follows: If f_0 is the nth harmonic of the transit-time frequency, the output voltages will have a waveform consisting of a series of damped sinusoids, reinforced every nth cycle. The diode, however, has during domain transit, an internal impedance whose real part can be negative, so that the amplitudes of the output voltage can also remain constant or even grow between the domain-pulses. When the domain arrives at the anode, the diode presents a different impedance, whose real part might then cause a corresponding decrease in oscillation amplitude again. This mode of oscillation can, therefore, have either various amplitude fluctuations or constant-amplitude oscillations.

If the resonance voltage is large enough, so that it can influence the domain nucleation and extinction, we have the so-called '*resonant modes*'.

For the understanding of these modes it is useful to know the current-voltage characteristics of a Gunn diode, as shown in Fig. 4.8 (102c). Subtracting the voltage outside the domain, we find the diode current versus domain voltage, as shown in Fig. 4.9. Both these figures show, that the current rises with applied voltage, until the threshold for domain formation

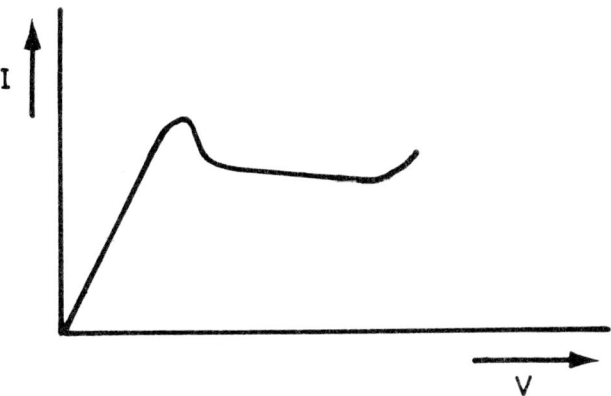

Fig. 4.8   Current I versus voltage V of Gunn oscillator.

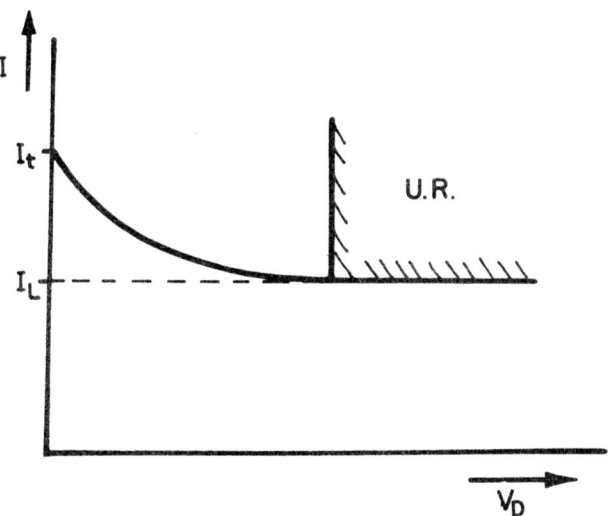

Fig. 4.9   Current I versus excess domain voltage V_D (I_t =threshold current for domain formation, I_L =limiting value for stable operation, U.R.= unsteady region).

is reached, from which point onwards, the current decreases. If the applied diode voltage is further increased, one reaches voltages which cause impact and field ionization and the oscillations become unstable.

If a load R_L is applied to the oscillator, we have to introduce a load line into Fig. 4.9, as

$$V_B = V_D + I(R_0 + R_L) \tag{4.6}$$

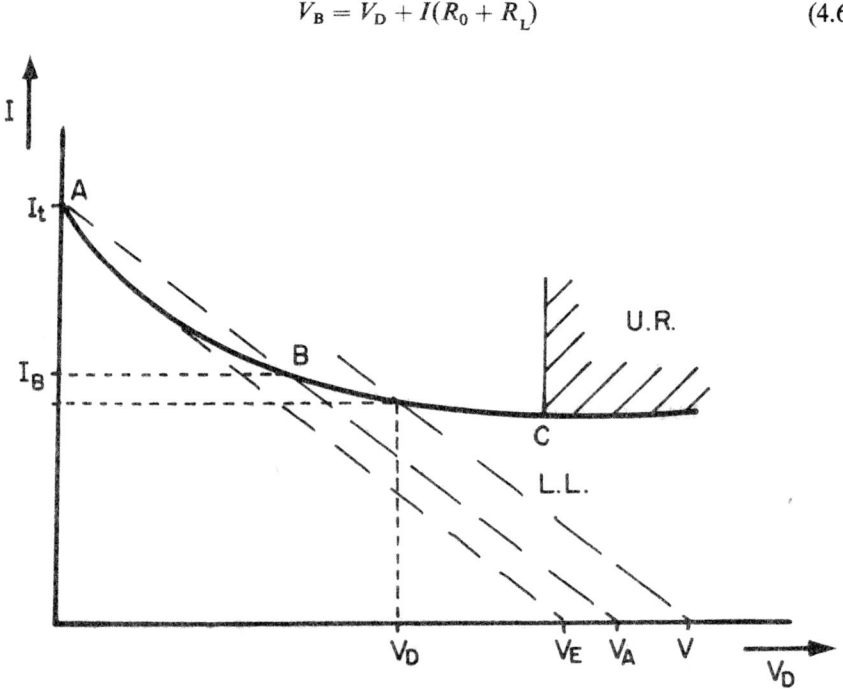

Fig. 4.10 Current I versus excess domain voltage V_D with load line L.L (V_A = threshold voltage for domain formation, I_B = diode current for domain in transit, U.R. = unsteady region).

with $R_0 \cong$ resistance of crystal outside the domain

$$\cong \frac{l \mathscr{E}_R}{I}$$

The slope of the load line is given by $-1/(R_0+R_L)$, as shown in Fig. 4.10. On this figure we can also see the threshold current I_t for oscillations. If we increase the applied voltage V_B from the value $V_B = 0$, we find that I increases linearly until I_t is reached. Then the operating point will jump from A to B and the diode current drops to I_B. For a further increase of V_B, the operating point will finally reach C, where the unsteady region begins.

If a domain has been nucleated by a voltage larger than V_A, the applied voltage can be decreased without extinction of domain, unless it becomes smaller than V_E (see Fig. 4.10).

When the combination of the bias voltage and the microwave voltage of a resonant circuit across the diode causes the applied voltage to swing from V_1 to V_2 in Fig. 4.11, a domain will form as soon as the operating point A has

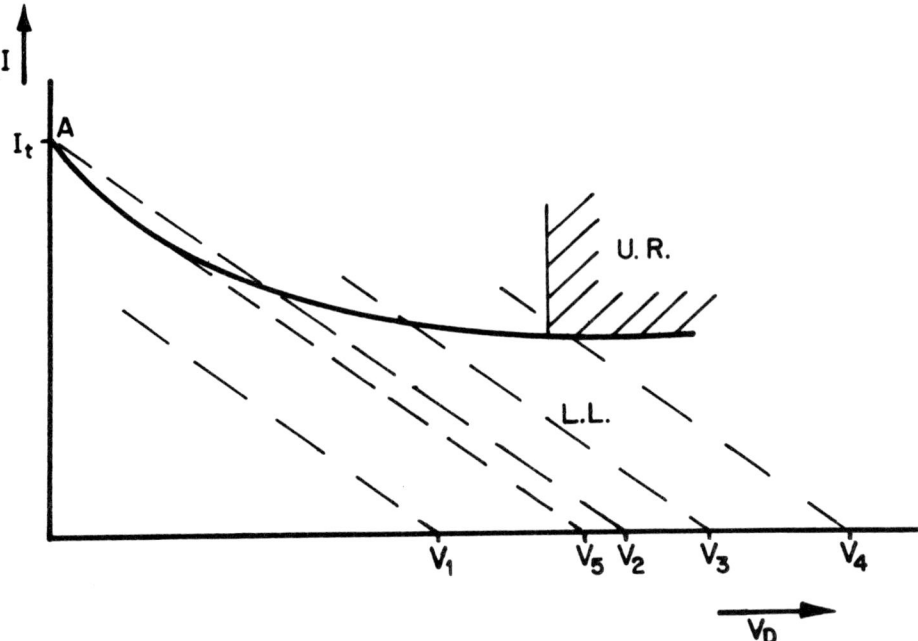

Fig. 4.11 I versus V_D with load line L.L. for u.v.r. and o.v.r. mode.

been reached. The formation of a domain will cause a current drop, which means, the diode presents a negative resistance to the resonance circuit. For a subsequent decrease in applied voltage from V_2 to V_1, the domain will be extinguished on its transit and the diode current will increase again. The diode current is therefore counteracting the ohmic loss-current of the resonant circuit and the oscillations will grow. The frequency of oscillation is determined by the resonance frequency of the external circuit (and to a small extent by the load admittance of the diode). The period of oscillation must be smaller (or much greater) than the transit-time t_d of a domain. As the diode-current waveform resembles a square wave, the efficiency will be higher than in transit-time modes. This mode has been called the *Under-Voltage Resonant Mode*.

If the bias voltage is increased further, so that the total voltage across the diode swings from V_3 to V_4 in Fig. 4.11, the crystal will first have one domain. As soon as the unsteady region is reached, the voltage is so high that a second domain might form at the cathode and the original one will be extinguished by the new one. The fact that normally no two domains can exist simultaneously in series, can be explained by the voltage-controlled negative resistance characteristics. However, why the new domain often takes over the original one is obscure. The effect of the domain extinction process means that no domain will reach the anode if the resonance period is again smaller than the transit time. As a reduction in current occurs for an increase in voltage from V_3 to V_4, a negative resistance is exhibited. The current change is of a small value only and this mode is therefore less efficient. Additionally it will be rather noisy, as the current in the unsteady region is fluctuating, and the mode will be a little non-coherent. This mode has been called the *Over-Voltage Resonant Mode*.

A third type of resonance mode is possible. If the applied voltage across the diode oscillates between V_5 and V_2 in Fig. 4.11, a domain formed during the positive period cannot be extinguished by the negative period. However, if the transit time t_d is related to the oscillation period T' by the following relation:

$$\tfrac{1}{2}T' < t_d < T'$$

then no further domain can be nucleated during the remaining time of the period, when the current will be increased to a value somewhat smaller than I_t. Again, if one Fourier-analyzes the resultant current function, the current of the fundamental frequency, which is equal to the circuit-resonance frequency, will exhibit a negative resistance effect. This mode has been called: *Mixed Mode*.

The most important contribution towards an understanding of these resonant modes, as described above, has been made by Gunn (102b). He employed the powerful research tool of capacitive probes along the crystal. This enables one to determine fast changes in potential and field occurring inside the device.

4.1.4 Space-Charge Wave Amplifier

Now we have to discuss an instability in GaAs, which occurs if $n.\, l < 10^{12}\text{cm}^{-2}$†, i.e., if the crystal is too short for domain formation. In this case, semiconductor-plasma instabilities set in between the streams of two different types of particles, the light and heavy electrons. Thim *et al.* (277), McCumber and Chynoweth (187), Mahrous *et al.* (179), McWhorter and Foyt (191a), and Hakki (104b), have essentially clarified this mode of operation.

It can give first a convective instability, which means, the diode will act as a reflection amplifier. For higher bias voltages, the gain is so large that only a small feedback via the external circuit will cause the diode to start oscillating. The direct biasing current will not decrease during the instability, as we have seen with the domain formation (see Fig. 4.8).

† Ridley (238a) obtained the above value, whereas McCumber and Chynoweth (187) found a value of $n.\, l = 2.10^{11}\,\text{cm}^{-2}$.

Neglecting diffusion, the steady-state current density J is given by

$$J = e\mathscr{E}(\mu_1 n_L + \mu_2 n_u) \tag{4.7}$$

(μ_1 and μ_2 are the mobilities and n_L and n_u the electron densities of the lower and upper valleys respectively).

The Poisson equation is:

$$\frac{d\mathscr{E}}{dx} = \frac{e}{\epsilon}(n_L + n_u - n_0) \tag{4.8}$$

In order to obtain an analytical solution, an approximation to the function of Fig. 4.3 can be used. The boundary condition is that $\mathscr{E} = 0$ at $x = 0$. With a small-signal analysis (i.e. a time-dependence of the form exp $(j\omega t)$ is used and only first-order terms are included), and the relation

$$\tilde{\jmath} + j\omega\epsilon\,\tilde{\mathscr{E}} = \tilde{\jmath}_t \tag{4.9}$$

($\tilde{\jmath}_t$ is the total alternating current density and the curly line denotes a small-signal quantity), one can find the terminal impedance

$$Z_s = \frac{1}{j\omega\epsilon A}\left[l - \frac{1}{\tilde{\jmath}_t} \int_0^l \tilde{\jmath}\,dx \right] \tag{4.10}$$

(A = cross-sectional area). The impedance $Z_s = R + jX$ can be found analytically, giving the results of Fig. 4.12, where R_0 = low-field resistance of the specimen, and where the crystal data are: $l = 100\,\mu$, $\rho = 100\,\Omega$ cm, $\mu_1 = 5000$ cm^2/V sec; $\mu_2 \simeq 0$, $n_0 = 1.25 \cdot 10^{13}$cm^{-3}. It can be seen, how a negative resistance effect occurs over limited frequency ranges.

This amplification mode has been studied under various aspects, such as a non-uniform doping profile (256), thermal effects (277c), and near-intrinsic crystals (164a), and the general conditions for space-charge-wave growth and differential negative resistance have been investigated (246).

Mahrous et al. (179) have shown that trapping damps out the negative conductance of Fig. 4.12. However, as the carrier lifetime measured so far (123c), shows a value of about 200 nsec, this might have a negligible effect only.

Heinle (117) has shown that the condition of Ridley (238a) [equation (4.5aa)], is not given by a constant, but depends also on the applied electric field $\mathscr{E}$. For field values just above the threshold for the transferred electron effect, the boundary is given at very large $n \cdot l$ values, for $\mathscr{E} \simeq 10$ kV/cm it is about $n \cdot l = 2 \cdot 10^{11}$cm^{-2} and for higher fields, the required $n \cdot l$ increases again. This means one can switch

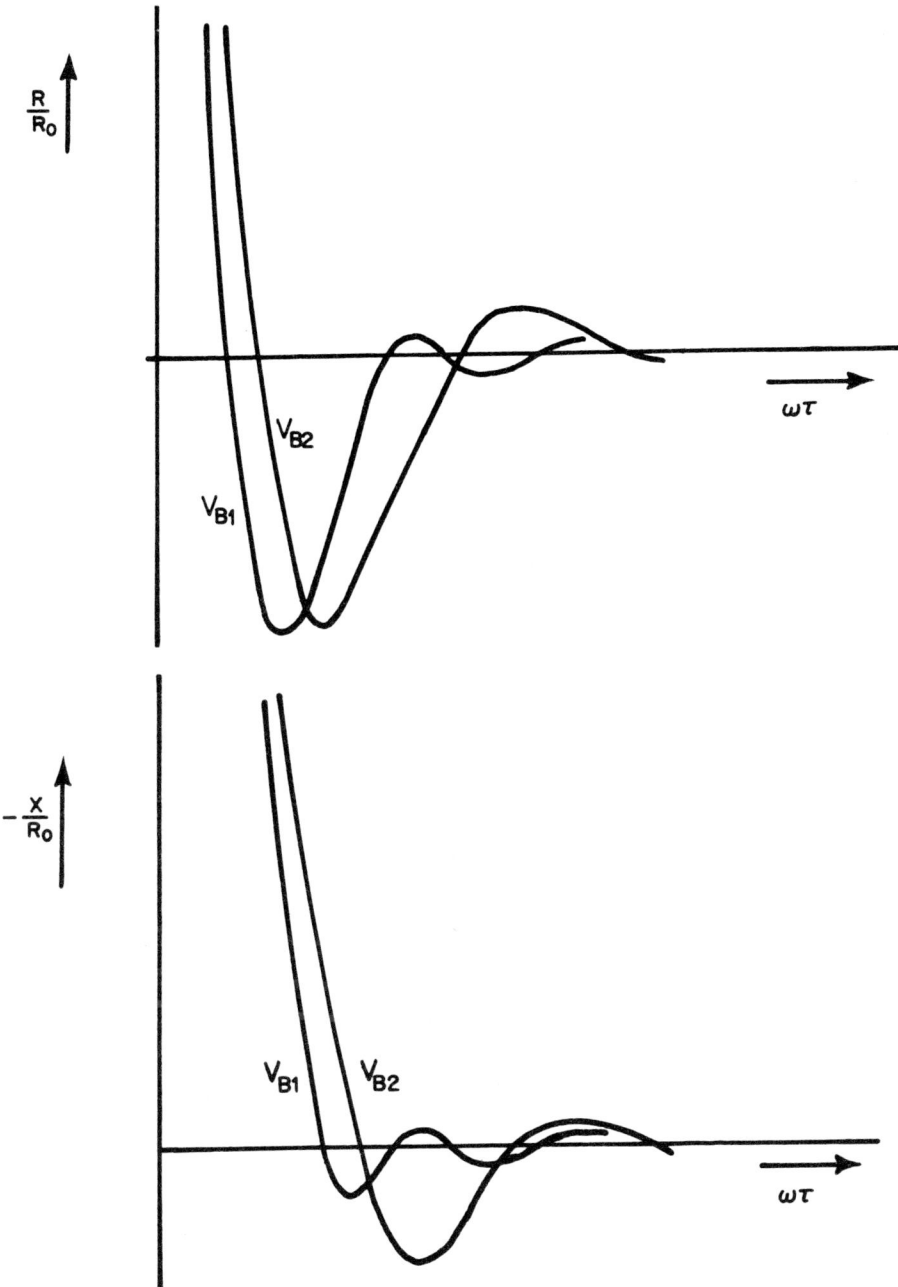

Fig. 4.12 Complex impedance $R+jX$ of a Gunn diode amplifier ($V_{B1} = 1.1\ V_t$; $V_{B2} = 1.6\ V_t$; V_t=threshold voltage; $\tau = \epsilon/(e\ \mu_l n_0)$; R_0 = low-field diode resistance).

from domain-formation mode into the amplifier mode only by a change of applied voltage.

Mahrous *et al.* (179) have proposed, that one can switch a diode with $n.l = 10^{12} \mathrm{cm}^{-2}$ from the domain mode into the amplifier one by the application of a suitable load impedance. With the help of a mathematical treatment based on Nyquist's diagram (see Chapter III, p. 67), one can in fact show that this effect can be achieved by a change in load. Experiments have shown the following: When diodes are inserted into a coaxial cavity, they exhibit oscillations with accompanied reduction in dc current, as shown by Fig. 4.8. This indicates the formation of domains. The diodes were then inserted into a variable impedance circuit, which incorporated a line stretcher, a T-junction, a short-circuit stub and a 50 Ω load resistance. By adjusting the line stretcher and the short-circuited stub, any required impedance could be presented to the diode. With suitable impedances, oscillations were suppressed. With the help of a directional coupler, one could find then large reflection-power gain. Increasing the applied voltage appreciably caused the diode to oscillate again, however, without the typical decrease in dc current as shown in Fig. 4.8. It can be assumed that these are negative resistance oscillations, at the resonant frequency of the circuit.

4.1.5 The lsa Oscillator

A further mode of operation has been discovered by Copeland (62a). It arises if the biasing voltage is larger than twice the threshold voltage for domain formation. Copeland (62) wrote earlier that there are the following four distinct classes of solution for equations (4.1) and (4.2), corresponding to four possible sets of boundary conditions, namely

(1)　the crystal is separated into two different field regions, with the low field near the cathode (accumulation layer mode)
(2)　the same as (1) except that the low field area is near the anode (depletion layer mode)
(3)　the high field domain (= the Gunn-effect domain) and
(4)　the low field domain.

It is possible to obtain oscillations with the first of these modes (the accumulation layer mode) as shown experimentally by Shaw and Shuskus (252), Copeland (62a, 62b), Kennedy (150, 150b), and others (81). These modes are more efficient as it is not only the narrow domain, which is producing microwave power, with the remainder of the crystal dissipative, but a large part of the diode is actively engaged in the transformation of dc into microwave power. It is interesting to see some experimental results of this high field mode (which has also been called the lsa† mode), as seen in Fig. 4.13. This mode is of great importance for many applications.

The frequency of operation is higher than the reciprocal of the carrier transit time and is determined by the resonance frequency of the external circuit. The

† lsa = limited space-charge accumulation.

conditions for an lsa mode are that the ratio of operating frequency f to electron density n must lie within a certain range and the tuned circuit must be loaded such that the voltage across the device swings below the threshold voltage during each cycle. The oscillator can be tuned up to 50% by changing the resonance circuit.

The electric field across the diode is swinging from below the threshold value

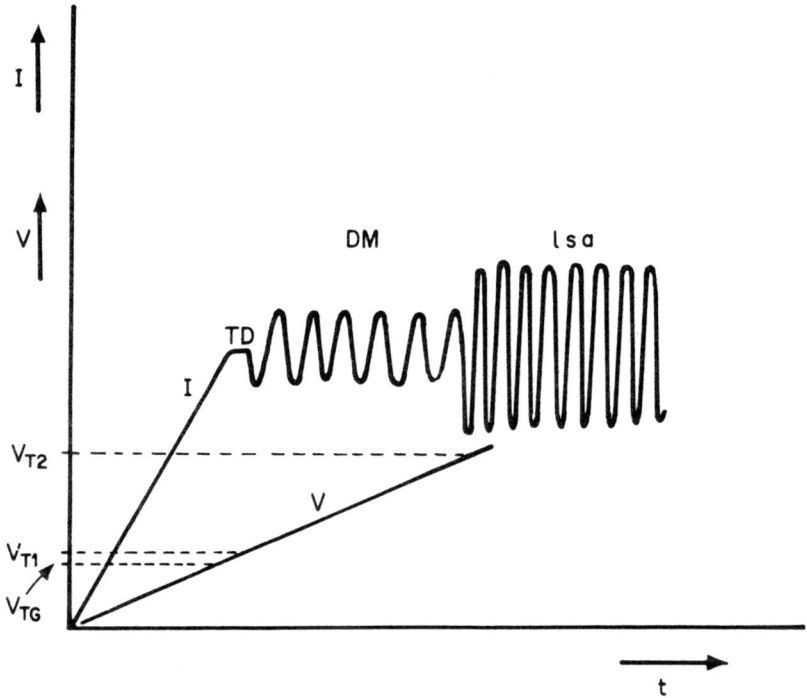

Fig. 4.13 Different modes of Gunn diodes for increasing applied voltage V: (1) ohmic behaviour for low voltages; (2) current reduction owing to a trapped domain for $V_{TG} < V < V_{T1}$, (3) domain oscillation for $V_{T1} < V < V_{T2}$, (4) lsa mode of oscillations for $V_{T2} < V$.

to a value more than twice the threshold one so quickly, that a domain cannot form. There is only an accumulation layer near the cathode and the rest of the diode is in the negative resistance state. The condition for this effect is

$$1/f \leqslant 3\epsilon/(n|\mu| e)$$

(ϵ = permittivity, $|\mu|$ = average negative electron mobility, e = electronic charge).

During the negative swing the accumulation layer must disappear, which is only possible for a short dielectric relaxation time, i.e.

$$1/f \gg \frac{\epsilon}{n\mu_l e}$$

(μ_l = low field mobility).

With $\epsilon \simeq 10^{-10}$ F/m, $\mu_l = 0.5$ m^2/Vsec, $|\mu| = -0.01$ m^2/Vsec, the above-mentioned condition for the lsa mode is given by the following relation:

$$2 \times 10^5 \gg \frac{n}{f} \gg 1.4 . 10^3 \left[\frac{\text{sec}}{\text{cm}^3} \right] \tag{4.11}$$

Experiments give the following impressive results for the lsa mode of operation:

frequency/GHz	9.2	30	88
CW output power/mW	100	63	22 (62c)
n/cm^{-3}	1.2×10^{15}	3×10^{15}	
n/f	1.4×10^5	1×10^5	
efficiency/%		1.5	2

It is, however, difficult to produce suitable GaAs crystals which show the lsa mode. Therefore, only a few laboratories have been able to measure these high-frequency oscillations so far, in spite of its enormous commercial interest. Detailed theoretical work has shown, that the lsa mode is not necessarily a mode with an approximately uniform field distribution, which swings as a whole between the two states of above and below the threshold field $\mathscr{E}_t$ for the electron transfer to the satellite valley. It is possible that high-field domains are superimposed on the overall field, which has still to be above $\mathscr{E}_t$ if one speaks about the lsa mode, in accordance with general agreement. Theoretical results by Thim (277h) indicate, in fact, that domains always form in samples with $nl > 10^{12}$ cm^{-2} owing to random doping fluctuations, and that accumulation layer modes occur only in crystals of $nl < 10^{12}$ cm^{-2}.

It has been found experimentally, that $l . n$ must not be too large, otherwise accidentally-formed high-field domains would damage the crystal.

Various authors have presented analytic studies of the lsa mode (36a, 117a). This is of value for a correct design of suitable GaAs oscillators.

4.1.6 Further Phenomena

If one utilizes the negative slope produced by domain formation, as shown in Fig. 4.8, one can obtain negative resistance gain. For this effect, the device has to oscillate with a frequency given by the transit time of domains. If the bias voltage is then slightly increased, the time-averaged current decreases.

This can be utilized either for reflection gain (277d) at a frequency far enough away from the domain oscillation, or for neutralizing losses of resonant circuits (138). The latter effect was known from experiments in connection with domain-formation oscillation, as a stray resonance of the circuit could suddenly break into continuous oscillations, which were then superimposed on the wave-form caused by travelling domains. Using suitable filters for the two frequencies involved, one can employ the reflection gain effect as an amplifier of very wide bandwidth. This is, in fact, the important advantage; the reflection gain owing to domain formation is more or less constant for all frequencies, except for the resonance of the domain-transit time, whereas the small-signal gain of dual-carrier-type streaming is very dispersive, as shown by Fig. 4.12. Therefore, this domain reflection gain could be of great importance for technical applications.

There are numerous further effects, which have been observed by various research workers. Illumination of cooled Gunn-oscillators resulted in an abrupt shift from the transit-time frequency mode to a higher frequency (251). This could possibly be explained by high-field trapping, which is increased by higher illumination intensity.

With diodes of large $n . l$ product, infrared radiation of band-gap frequency has been emitted by travelling high-field domains and attributed to impact ionization (116, 261, 261a). Associated with this infrared emission a current-controlled instability has also been observed, together with broad-band microwave emission (173, 304) immediately after the Gunn-effect instability has set in. The infrared radiation is believed to be a result of radiative recombination associated with the impact ionization in the domain, whose field is estimated to be greater than 75 kV/cm in these cases. The negative resistance observed seems to be caused by avalanche injection instabilities, similar to the phenomena described in the following section, 4.2. Thim and Knight (277e) have performed potential-profile measurements on diodes exhibiting this current-controlled negative resistance. They found very high electric fields near the anode contacts. This shows that avalanching will most likely also occur near the anode.

4.2 The Avalanche Effect

The most important competitor of the Gunn diode as an oscillator is the avalanche diode, often called IMPATT (from IMPact Avalanche and Transit Time). Bell Telephone Laboratories reported already in February 1967 that they had obtained 1.1 W CW operation at 12 GHz with 8% efficiency, and the output power has been increased since then to many watts by very skilful heat-sinking.

The effect can be explained if one takes into account the avalanche mechanism in semiconductors for very high applied electric fields, as first proposed by Read (236) and theoretically further developed by Misawa (196a), and others.

4.2.1. The Read Diode

A suitable epitaxial sandwich of various doping layers can give a depletion layer of fixed width in a relatively weakly-doped region bounded by highly conductive end regions, if a reverse bias is applied. An example is the n^+-p-i-p^+ structure, as shown in Fig. 4.14. The applied voltage is high enough, so that the space-charge

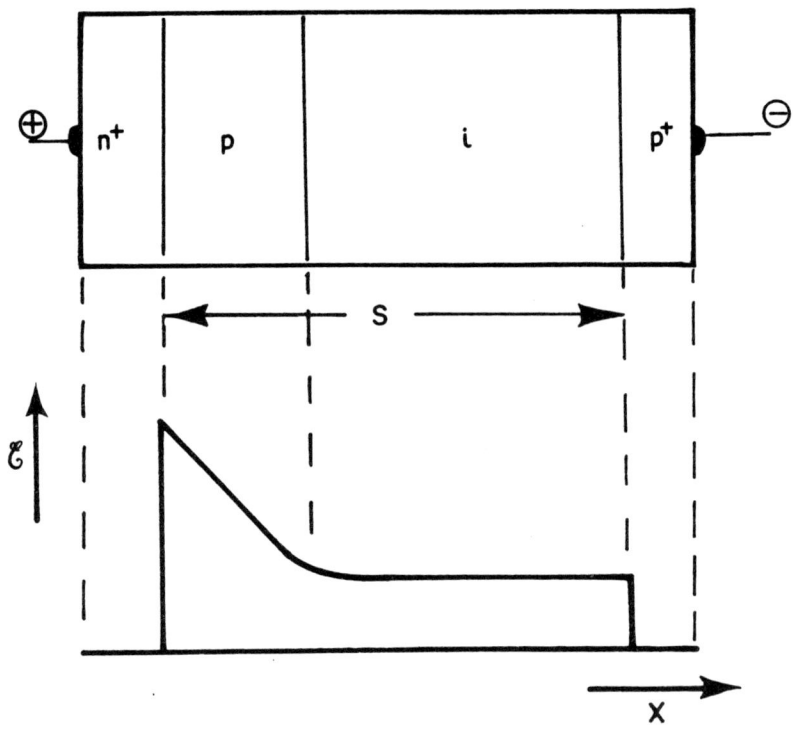

Fig. 4.14   Structure of Read diode and resulting field distribution (S = space-charge layer, + denotes high doping, i = intrinsic).

region always extends from the n^+-p junction to the i-p^+ junction. The maximum field, which occurs at the n^+-p junction, is of the order of several hundred kV/cm, just below the value for electron-hole pair generation by impact ionization or the Zener effect. The electrons will move to the n^+ region, whereas the holes travel across the entire space-charge region to the p^+ layer. The field in the space-charge region is so high that carriers move with a field-independent velocity v. Their transit time is

$$\tau_t = \frac{w_s}{v} \tag{4.12}$$

where w_s is the width of the space-charge region. When a bunch of holes is generated by a short increase in applied voltage, they will arrive at the p^+ electrode after some delay, giving a current pulse I_e out of phase with the applied-voltage pulse. If the device is placed in a cavity, and the resonance frequency is

$$f_0 = \frac{1}{2\tau_t}$$

the diode presents a negative resistance to the resonant circuit by its conductive current I_e.

Additionally, there is a displacement, or capacitive current I_c, which charges and discharges the diode as a capacitor. This current produces a detuning effect of the cavity, which has to be taken into account for the determination of the correct f_0.

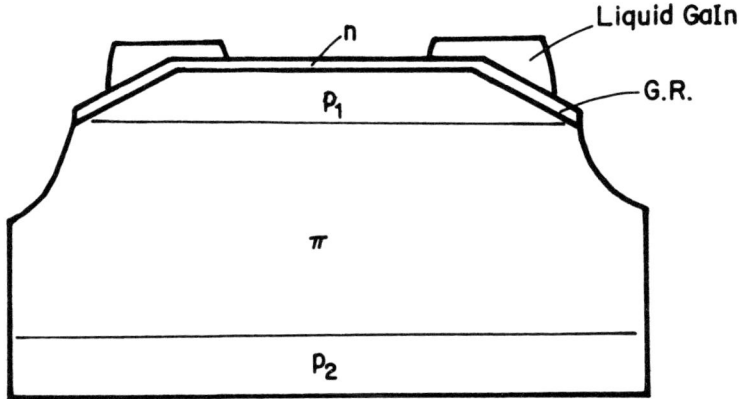

Fig. 4.15 Schematic cross-section of $np\pi p$ structure with guard ring G.R. (doping levels in cm^{-3}: n: 10^{19}; p_1: 10^{13}; π: 6.10^{12}; p_2: 3.10^{16}).

The diode has to be biased so that the peak field is above the threshold value $\mathcal{E}_{ta}$ for avalanching during the positive half of the voltage cycle and below $\mathcal{E}_{ta}$ during the negative half. Avalanching can occur either by impact ionization or as a result of the Zener effect, which means ionization by high electric fields.

Read predicted large power output at high conversion efficiencies in his analysis (236). However, in spite of considerable effort, it remained very difficult to build an experimental microwave device owing to the presence of field inhomogeneities causing microplasmas. These are well-known phenomena occurring usually in p–n junctions biased strongly in the reverse direction (103). They represent highly localized breakdown regions with intense carrier multiplication, and they have very high effective carrier temperatures. One of Read's basic assumptions is that the multiplication must be uniform and high over the whole junction area. In order to fulfill these conditions more easily, Lee et al. (170, 170a) fabricated

a low-frequency structure (180 MHz) at moderate impedance levels (5000 Ω).
The device was a $np\pi p$ structure, produced by vacuum diffusion techniques (Ga
and As into 2000 Ω cm–Si), and was free of microplasmas (see Fig. 4.15).
A special guard-ring structure was generated by two masking and etching steps in
order to avoid surface inhomogeneities. The operating bias was about 600 V.

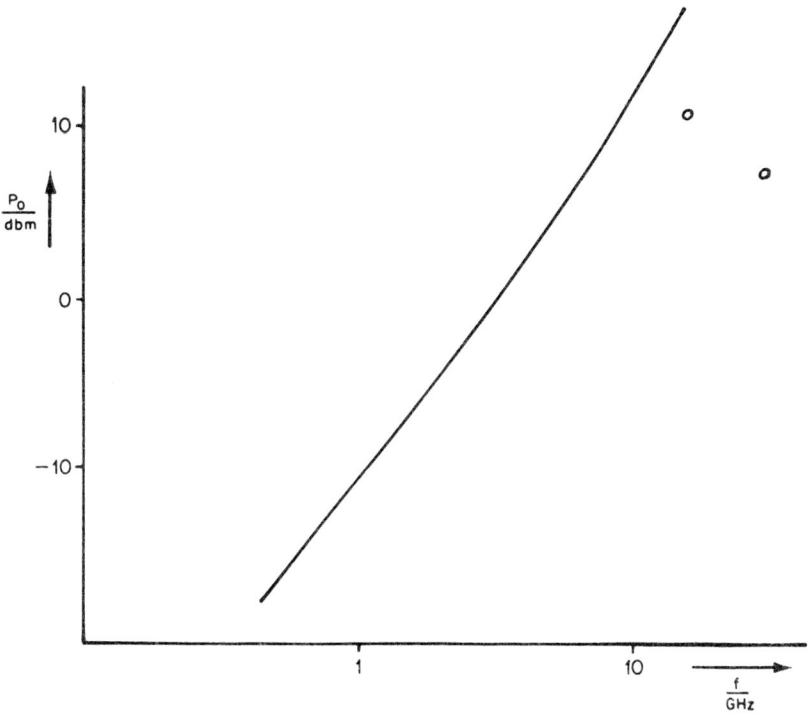

Fig. 4.16   Output power P_0 versus frequency of p-n diode, related to: 0 dbm = 1 mW.
(results for coaxial-cavity mounting, except two values indicated by $\bigcirc$, which were
obtained in waveguide mounting).

The oscillations could be tuned continuously from 110 to 250 MHz in the
fundamental mode. No oscillations could be observed at the second harmonic,
whereas a 540 MHz-output could be detected as the third harmonic. These
results verified Read's predictions.

At about the same time, Johnston *et al.* (141) obtained microwave oscillations
from p-n Silicon diodes biased in the reverse direction. The diodes were made by
boron diffusion into 0.15 Ω cm n-type silicon. Their results are shown in Fig.
4.16. They cannot be explained by the Read-diode model any more.

Höfflinger (126a) obtained microwave oscillations with diodes having the
doping structure p^{++}-n-n^{++} and p^{++}-n^{+}-n-n^{++}. Large power outputs of up to

3 W under pulsed conditions were obtained for frequencies up to 8 GHz. The absence of a lower cut-off frequency as predicted by Read's model, showed that transit-time effects were not essential and it was suggested that some space-charge effects were involved.

Both these latter results required a new explanation, which was in fact, presented by a small-signal analysis developed by Misawa (196a)(and other authors), and described in the following section.

4.2.2   The Misawa Instability

Use is made of the effect that carriers drift with a velocity which is independent of the field, if the applied field is larger than a given value $\&$. A density perturbation with its local electric field does not then spread out, but propagates without attenuation in the direction of the drift velocity of the carriers.

The generation-rate of electron-hole pairs is larger both when the electric field is stronger and when there is a higher carrier density. If a density perturbation travels through the crystal, the maximum density will be in its centre, whereas the highest field appears at the maximum boundary slopes. For a periodic-wave perturbation, this means that the field wave lags the electron density wave by 90°. The electron-hole pair generation will have its peak value then just before the maximum electron-density value arrives and its smallest values after the density peak has passed (see Fig. 4.17). This means that in the positive half cycle of the electron-density wave, the number of electrons increases, whereas it decreases during the negative half cycle. The holes are dragged by the electron-density wave, though drifting in the opposite direction, and lag the field by more than 90°. Thus the ohmic losses due to both electron and hole currents are negative in this case. This means that there are growing space-charge waves. The instability is produced if the avalanching plasma is not restricted by boundaries, such as in a p-n junction, which is the easiest device for the production of an avalanching plasma. Therefore, the theory has to be extended if boundaries are given for a confined plasma, as shown in Fig. 4.18. Electrons enter from the left and holes from the right. When an impulsive current is applied, it produces charge spikes at both edges of the space-charge region. This corresponds to a momentary widening of the space-charge region. However, the charge in the spikes is given mainly by immobile charge carriers of ionized impurities, since the saturation current of a p-n junction is very small. The charge spikes have to wait to be neutralized by carriers generated by avalanche. The spikes raise the field in the space-charge region by a constant amount, which however, causes an increased electron-hole production. When the spikes are finally neutralized, a higher carrier density is available causing further avalanching. This causes a narrowing of the space-charge region, the field is decreased, and avalanching decreases. This, however, brings about a reversal to the original state again and the process repeats itself, with growing amplitudes.

It is very instructive to discuss the small-signal analysis of this instability. The relevant equations are:

(1)　Poisson's equation (equation 2.3),

(2)　the continuity equations [equations (2.36) and 2.41)] with the approximation for the generation rate g_c (equation 2.43) and

(3)　the current equation, neglecting diffusion.

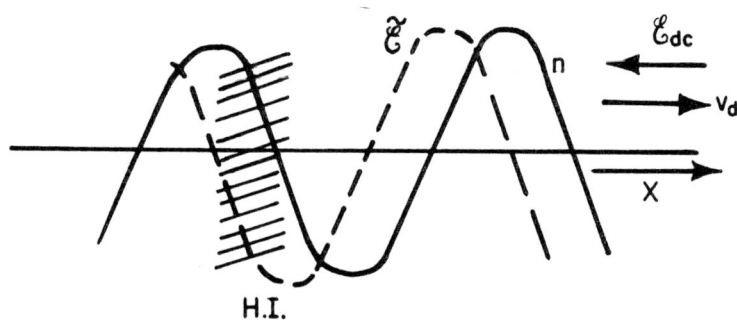

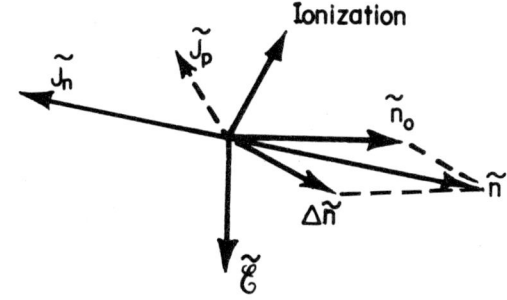

Fig. 4.17　Instability of an avalanching electron-hole plasma (H.I.=highest-ionization region, $\tilde{j}_n$ =electron-current density, $\tilde{\mathscr{E}}$ =a.c. field produced by density variation, $\tilde{n}_0$=original density, $\Delta\tilde{n}$ = change of density by ionization, $\tilde{n} = \Delta\tilde{n} + \tilde{n}_0$).

Assuming the time-dependent part to vary as exp ($j\omega t$), the d.c. field to be independent of x and avalanching to occur uniformly along the space-charge layer, a small-signal solution of the form exp $j(\omega t - kx)$ is possible. The resultant dispersion equation is found to be

$$k^2 + 2\alpha_i' J_{to} \frac{1}{\epsilon v} - j2\alpha_i \frac{\omega}{v} - \frac{\omega^2}{v^2} = 0 \qquad (4.14)$$

where $\alpha_i' = d\alpha_i/d\mathscr{E}$; α_i = ionization rate for electrons and holes. J_{to} = total d.c. current, i.e., the sum of electron and hole currents.

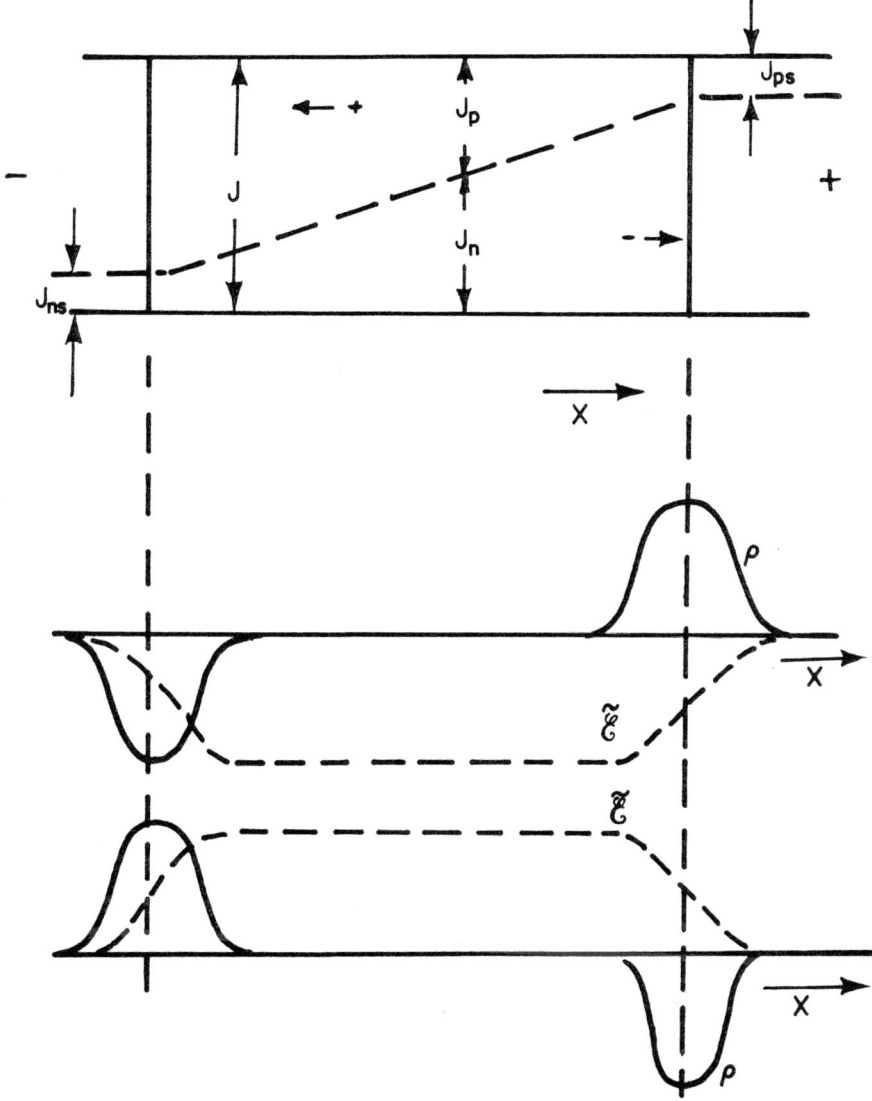

Fig. 4.18   Space-charge region of a *p-n* junction and two phases of the oscillation (ρ=charge density, J_{ns}, J_{ps}=current density owing to electrons and holes entering the space-charge region, J=total current density).

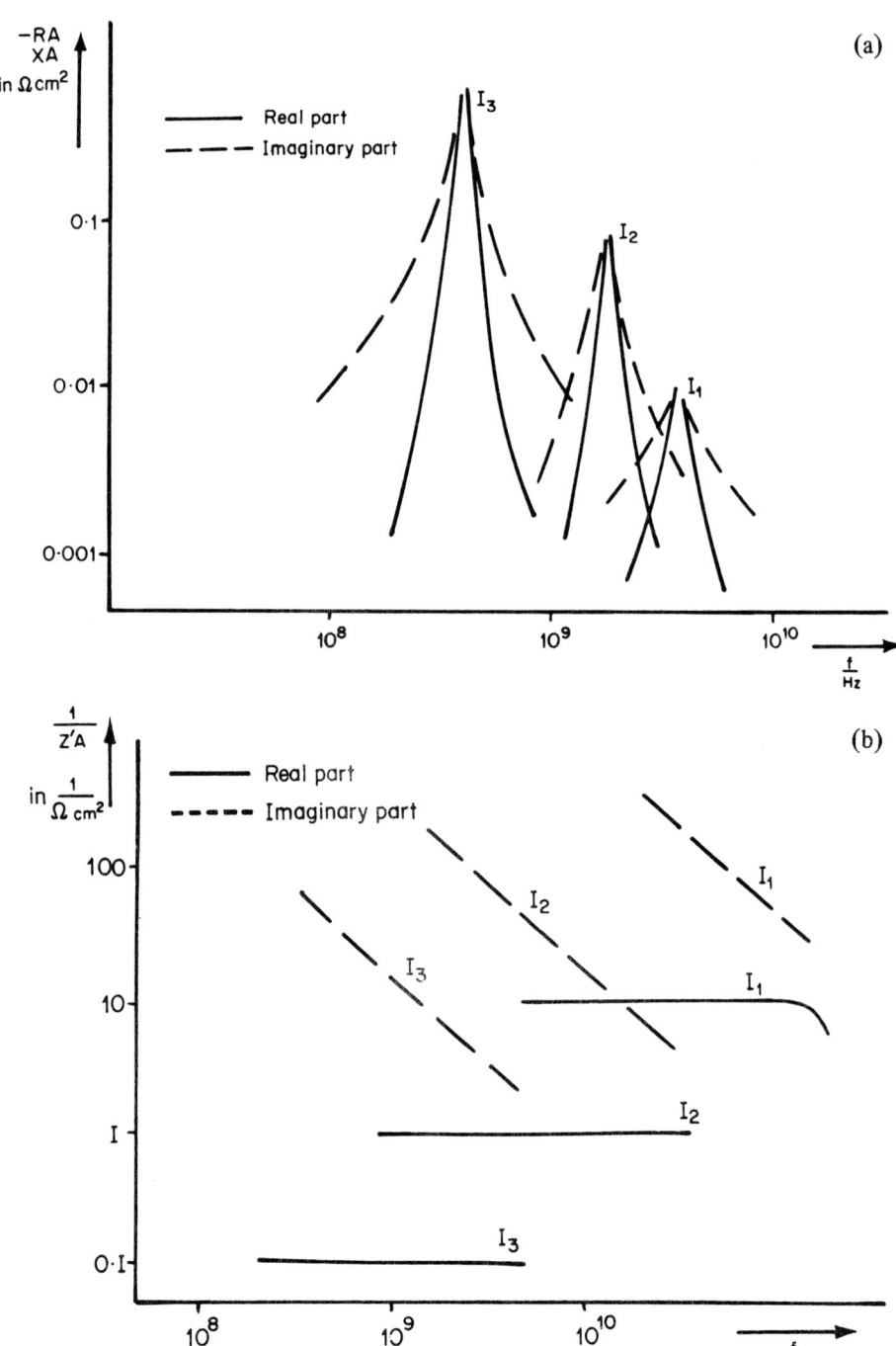

This gives

$$j\omega = \alpha_i v \pm \sqrt{(\alpha_i^2 v^2 - 2\alpha_i' J_{to} \frac{v}{\epsilon} - k^2 v^2)} \tag{4.15}$$

which shows that one can have a temporally-growing wave for real k.
If one takes

$$k = \pm \sqrt{\left(\frac{\omega^2}{v^2} - 2\alpha_i' J_{to} \frac{1}{\epsilon v} + j2\omega\alpha_i \frac{1}{v} \right)} \tag{4.16}$$

one sees, that a saddle point occurs at $k = 0$, i.e. there is an absolute instability.
In the p–n junction case, the boundary conditions are:

$$\tilde{J}_n(x = 0) = \tilde{J}_{ns} \tag{4.17}$$

$$\tilde{J}_p(x = 1) = \tilde{J}_{ps} \tag{4.18}$$

where $\sim$ indicates the ac part. One then obtains analytic solutions to the field $\tilde{\mathscr{E}}$ and currents $\tilde{J}_n$ and $\tilde{J}_p$.

Taking

$$\tilde{V} = -\int_0^x \tilde{\mathscr{E}} dx \tag{4.19}$$

for the a.c. voltage of the diode, one obtains an expression for the impedance

$$Z_s = \frac{\tilde{V}}{\tilde{J}} \tag{4.20}$$

For a numerical example, namely the width of the depletion layer 5 μ, and a silicon diode, one can obtain the impedance as a function of frequency and bias current, as shown in Fig. 4.19a.

The equivalent circuit is given in Fig. 4.20. If the capacitance C is chosen to be equal to the depletion layer capacitance, the inductance L and the negative resistance $-R$ are fairly frequency-independent, as can be seen in Fig. 4.19b, where the admittance of the avalanching effect is given. It can be seen that the admittance is approximately proportional to the bias current, whereas the

Fig. 4.19   Small-signal impedance Z (a) and admittance $1/Z'$ (b) of avalanche diode ($Z = -R + jX$, where X is inductive for lower frequencies from resonance, and capacitive for high frequencies; $1/Z' = -G + jY_L$, where the contribution from the depletion layer capacitance is subtracted; $I_1 = 10^{-3}$ A/cm^2; $I_2 = 10^{-4}$ A/cm^2; $I_3 = 10^{-5}$ A/cm^2; A is the cross-sectional surface of the diode).

inductance is inversely proportional. Hence, the resonance frequency is proportional to the square root of the bias current.

For the study of the oscillation threshold and build-up rate of oscillation, it is useful to know Q as a function of frequency. Q is defined as the angular frequency ω times the ratio of the average stored energy to the average energy dissipation per unit time, i.e.

$$Q = \frac{\omega \int_0^1 \langle E \rangle \, dx}{-\int_0^1 \left\langle \dfrac{dE}{dt} \right\rangle dx} \tag{4.21}$$

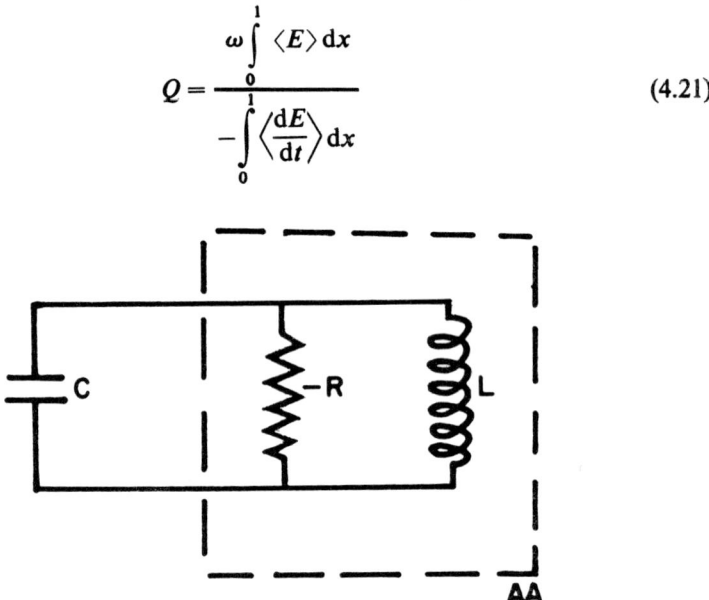

Fig. 4.20 Equivalent circuit of avalanching p-n diode. (AA=admittance due to avalanche).

where the time average of power dissipation is given by:

$$-\left\langle \frac{dE}{dt} \right\rangle = \tfrac{1}{2} \operatorname{Re} \{(\tilde{J}_n + \tilde{J}_p) \, \tilde{\mathscr{E}}^* \} \tag{4.22}$$

(* indicates a complex conjugate value) and the energy stored as the field energy is:

$$\langle E \rangle = \tfrac{1}{2} \operatorname{Re} \frac{|\tilde{\mathscr{E}}|^2 \epsilon}{2} \tag{4.23}$$

Figure 4.21 gives Q versus f, where one sees that a small negative Q, which is preferable for a stable operation, occurs at low f for a given bias current and at high currents for a given f.

4.2.3. Further Avalanche-Instability Studies

Stimulated by Read's proposal (236), entirely parallel work was performed in the Soviet Union by a large team (285). When they reported their results in *Radio-Technika i Elektronika* in November, 1966, they were not only able to present their theoretical work, but could describe a whole range of fabricated microwave devices for ready use. According to their paper, their first microwave avalanching diode was built already in 1959. The Ge diode was a *p–n* junction

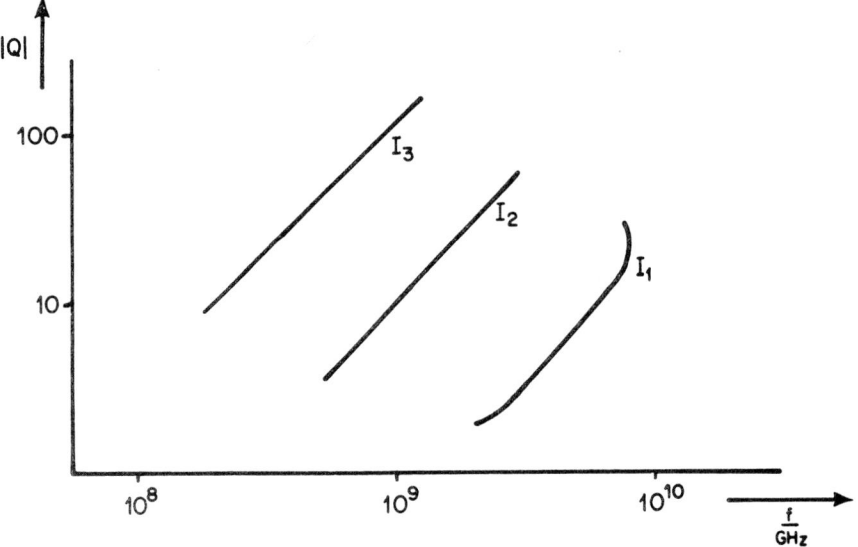

Fig. 4.21 Small-signal negative Q ($I_1 = 10^{-3}$ A/cm^2; $I_2 = 10^{-4}$ A/cm^2; $I_3 = 10^{-5}$ A/cm^2).

diode, placed in an r.f. cavity. Microwaves of a few milliwatts were generated for biasing voltages of about 30 V, when a direct current of about 15 mA was flowing. In underexcited operation near the oscillation threshold regenerative microwave amplification with 15-20 dB gain was observed.

The differential diode resistance at oscillations was 50 to 300 kΩ. This enabled about 1% efficient microwave generation. The theory was developed along a slightly different line from that of Misawa (196a). Impact ionization is assumed to occur in that part of the junction which exhibits the strongest field – the so-called 'multiplication layer'. The carriers produced, travel then across the remainder of the junction and this transit time causes the time-lag between the carrier production at a high field, and the current pulse, when the microwave field has reverted to a negative value. Thus, a negative resistance effect is observed for a limited frequency range. The carriers drift away from the 'multiplication layer' with a field-independent velocity, owing to optical-phonon interaction, and intervalley scattering, if this is present.

Using Poisson's equation, the continuity equation and the total-current expression, the small-signal diode impedance

$$Z_s = R + jX$$

was obtained. The equivalent circuit was found to be conveniently expressed by a parallel LC network with a negative resistance R and a small reactance X in series. R and X are given as a function of diode current, where R becomes very strongly negative for a correctly-chosen value of $\omega\tau_t \simeq 0.5$ (τ_t = transit time and ω being the angular frequency). X is first negative for small currents and switches at the point of maximum negative R suddenly to positive values. The experimental results show a surprisingly good agreement with theory.

In short, we can say that the general operation of an avalanche oscillator can be understood as the result of the following two effects: (a) The generation rate of carriers, being dependent on the product of voltage and current density, is out of phase with both, so that, for an abrupt junction, the current can lag appreciably behind the electric field. (b) A further phase lag can be introduced by an intrinsic drift region of suitable length.

The analysis by Misawa (196a) stimulated further theoretical investigations. Chang (55) analyzed PIN avalanching photodiodes considering unequal ionization rates for holes and electrons (β_h and α_n), and unequal scattering-limited velocities (v_p and v_n). He studied the question of frequency response for various cases of photon absorption [i.e. absorption, (a) in the space-charge region, and (b) in the p-region], in particular in view of the cut-off frequency and the gain bandwidth product, which is given as the product of cut-off frequency and the so-called 'd.c. multiplication factor'. It was found that a change in v_p and v_n does not affect the d.c. multiplication factor. When $\alpha_n > \beta_h$, a higher d.c. multiplication factor is achieved, if photons are absorbed near the boundary between the p-region and the i-region. The cut-off frequency increases with the ratio α_n/β_h.

Fisher (80) studied the avalanching semiconductor junction for unequal ionization rates and drift velocities, and found threshold conditions for oscillation. It is assumed that impact ionization is confined to a very thin layer of thickness l_i within the depletion layer, a similar approach as that used by Val'd-Perlov and others (285). The junction impedance and the equivalent circuit derived take, however, a different form here, so that it is difficult to compare them with the Soviet results. However, good agreement is shown with Misawa's results (196a).

Further work was also performed on the Q-factor, stability and time-dependence of Read Structures (170b, 170c). Parametric effects have been studied which arise from the nonlinearity of the avalanche (85). It has been shown that the IMPATT diodes can exhibit a parametric negative resistance. By adjusting external circuits and the direct current of the diode, one can realize parametric oscillators and amplifiers.

Recently, very high efficiencies (258.1) were reported for a subharmonic of the microwave frequency considered so far, and high CW and pulsed output powers from 0.5 to 4 GHz have been obtained with Ge and Si diodes by employing suitable two-frequency microwave resonators. Theoretical efficiencies of up to 70% (!) have been calculated.

Another proposal is of some interest here, as it makes use of conventional transistor structures, although it does not rely on avalanching processes. Shockley (255) had shown, that negative resistance can be obtained arising from transit-time effects, if the depletion layer extends across the whole base region because of large reverse-biasing (one says the base is 'punched through'). It was proposed by Yoshimura (305) in 1964, that one has two cases in a transistor which correspond to the vacuum tube, where one can either have space-charge-limited emission or temperature-limited emission. Shockley's oscillator is equivalent to the space-charge-limited valve. In an ordinary transistor, minority carriers are injected into the depletion layer between base and collector. This injection is limited by emitter current. This mode corresponds to a temperature-limited valve. By using an equation, which relates current, voltage, electron velocity and electron current, the so-called Llewellyn-Peterson equations (174), a negative resistance is obtained.

Summarizing, one can say that the principal structures for IMPATT devices are Read's *pnin*-type diodes (236), the *pin* device (196a) and the simple *pn* diode (196b). In general, increasing output can be obtained with higher bias current, and maximum output is given just before the diode burns out. This shows how useful good heat-sinking is, so that the devices can be driven harder. *Pin* diodes are less frequency-stable than Read diodes; the resonant frequency increases approximately as the square root of the bias current. The *pn* diodes are most useful for high-frequency operation, when it is difficult to control the required impurity profiles for the Read and *pin*-structure. For frequencies above 50 GHz, the space-charge region has to be less than 1 micron. As GaAs has a high carrier mobility, it is a promising material for high frequencies. It seems, therefore, that Read structures are most suited for low frequencies (less than 10 GHz) owing to their good frequency versus bias power stability; *pin* diodes for medium frequencies, as they require a convenient high bias voltage, owing to the large space-charge width; and *pn* diodes for very high frequency because of their constructional simplicity.

The main materials used have been Si, Ge and GaAs, although negative resistance avalanche effects have also been observed in n-CdTe (218) and InSb at 77°K (6h).

4.2.4 *General Experimental Results*

Several authors have reported experimental verifications of Misawa's theory, particularly the increase in operating frequency with growing current (see Fig. 4.21), and the dependence of operating frequency on the width of the depletion layer and the doping profile (i.e. boundary conditions J_{ns} and J_{ps}).

De Loach and Johnston (175) obtained from Si *p–n* diodes the results of Fig. 4.22, where the circuit of Fig. 4.23 was used. It is of interest, that these authors reported parametric action, i.e., a pump (avalanche transit-time generated) at 17.49 GHz delivers simultaneously power at two lower frequencies, 8.512 GHz and 8.982 GHz [see also Irvin (133) and Josenhans *et al.* (144a)].

Similar results were reported by Gilden and Hines (92), who investigated particularly the question of electronic tuning by changing the biasing current and

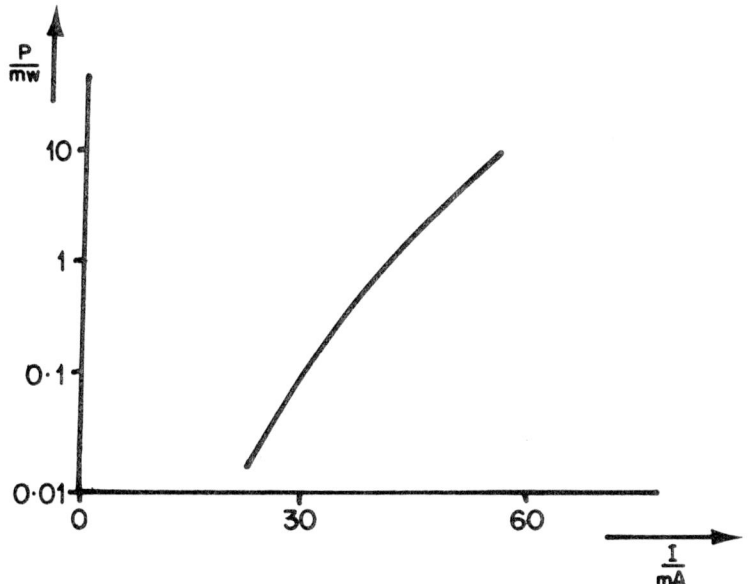

Fig. 4.22   Output power versus bias current for a *p-n* diode.

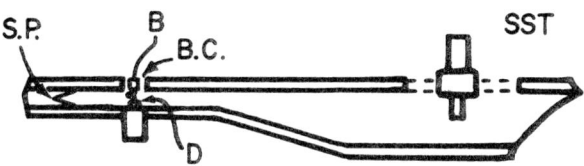

Fig. 4.23   Oscillator circuit (S.P.=sliding piston, D=diode, B=bias voltage, B.C.=by-pass capacitor, SST=slide screw tuner).

cavity dimensions at X-Band. Irvin (133) investigated GaAs *p-n* diodes, as this material has a higher scattering-limited velocity than Si, so that possibly higher frequencies can be produced. Unfortunately, this semiconductor has a higher defect density and a larger thermal resistivity than Si, so that any GaAs avalanche diode would only be of possible advantage for pulsed operation. Irvin's results are at 27 GHz under pulsed condition. It can be suspected that the Gunn-effect produces an enhanced bunching of the avalanche-produced electrons, though this effect does not seem to be of great significance. Higgins *et al.* (121) report about avalanche oscillations of GaAs varactor diodes, obtaining CW power at about 14 GHz.

After these first results, among which one has to count also the microwave oscillators reported by Val'd-Perlov *et al.* (285), a range of papers gave exciting experimental achievements: Si *pn* junctions gave more than 300 mW CW at 39 GHz (271); Si *pnn*[+] devices produced 435 W pulsed at 425 MHz (230); or Si *pn* junctions yielded 75 mW at 115 GHz and possibly 1 mW at 300 GHz (38), just to quote a few examples. These high output powers have been achieved by a thorough study of the heat-sinking problem (271a, 271b). The thermal flux density has been raised considerably. As an example, a medium frequency *pin* diode has a 3 μ space-charge width and an active region of about 100 μ^2. It operates CW at 5% efficiency and 10 W input, generating 400 MW/cm^3 and yielding a thermal flow of 120 kW/cm^2 into the heat sink.

Problems are posed by 'hot spots' owing to non-uniform current flow across the junction. Some effects actually tend to reduce the hot spot problem, particularly at higher frequencies, namely : (*a*) the avalanche field has a positive temperature coefficient, i.e. increasing temperature increases also the breakdown voltage, so that a current reduction occurs in the hot spot; (*b*) the local regions of excess current seem to exhibit an effective series resistance (92), which limits the local current rise. Further power increase can be obtained by phase locking (70, 96, 253).

Of interest are results of noise measurements at 6 GHz by Josenhans (144) on avalanche diodes and Gunn-oscillators, where FM noise was found to be of a very similar level for both oscillator types, and AM noise was smaller for the Gunn-diode.

The avalanche ionization mechanism is inherently noisy. Noise figures of up to 40 dB (124) are common. Circuits have been developed which incorporate a number of individual locked diodes, such that the signal-frequency outputs add in phase, whereas the noise contributions do not. Appreciable noise figure reduction can be obtained thus. Ge and GaAs are advantageous for lower noise figures, and some GaAs IMPATTS have shown less than 30 dB noise.

The theoretical noise results (124) have been verified experimentally (103a). It was found that there are three noise contributions: (*a*) the inherent avalanche noise, which is proportional to V_b^2/I_a (V_b = breakdown voltage and I_a = avalanche current), (*b*) noise caused by non-uniformities of the avalanche break-down, which can even be observed in microplasma-free diodes, and (*c*) an excess noise at high current densities which seems to be caused by thermal effects. The contributions (*b*) and (*c*) are very temperature-dependent.

Avalanche diodes can also be used as a reflection-gain amplifier, as illustrated in Fig. 4.24, where the gain G is given by the expression:

$$G = \left(\frac{R_d - R_L}{R_d + R_L}\right)^2 \tag{4.24}$$

(R_d = negative resistance of diode, R_L = load resistance).

This shows that one obtains gain if R_d is negative. The device becomes unstable, however, if $R_d + R_L < 0$. De Loach et al. (175) obtained 20 dB gain at 11.5 GHz, with a 3 dB bandwidth of 20 MHz. The noise figures were about 60 dB. Other workers (249) found power outputs of 40 mW CW with 15 dB power gain over a tuning range from 8 to 12 GHz from Si np diodes, and transmission gain was observed with avalanching Ge varactor diodes (266a).

Diodes with sandwich structures very close to that described by Read were measured (175), and CW output at 5 GHz was obtained. Avalanche oscillations were also observed from pvn varactor diodes at about 4 GHz (214). Low-frequency oscillations in p^+nn^+ avalanche devices (126b) at low transit angles

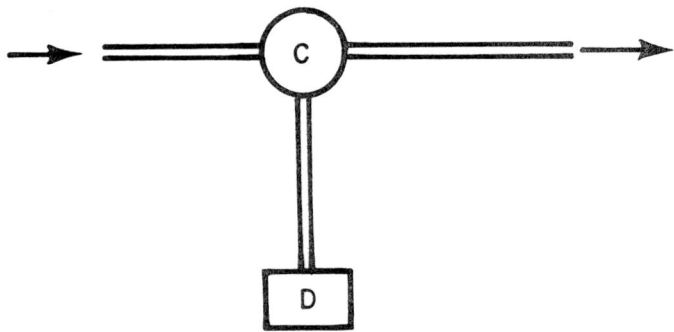

Fig. 4.24   Amplifier circuit (C = circulator, D = reflection-gain diode).

have been reported. They could be of interest at low frequencies where otherwise long space-charge layers and consequently, high breakdown voltages would make the normal transit-time mode inconvenient. GaAs $p\pi p$ structures with a high-resistivity layer approximately 1 μ thick, showed breakdown with accompanying light emission (294). This is a similar phenomenon to that observed in connection with the high domain fields of Gunn oscillators (116). This property could possibly be exploited for new device developments.

It has been observed (181) that a pulsed reverse-biased diode can oscillate at several frequencies. They occur at different well-defined time sections of the applied pulses. For example, the leading edge of a particular microwave signal appeared only 0.2 μsec after the application of the pulsed bias, and under certain conditions, this first mode was replaced after a further time interval by another one. The transient phenomena occurring during the onset of oscillations can be of importance for many novel devices and are the reason for the Gunn-effect domain being of advantage for applications such as ultra-fast logic circuitry (see next chapter).

It is of great practical interest, that two frequency-locked avalanche oscillators were not phase-locked (259). The relative phase shift could be accomplished electronically by bias current variation, without appreciable change in output power. This property can be utilized for phase modulation techniques.

Large transmission on/off ratios were obtained from an X-Band *pin* diode switch (67), attributed to the generation of a microwave negative resistance of the IMPATT effect. The negative resistance cancels any diode losses and produces a wideband zero loss wave-guide switch.

Rieke diagrams, which consist of contours of constant power and frequency pulling plotted on a Smith Chart, have commonly been used to show the performance of microwave tubes as a function of load impedance. They have been employed in connection with IMPATT diodes (66). It was found that the output signal is most noisy where the gradient of the frequency-pulling contours is steep.

Solid-state plasmas can often provide a convenient tool for investigating plasma instabilities in general, particularly in relation to Penning discharges and similar effects, because the collision frequencies are comparable. Kakihana (146) could therefore verify a current oscillation predicted by Simon for a partially-ionized inhomogeneous plasma, by simulating this problem with a *pin* Ge diode at $77°K$ under a transverse magnetic field. This result shows how not only the well-established field of the gas-plasma studies has stimulated the new semiconductor-plasma work, but how electron-hole plasmas can help now in the further development of knowledge of electron-ion instabilities.

Very low-frequency oscillations and fast pulses have been obtained from commercially-available low-frequency transistors with the base-collector junction reverse-biased and the emitter either open-circuited or connected to the base via a resistor (59). They are caused by a succession of discharges owing to the space-charge region extending to the base-emitter junction, and operate in a similar manner to discharges in gas tubes with the additional possibility of controlling the repetition frequency by means of the resistor between emitter and base. The theory of avalanche injection in transistors for fast pulses is given by Mizushima and Okamoto (200).

4.3   The Electroacoustic Effect

4.3.1   Electroacoustic Gain

If electrons drift faster than the sound velocity v_s and certain conditions are satisfied, they amplify the electric field associated with the sound wave (142). This effect was measured first in piezoelectric semiconductors such as CdS (129). However, acoustic gain has also been observed with deformation potential waves in Ge (229). The deformation-potential coupling is usually weaker than piezoelectric coupling. However, relatively strong interaction can occur as a consequence of the multi-valley nature of the conduction bands in Ge. Weinreich *et al.* (293) showed that in a many-valley semiconductor, the electron-phonon interaction could remain unscreened by the space charge. In this case the amplification increases with increasing electron density. The gain parameter has been developed by Spector (262, 262a), who bases his treatment on previous theoretical work on electron-phonon interaction in many-valley semiconductors (194). The theory has been extended by Gantsevich and Gurevich (89) and others (83). The experimental results showed gain of more than 20 dB/cm at 9 GHz (229). The effect was observed in n-type Ge doped with 10^{16} atoms/cm^3 of As at 4°K; The field was applied in the (100) direction and d.c. pulses of up to 20 A were used. The acoustic wave was generated at one end of the crystal by a ferromagnetic-film transducer. The main application of this gain mechanism is the study of the physics of electrons and phonons in two-valley semiconductors.

The small-signal dispersion characteristics for piezoelectric semiconductors and photoconductors has been obtained by White (298) and others (30, 202, 202a, 260).

Under the condition that the mean free path of the electrons is shorter than the acoustic wavelength, the piezoelectric equations [equation (2.45) b and c] , (or correspondingly the deformation potential equations); the acoustic-wave equation [equation (2.45e)] ; and the continuity equation [equation (2.36)] lead to the dispersion equation if a small-signal approximation is used, i.e.

$$\mathscr{E} = \mathscr{E}_0 + \mathscr{E}_1 \exp j(kx - \omega t) \qquad (4.25)$$

and

$$u = u_0 \exp j(kx - \omega t) \qquad (4.26)$$

where $\mathscr{E}_0$ = d.c. electric field
$\mathscr{E}_1$ = amplitude of alternating field
k = $j\alpha + \omega/v_{ph}$
α = attenuation constant
u = physical displacement of medium.

One can approximate: $K^2 \ll 1$ and $|\alpha| \ll \omega/v_s$ (v_s = sound velocity in the crystal, K is given by the relation $e_p^2/(\epsilon e_e) = K^2/(1 - K^2)$ and is called the electro-mechanical coupling coefficient). One then finds the solution:

$$\alpha = \frac{K^2}{2} \frac{\omega_d}{v_s \gamma} \left[1 + \frac{\omega_d^2}{\gamma^2 \omega^2} \left(1 + \frac{\omega^2}{\omega_d \omega_D} \right)^2 \right]^{-1} \qquad (4.27)$$

[$\omega_d = \sigma/\epsilon$, dielectric relaxation frequency; σ = conductivity; ϵ = dielectric constant; $\omega_D = v_s^2/D$, diffusion frequency; D = diffusion constant; $\gamma = 1 - (v_d/v_s)$]. The solution is given in Fig. 4.25.

Acoustic gains have been measured (30) and the results agree quite well with the theoretical findings (see Fig. 4.25). The experimental set-up is shown in Fig. 4.26.

The theory presented so far, does not deal with large signal phenomena. If one wants to study gain saturation, one is not able to make use of such experimental

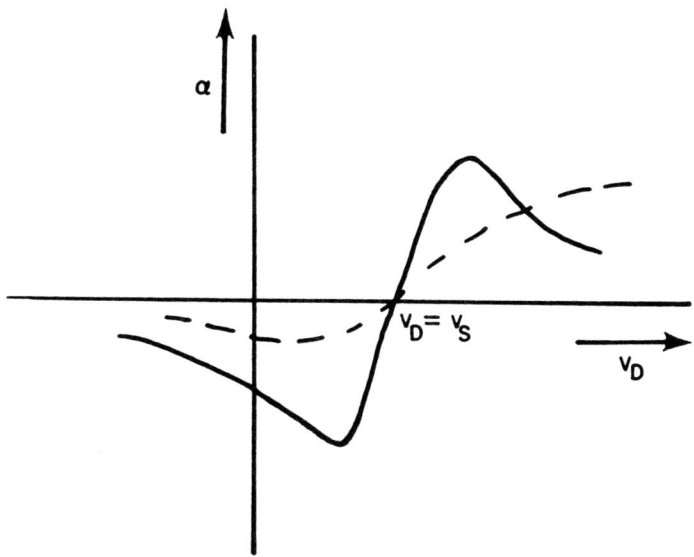

Fig. 4.25 Gain α versus drift velocity v_d (v_s=sound velocity, —— = theoretical, - - - = experimental).

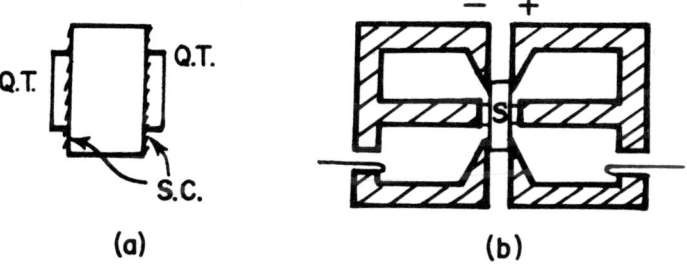

Fig. 4.26 Experimental set-up for acoustoelectric amplifier: (a) Sandwich of CdS crystal with two quartz transducers QT, the surfaces S.C. are coated with In for ohmic contacts. (b) Re-entrant cavity, with amplifying sandwich S inserted.

results as, for example, the various constants of piezoelectric materials, which have been reviewed very well (26). One then has to measure the fields and the acoustic flux along the crystal for gain saturation conditions. Maines studied the field distribution using Pockel's effect by measuring the phase shift of a light beam from an He–Ne gas laser, when passing down the CdS crystal in two different directions (180). Using light scattering and the photoelastic effect, Zucker and Zemon investigated the frequency spectrum of giant acoustic shear wave packets (309). In order to study the values of the effective third and fourth-order elastic constants in CdS, two signals at 14 and 16 MHz were applied to the crystal via a transducer (185). At the output transducer, the frequencies 28, 30 and 32 MHz were measured, indicating the occurrence of a large-amplitude three-phonon process. A similar experiment employed three input frequencies and the output gave the sum frequencies produced by four-phonon processes. Hanlon (107) found evidence of noise, producing strong gain limitations, in contrast to earlier assumptions that gain saturation is only caused by limitations of the basic amplification properties. This noise is closely related to the onset of non-ohmic I–V characteristics, as described below. In particular, he found the maximum ultrasonic gain limited to about 80 dB. This gain limitation by inherent crystal noise could be a much more important limitation than the other gain-limiting effects, such as non-uniformities of the crystal conductivity (65), heating (154, 299) and electron traps (97, 147c). On the other hand, White showed that a decrease in gain occurs, because the inner parts of the crystal will reach a higher operating temperature than the outer ones (299). Kalashnikov et al. (147c) found experimentally how various trapping levels could be responsible for a gain decrease. They illuminated photoconductive CdS using light filters and made transient measurements after the onset of illumination. Ogawa and Kojima (212) have determined changes in piezoelectric constants, which can also have a pronounced influence on gain. Prohofsky (231) was able to show that some gain limitation will ultimately result as the drift velocity of carriers will be reduced by momentum loss, causing a reduction in the gain parameter (see Fig. 4.28). It was subsequently suggested (119) that it is not permissible for this large-signal case to use the linearized approximations of White, which are used for the results of Fig. 4.25.

Electroacoustic gain interactions in III–V compounds, particularly in GaAs, were studied by Hickernell (120), who found a gain of 9 dB/cm, which is consistent with an electromechanical coupling factor of 0.075 for GaAs.

A further development was achieved by making evaporated-layer CdS transducers that could produce either longitudinal waves (if the acoustic-wave vector is parallel to the hexagonal axis, the C axis) or 'shear waves' (acoustic-wave vector is perpendicular to the C axis.) This technique provided a higher coupling efficiency and higher frequencies of operation, i.e. from 100 to 1800 MHz. The main application of these devices is not their use as an amplifier, as it is not competitive enough with conventional amplifiers of this frequency. It has been suggested to employ these electroacoustic devices for high-frequency delay lines and in memory units for computers. Some interesting results have been obtained by Robertson and Ash. By shaping the resistivity profile and applied voltage, specific circuit functions were obtained, which could enable the use of these devices in pulse logic applications (239).

The electroacoustic-gain phenomena discussed here are a type of travelling wave amplification, which is based on a similar interaction as that in Travelling Wave Tubes (260a). This fact has shown that microwave gain can be obtained also in semiconductor devices if slow waves are made to interact with a carrier stream.

Several suggestions for suitable slow wave structures along the outside of the crystal have been made, however, none of the proposed systems has yet led to an actual amplifier. The difficulty is that no good coupling coefficient between the bulk carrier stream and the slow-wave structure can be achieved owing to the surface properties of the semiconductor and the very small plasma wavelength. A better approach is given by the use of surface elastic waves, which travel only along the surface and do not penetrate into the bulk. White (299a) was able to report amplification with a continuous drift field in CdS, and presented the underlying theory. The surface of the piezoelectric solid represents a very low-velocity, piezoelectric, slow-wave structure. The surface waves can therefore interact with drifting carriers in the bulk near the surface. The method of generating surface waves involves either mode conversion from bulk to surface waves (14), or the application of suitable stresses near the surface of the solid by a periodic electrode on the piezoelectric surface (299a); if a periodic electric field is then produced by this electrode, piezoelectric waves are generated. Surface-wave amplification has the following advantages: (a) The interaction will only be with carriers very near to the surface. Therefore the conductivity can be very small away from the surface, so that dc-current heat would only be produced in a thin and extensive layer, which is very suitable for efficient heat-sinking. CW operation can now be envisaged (14). (b) The surface-wave transducers can be made to produce virtually negligible wave reflection, so that we can expect greater electronic stability.

Thin-film devices of CdS are of equally great interest here. However, they have been reported to exhibit various further effects of instabilities. Single-crystal CdS films have been studied for a switching behaviour which relies on breakdown, and negative resistance effects have been observed (273). Polycrystalline CdS thin films have been vapour deposited on a ruby substrate (183). When this device was illuminated with white light and when a field of several kV/cm was applied, high-frequency current oscillations were observed (183).

4.3.2 Electroacoustic Oscillations

Technical applications might be possible with the continuous current oscillations such as the ones observed in CdS (45, 216, 290) CdSe (153a), CdTe (153b), GaAs (114) and other materials. They are caused by the electroacoustic gain phenomena. They occur after the field value for current saturation has been reached. This saturation of the I–V characteristics is in fact closely related to the electroacoustic interactions discussed above. It has been studied theoretically (134, 201, 220, 233, 307) and experimentally (134a, 189, 199). In particular, McFee *et al.* (189a) have shown by transient measurements after the application of the bias voltage at the photoconducting crystal, how a phonon domain is nucleated and travels towards the positive electrode, where it is transformed into a stationary domain. The current saturation is, therefore, caused by a stationary high-field domain. Similar phenomena have been observed in current-saturated semiconduct-ing CdS (182). Some phenomena observed can be treated by an analysis including trapping of carriers (154a, 282), which reduces the effective drift velocity. In particular, the field-dependence of trapping can be expected to be responsible for some of the current saturation phenomena and low-frequency oscillations as discussed in the next section. Rannestad (235) has shown that one can obtain current saturation by acoustoelectric amplification either with the transverse or the longitudinal acoustic waves, and that the gain in the transverse mode is usually larger than the gain in the longitudinal mode.

Of interest is a two-step current saturation with CdS in some experiments where the ohmic contacts have been prepared by direct indium diffusion in vapour phase within a sealed vessel (13). Therefore, it can be assumed that the contact quality is of great importance for the saturation phenomena.

n-GaAs exhibited two types of current saturation, one is caused by the electro-acoustic-gain phenomena at about 200–500 V/cm and the other one seems to be associated with the electron transfer to satellite valleys at about 3000 V/cm as described in section 4.1 (132).

Acoustoelectric current oscillations fall into two distinct categories, namely those observed with semiconductive and those with photoconductive semicon-ductors, particularly CdS The first type occurs in CdS crystals of about 1 Ωcm resistivity and does not rely on any carrier generation by illumination. These oscillations are caused by the production of clearly-defined travelling high-field domains which are very similar to the domains of the Gunn effect (115). These domains travel across the crystal with the velocity of sound. The effect can be understood as a negative resistance phenomenon produced by the fact that an incremental increase in the acoustoelectric field can be greater than the incremental increase in the applied field (see section 3.3 p. 71). This will cause the total current through the sample to be a decreasing function of applied field so that the J–$\mathscr{E}$ curve will become negative. It is not required to have the acoustic flux being reflected and returned to the cathode so that a loop gain in excess of unity is obtained. As soon as one domain has reached the anode and is extinguished there, a new one is formed at some nucleating centre near the cathode electrode. Before a domain is nucleated the I–V relation is ohmic. A domain will cause current saturation during its transit. The current oscillation occurs therefore between a high-current value, which is given by the low-field resistance of the crystal, and a saturated-current value. Typical domain fields are more than 3×10^4 V/cm, the domain width is more than 150μ. Domains have been studied by probe contacts along the crystal (115), by optical transmission, i.e. Brillouin scattering by a moving domain giving its phonon intensity (297), and by microwave transmission measurements (125, 227). Impact ionization occurs in CdS at fields higher than 2.1×10^3 V/cm, as determined by a measurement of the Hall voltage and conductivity (199a). This phenomenon will therefore occur inside the travelling domain with its high field value. Balberg and Many (15) developed a technique for studying the acoustic wave properties of a high-field domain by terminating the bias pulse before the domain reaches the anode and by measuring the current decay.

These electroacoustic domain effects have not only been studied in semiconducting CdS (further publications are 44, 134c, 263) but also in GaAs (32, 41, 153c) and in InSb (153e, 284) (see pages 127-128). Hervouet (119b) has shown theoretically that a transverse magnetic field increases the piezoelectric amplification, and Ishida and Inuishi (134b) measured a differential negative resistance in semiconducting CdS with travelling domains.

The second type of acoustoelectric oscillations occurs in photoconductive CdS, which is illuminated so that the optimum carrier density for amplification can be set up. It has been found that these crystals show then only damped oscillations leading to current saturation as discussed by McFee et al. (189a) and others (81.1), if the illumination is either uniform or stronger near the anode electrode (115). On the other hand, continuous current oscillations with frequencies around 1 MHz or less have been observed, if the crystal half near the negative electrode is illuminated and a sufficiently large drift field is applied. Many people have been investigating this effect (21, 21a, 105, 130, 134d, 153, 153g, 279, 303). A possible analysis has been suggested by Froom (84).

It has now been quite well established with the help of capacitive probes (134d, 134e) and ohmic probes (147b), that stationary and moving field domains exist simultaneously in the crystal. In many cases, the oscillatory phenomena are caused by the travelling domains, whose height is about 10^3-10^4 V/cm and whose width is of the order of millimeters (115). The domain width is therefore comparable to the sample length and the domain velocity is not well defined. The oscillation frequency changes to some degree with applied voltage and intensity of illumination (115). In fact, one can observe a continuous variation of frequency with applied voltage or illumination, and a sudden change by about a factor of two. The first effect can be explained by the fact that an increase in illumination causes an increase in conductivity near the cathode, so that the electric field can fall there below the threshold value for an acoustoelectric interaction. Therefore, the transit length of the domain is shortened. The second phenomenon of frequency change is related to the presence of stationary domains. If the whole crystal is illuminated except for a very narrow strip near the positive electrode, Hartnagel and Gay (90, 90a, 111) found the frequency to vary in steps by changing the position of the shielding strip. Between the frequency change-overs a beating effect was often observed which involved the two neighbouring frequencies. These effects depended very sensitively on the position of the narrow mask and on the background illumination of the masked strip. They could possibly be utilized for practical devices in order to measure very small displacements (length or thickness gauges, seismographic applications) or light-levels.

Of interest are also interaction phenomena of microwaves and supersonic electrons (105a, 105b), the influence of high phonon fluxes on X-ray reflectivity (204) and the changes in CdS conductivity by microwave phonons travelling across the crystal (10). Similarly, emission of microwaves has been reported from n-CdS (197, 276) and from n-InSb (9b), both under electroacoustic interaction conditions. Great potentiality is shown by new CdS oscillator structures (180a, 180b, 298a), which consist of a thin platelet of photoconducting CdS. Ohmic contacts are evaporated on the two large surfaces of the crystal, which is also illuminated through these contacts, which are kept transparent. When a large voltage is applied, so that the drift velocity is large enough for electroacoustic interactions, acoustic waves are amplified on their trajectory towards the anode, reflected there, and slightly attenuated on their return towards the cathode. As the net gain is still more than one for good surface reflection, oscillations are observed at frequencies which are given by the resonance of the CdS platelet. The thin crystal acts like a resonant cavity and can also be considered as the acoustic analogue to a laser. Coherent oscillations up to 900 MHz have been observed with a CdS crystal of 0.1 mm thickness (298a), and ZnO platelets have produced microwaves up to 5 GHz (180c).

It is worth mentioning that acoustoelectric current oscillations have also been observed in various III–V compounds namely p-GaSb (258), n-GaAs (32, 119a, 153c), and n- and p-InSb (41, 284); and in InSb (153d, 153e) in the presence of a transverse magnetic field, causing some magneto resistance effect (see pages 127-128).

4.3.3   Further Electroacoustic Instabilities

Various novel instabilities have been studied which rely on electroacoustic interactions.

High-mobility piezoelectric semiconductors are not usually suitable for microwave amplification of acoustic waves, as excessive power dissipation occurs under optimum gain conditions. The analysis leading to equation (4.27) shows that the maximum gain occurs at the frequency

$$\omega_m = \sqrt{(\omega_d\,\omega_D)} = \sqrt{\left(\frac{ne^2\,v_s^2}{\epsilon kT}\right)}$$

and the drift velocity

$$v_{dm} = \left[1 + 2\,\sqrt{\left(\frac{\omega_d}{\omega_D}\right)}\right]\,v_s = \left(1 + 2\,\frac{\omega_m\,\mu kT}{v_s^2\,e}\right)v_s.$$

It can be seen from these expressions that the optimum frequency ω_m is independent of mobility μ, whereas the optimum drift velocity v_{dm} depends on μ, and would, therefore, have to be much larger than v_s for high mobility materials. If d.c. electric and magnetic fields are present, which are perpendicular to the drift velocity v_d and to each other, the effective carrier mobility can be reduced for maximum-gain operation (263.1) and the maximum gain is achieved with much lower bias-power dissipation than in a conventional CdS configuration (284a). The Hall electric field produced will be short-circuited by plate electrodes, which permit in addition efficient heat-sinking. Weller *et al.* (296) have shown that gain can in fact be obtained with such a structure at 77°K and with B = 6250 Gauss, and with ZnO transducers for 370 and 655 MHz.

Gulyaev has shown that a negative differential conductivity is possible in semi-conducting acoustoelectric instabilities (100). Coherent emission of optical phonons for current oscillations was studied for GaAs and InAs theoretically (268). When the sound wave has very large amplitudes, electrons can be considered to be trapped in the field associated with the sound wave. It has been shown theoretically by Beale (23) that the current density-field characteristic may then show an insta-bility. It is caused by the phenomenon that electrons escaping from the trap are heated by the field and, by sharing their energy with other trapped electrons, cause further electrons to escape, thus producing an unstable avalanching effect. Of interest is also a general study of the effects of trapping of particles by waves (177). It has been shown that strong amplification of acoustic waves can occur in materials with strain-dependent dielectric constants (222). The analysis of this effect can be reduced to the analysis of acoustoelectric amplification, where the piezoelectric constant is assumed proportional to the applied electric field and to the dielectric constant (213).

4.4 Two-Stream Interactions and Other Effects

4.4.1 Two-Stream Instabilities

In this section we shall discuss several types of instabilities which have mostly occurred in both gaseous and semiconductor plasmas. Effects observed in one type of medium stimulated work in the other one.

The two most important plasma properties are the natural resonance frequency, which is called the plasma frequency ω_p, and the shielding effect against any disturbance, which is effective approximately within a length, which is termed the Debye length L_D. The two expressions are related to the plasma density n_p, the charge-carrier mass m, the plasma temperature T and the permittivity ϵ as follows:

$$\omega_p = \sqrt{\left(\frac{n_p e^2}{\epsilon m}\right)} ; \quad L_D = \sqrt{\left(\frac{\epsilon k T}{n_p e^2}\right)}$$

One can classify plasmas by dividing them into the following three types: (a) an uncompensated plasma occurs, if charge neutrality is being produced with one type of 'carrier' being immobile; (b) a compensated one is, for example, given in an extrinsic semiconductor, and (c) a non-equilibrium phase. The last is present if the carriers are not required to neutralize fixed ionic charges and are produced by injection from current-carrying contacts, by impact ionization and by optical generation.

If a voltage is applied at a plasma the positively-charged carriers move in the opposite direction to the negative ones. Gaseous plasmas exhibit then an instability caused by an interaction between one of the modes of the electron beam and a mode of the counter-streaming ion beam. The feedback mechanism is the same as employed for gain in a two-beam microwave tube. It has been suggested by various authors that such an instability might be observed in semiconductors with a high mobility, as the unfavourable effect of high collision frequencies of solid state devices could be reduced sufficiently. This instability would then occur in a longitudinal electric field in the absence of a magnetic field. Pines and Schrieffer (224) analyzed this phenomenon for InSb at $77°K$. They found that several requirements had to be satisfied, namely:

(a) $\omega \tau_{\pm} \gg 1$, where ω is the frequency of the instability and $\tau_{\pm}$ are the hole and electron scattering times;

(b) the drift velocity has to be as large as possible with respect to the electron thermal velocity, i.e.

$$v_d \geqslant 0.22 \sqrt{\left(\frac{2kT_e}{m^*}\right)}$$

(c) $m_e^* \ll m_h^*$, i.e. intrinsic or near-intrinsic material with a large ratio of hole to electron effective mass; and

(d) $T_e \gg T_h$, i.e. a large ratio of electron to hole effective temperatures.

Jackson (137) has found the required drift velocity v_d for the instability threshold if $T_e = T_h$, namely:

$$v_d = 0.93 \sqrt{\left(\frac{2kT}{m_e^*}\right)} \left[1 + \sqrt{\left(\frac{m_e^*}{m_h^*}\right)}\right] \quad \text{(see Fig. 3.11).}$$

It seems that the required temperature conditions cannot be achieved in InSb, as the drift velocity and the temperature ratio T_e/T_h have to be too high for the onset of growing waves. Another material is Bi (191), which might be suitable for this effect. However, no experimental evidence of this effect has been reported so far. The major disadvantage is the high value of Landau damping as the thermal velocities are of the same order of magnitude as the drift velocity. Harrison (110) investigated the longitudinal instabilities for degenerate plasmas theoretically and

found that instabilities might be possible provided the Fermi velocities of the two
carrier types differ sufficiently.

Köchner's study (161) neglects the important Landau damping. Tosima and
Hirota (280) described an instability which is assisted by collisions. Robinson and
Swartz (240), treated a structure consisting of adjacent InSb p and n layers, such
that Pines and Schrieffer's condition of $T_e \gg T_h$ can be fulfilled if the crystal is in
contact with liquid helium, and if a current passes only through the n-region, which
would produce an elevated T_e. The instability has therefore been reduced to that
of surface waves. Of interest in this context is a suggestion by Blötekjaer (30a) on
theoretical grounds that there exists a possibility that electrons may be cooled
rather than heated if strong optical phonon scattering predominates, which causes
a large transfer of energy to phonons.

A study of plasma oscillations in nonpolar semiconductors for $1/t_{e,h} \ll \omega \ll \omega_{n,h}$
and $\omega\tau_{ep,h} \ll 1$ has been performed by Gordeyev (95), where $t_{e,h}$ are the carrier
life-times and $\tau_{ep,h}$ are the average collision times between carriers and phonons.
Other researchers (146a) have studied the effect of the band-structure of Bi and
pyrolytic graphite on two-stream instabilities.

Microwave emission from magnetic-field-free semiconductor plasma has been
reported by several authors. Ancker-Johnson (6g) found that the special condition
required is an applied voltage of decreasing steps. Some plasma produced during the
first voltage step gives some usually unobtainable conductance conditions during
the subsequent lower voltage steps, and noise emission at X-Band occurred from
p-InSb at 77°K. The emitted frequency ranged from 6.55 to 15 GHz for applied
fields of 91–98 V/cm and 17.5–20 mA currents. The resistivity was 5.4 Ω cm. On
the other hand, one has also found emission from InSb without a magnetic field,
if only very short bias pulses were applied (296.1). However, the nature of these
instabilities is still obscure.

4.4.2 Microwave Emission from InSb with Electric and Magnetic Fields Present

Many authors have observed microwave emission in the presence of both electric
and magnetic fields from InSb, as discovered first by Larrabee (168a) and
Hicinbothem (168b). They observed microwave emission of up to 44 GHz in InSb
at 77°K. The crystal was in the form of a rod placed as an inductive post in a
waveguide. The ends protruded through two insulated holes in the top and bottom
waveguide surfaces. The waveguide containing the InSb post was immersed into a
dewar flask with liquid nitrogen. The interior of the waveguide was pressurized
with gaseous helium in order to prevent frosting inside it. The drift field was
applied in a pulsed form (1.3 μsec duration, ½ Hz repetition frequency). When a
critical value was exceeded for the electric and magnetic fields, microwave emission
and current oscillations were observed. The emitted frequencies ranged from 3 to
44 GHz, the electric and magnetic field was of 200 V/cm and 3 kG respectively,

and the pulsed current density was 3.10^4 A/cm^2. The microwave power was
1 μW at 15 GHz and 0.1 μW at 37 GHz. It is difficult to select one of the many
proposed theories as the correct one, as some of the experimental evidence usually
contradicts the theoretical results. It is very likely that it is a complex phenomenon
where several instability effects occur simultaneously.

Suzuki (269) reported about similar experimental results, which he summarized
as follows:

(1) Electron-hole pair generation is necessary for the effect.

(2) The microwave frequency is not monochromatic.

(3) A magnetic field transverse to the electric field was more effective than
a longitudinal one.

Buchsbaum et al. (43) then found microwave emission under similar conditions
with the threshold electric field of only 12 V/cm. This ruled out breakdown or
pinching effects. Better still, Musha et al. (206a) measured microwave emission
for $\mathscr{E} \geqslant 3$ V/cm and $B = 4$ kG. They observed noiselike emission, of almost constant
power level at any given electric field above threshold and spike emission of
relatively high power levels for a given electric field.

The results of Swartz and Robinson (272) are worth mentioning. Coherent
radiation was emitted from a rod of p-InSb, which has electron-injecting contacts
at each end, has recrystallized Suhl surfaces and is subjected to an electric and
magnetic field. Similarly, microwaves were emitted from a structure in which the
plane of a p-n junction is parallel to the main current flow. The application of 70 V
and 9000 Gauss to some samples produced noise radiation of 20 to 27 GHz, if the
angle between the electric and magnetic field ranged from 0° to 35°. Other samples
showed 20–50 MHz current oscillations for this range of angle. This low-frequency
observation could be explained by the 'oscillistor effect' (see p.138). For angles
greater than 36°, coherent microwave oscillations appear. Further experimental
results have been reported by many workers (74, 79, 162, 203, 203a, 270), in
particular emission up to 102 GHz has been found (225) and the instability effect
was observed at 4°K (25, 168c) and as high as 250°K (225a). Generally the results
seem to fall into a class with oscillations at low electric fields (43, 206a) and
another one with high field values (168a, 168b). The latter class seems to exhibit an
emission threshold above or at the threshold for impact ionization. Larrabee (168c)
showed that a minimum crystal length is required. He has also shown that the InSb
sample exhibits a current-controlled negative resistance in the MHz-frequency
range, when current oscillations occur. Some measurements demonstrate a complicated pattern of emission-intensity lobes as the magnetic-field direction is changed
either in the plane perpendicular to the applied electric field $\mathscr{E}$ (6f, 149a), or in the
plane which includes $\mathscr{E}$ (162). A review of the large amount of experimental
information obtained by the many experimenters has been written by B. Ancker-
Johnson (6i).

The experimental results have been discussed theoretically by a number of authors. Suzuki (270a) has shown that a gradient in carrier density perpendicular to the magnetic field can cause an instability. This is equivalent to the helical instability, discussed below, where however the magnetic field is in the direction of the drift velocity. The density gradient is assumed to be caused by the Lorenz force and by the asymmetry of the surface recombination velocities. Similarly, the theory presented by McNeill (190) makes use of this surface-density effect, often called the Suhl-effect (267). These explanations can take into account the nonuniformity of the various results observed with different crystals, as different crystal surfaces (and bulk imperfections) would show varying recombination rates.

Gueret (98, 98a) develops a theory along different assumptions. Inside a crystal the electrons drift approximately in the direction of the applied electric field in spite of the perpendicular magnetic field, owing to the finite dimensions of the crystal and owing to the Hall and Suhl effect setting up a transverse field which cancels the transverse drift to a certain degree. However, near the ohmic end contact, no tangential electric field can be set up and a strong transverse drift occurs there. This transverse drift is in fact the source of Gueret's instability, which requires a large number of holes to be injected at the contacts. The background of holes is required to maintain a low value of wave-phase velocity for a convective interaction to take place. He finds for example, a magnetic field of 1.4 kG suffices for the instability threshold, if as many holes as electrons are injected. In order to fit his theoretical results with experimental ones he has to assume, however, that the field is higher near the ohmic contacts than in the bulk.

Hasegawa (112, 112a) considers the situation where a reactive stream of electrons interacts with the holes which are regarded as a stationary resistive medium. Robinson (240a) computed collision-induced instabilities for B and v_d perpendicular to each other. A detailed study of the transient effects of avalanche-plasma production has been made by Ancker-Johnson (6e, 6h).

The other class of emission occurring at very low electric fields (9b, 43, 153f, 206a) has been explained quantum mechanically by stimulated emissions of phonons by the electrons drifting in a strong magnetic field (206), where electron transitions occur between Landau levels. The coupling between electrons and phonons takes place through the deformation potential and piezoelectric fields (see preceding section). The emitted phonons would somehow couple to the waveguide field at the semiconductor surface.

Using the approach of classical mechanics, one can treat the piezoelectric waves as being amplified by the drifting electrons (25a, 157, 242), whose drift velocity can be greatly reduced by the applied magnetic field for positive gain to occur (263.1). Such a treatment is strictly speaking incorrect, as for high-mobility semiconductors the mean free electron path is of the same order of magnitude as the acoustic wavelength and one ought to treat this problem quantum-mechanically. The gain mechanism between drifting electrons and acoustic lattice waves has been discussed in the previous section. In InSb, this effect causes high-field domains to travel along the crystal. As the phonon life-time increases with decreasing lattice temperature, the emission should be larger at $4°K$ than at $77°K$. This has in fact been observed (25a). It is a first verification of the presented theory.

It seems appropriate here to explain the significance of Landau levels which occur at high magnetic fields. For low electron densities, one can usually neglect

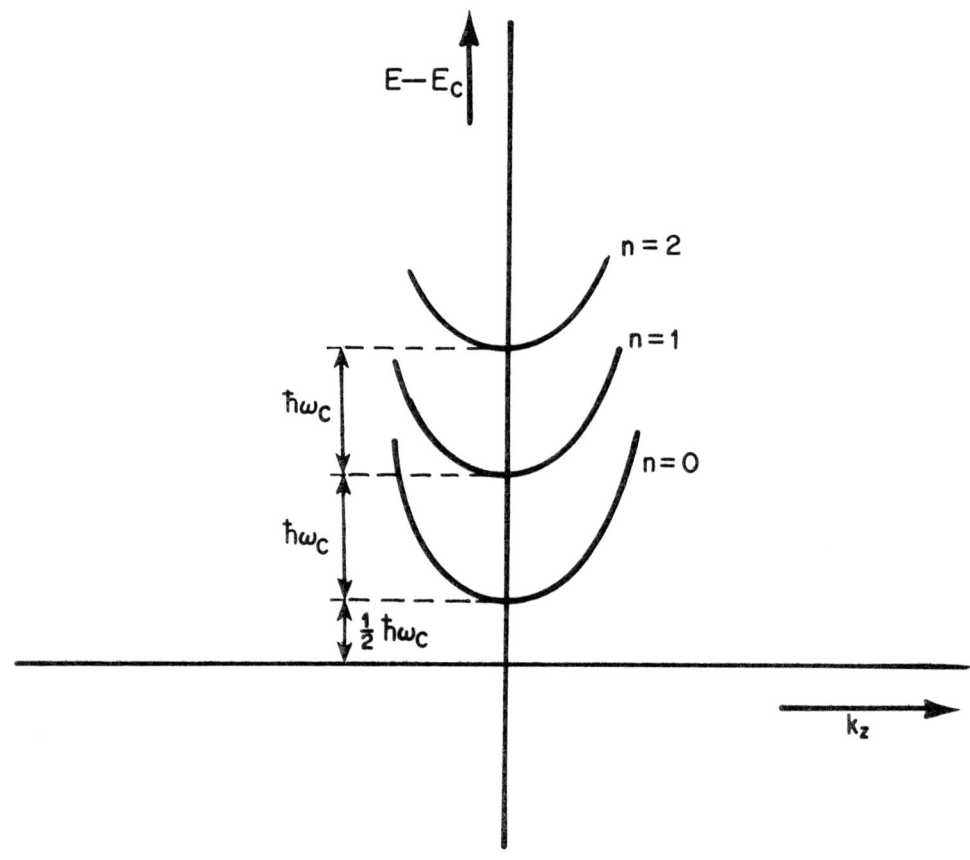

Fig. 4.27   Landau levels in a magnetic field.

the Pauli exclusion principle and assume a Maxwellian distribution function. For InSb at $77°K$ this holds for carrier densities up to about 10^{15} cm^{-3}. At higher densities, the distribution function follows Fermi-Dirac statistics. For sufficiently large magnetic fields, the conduction band splits into a succession of discrete levels called Landau levels (see Fig. 4.27) and this creates a redistribution of electrons. If an electron is subjected to a magnetic field in the z-direction, its motion in the transverse x-y plane will be a circular orbit, with angular frequency $\omega_c = eB/m^*$, referred to as the cyclotron frequency. If the radius of this orbit is very small, quantum mechanics imposes the restriction that the only permitted orbits are those with an angular momentum which is a multiple of $\hbar$, as was shown by Landau. The electron is free in the z-direction, but for directions normal to the magnetic field, it is trapped in the levels of the harmonic oscillator. This changes the expression for the density of states, S [see J. S. Blakemore (29)] which gives the number of electrons by the usual expression

$$n = \int_{E_c}^{\infty} Sf\,\mathrm{d}E$$

where f is the Fermi distribution function [see equation (1.33)].

Finally, microwave emission has also been observed from n-InAs (79a). The threshold field was 135 V/cm for 8.5 kG. The emission is again broadband and very similar to the one in InSb.

The emission described here can usually be called noise emission, which is the reason for its limited potential usefulness in device applications. However, the study of such effects might lead to a better understanding of instabilities in solid-state plasmas and ultimately produce technological advance.

4.4.3 Alfvén and Helicon Wave Instabilities

The treatment of the propagation of electromagnetic waves in gaseous plasmas (264) can be applied to solid-state plasmas (286.1), and it can easily be shown how recognition of the relationships has stimulated further research and brought about new knowledge.

H. Barkhausen noticed already during the First World War, that his radio receivers picked up descending 'whistles' and called this phenomenon 'whistlers' (18). It was not until several years later that it was found that they are associated with a particular low-frequency wave which can propagate even in very dense plasmas along magnetic field lines. These waves originate from lightning flashes. Whistlers propagate along the magnetic field lines of the earth in the ionospheric plasma and are in the kHz range.

It was Alfvén who first solved the dispersion relation for waves which occur in plasmas consisting of an equal number of positive and negative charge carriers. Although the results agreed with measurements on plasmas in outer space, little agreement with laboratory results could be found—until in 1959 Alfvén wave velocities were measured in a solid-state plasma. Galt et al. (88) were measuring the absorption coefficient of microwaves incident on the semimetal pure bismuth. Buchsbaum and Galt (43a) pointed out two years later that this was in fact a measurement of the velocity of Alfvén waves. The reflection coefficient for waves on a medium such as Bi should be very high. However, as there are as many holes as electrons, the waves are able to penetrate into the crystal and are absorbed there instead of being reflected. Owing to the light masses of electrons and holes in Bi, one was able to observe Alfvén waves at higher frequencies. The plasma dimensions could thus be made larger than the wavelengths involved and plasma boundaries could be neglected. Otherwise these would have an important effect on the wave propagation. Boundary effects were in fact responsible for the failure of finding agreement between theory and experimental results with gaseous plasmas. Naturally, the frequencies have also to be high enough for the collision effect to be negligible.

The equation of motion for n_s carriers of charge e_s and effective mass $m_s{}^*$ in a magnetic field H can be solved, if H is in the z-direction and circularly polarized radiation propagates along the z-axis. The following dispersion relation for transverse waves in the absence of scattering can then be obtained:

$$\frac{k^2}{k_L{}^2} = 1 + \sum_s \frac{\omega_{ps}{}^2}{\omega_{cs}(\omega a_s + \omega_{cs})} - \sum_s \frac{\omega_{ps}{}^2}{\omega\omega_{cs}a_s} \qquad (4.28)$$

(k = propagation constant,
  k_L = propagation constant owing to the lattice alone,
  s is summation index for electrons and holes,
  a_s = ± 1 according to the sign of the charge,
  ω_{ps} = $\sqrt{(n_s e_s{}^2/m_s\epsilon)}$ = plasma frequency,
  ω_{cs} = $e_s B/m_s$ = cyclotron frequency,
  n_s = carrier density,
  B = magnetic induction
  m_s = carrier mass)

If $\omega_{cs} \simeq \omega$, one has cyclotron waves, which are strongly attenuated (210).

Alfvén waves occur, if (a) the semiconductor is intrinsic, i.e. $\sum_s n_s a_s = 0$ and (b) $\omega_{cs} \gg \omega$.

Owing to condition (a), the second sum of equation (4.28) vanishes for Alfvén waves:

$$\sum_s \frac{\omega_{ps}{}^2}{\omega\omega_{cs}a_s} = \frac{e}{\epsilon\omega B} \sum_s n_s a_s \equiv 0$$

Alfvén wave propagation has subsequently been observed in bismuth by other authors (300).

The first sum of equation (4.28) can be rewritten as follows with the approximation $\omega \ll \omega_c$

$$\sum_s \frac{\omega_{ps}{}^2}{\omega_{cs}{}^2 a_s} = \frac{1}{\epsilon B^2} \sum_s n_s m_s = \frac{\mu_m \rho v_l{}^2}{B^2} = \frac{v_l{}^2}{V_a{}^2} \qquad (4.29)$$

where v_l is the velocity of light in the solid in the absence of the plasma,
V_a is defined as the Alfvén velocity, $V_a = B/\sqrt{(\mu_m \rho_m)}$,
$\rho_m = \sum_s n_s m_s$ is the mass density, and
μ_m is the permeability.
Therefore equation (4.28) reduces to

$$\frac{1}{u_a^2} = \frac{1}{v_l^2} + \frac{1}{V_a^2}$$

where $u_a = \omega/k$ is the phase velocity of the wave. If v_l is much larger than V_a, then u_a depends only on B and not on ω.

In the case of an extrinsic semiconductor plasma, when the second sum of equation (4.28) does not vanish, u_a depends on ω and Alfvén waves are not possible. In this case, the response to left-circularly polarized waves is not the same as for right-circularly polarized waves. A different wave occurs then whose phase velocity is given by the expression

$$v_H = \frac{v_l}{\omega_p} \sqrt{(\omega \omega_c)} \qquad (4.31)$$

These waves can also travel through plasmas whose densities are well above the cut-off densities. The existence of such waves had been suggested in metals (163), and Aigrain (3) predicted them in semiconductors. He called them 'Helicons'. One can attribute to them a characteristic mass. Using the relation $v_H = \omega/k$, we find with equation (4.31)

$$\omega = \frac{k^2 B}{\mu_m n e} \qquad (4.32)$$

The plane wave solution of the Schrödinger equation [see equation (1.4)] has the same dispersion law as equation (4.32), if the mass of the 'particle' is taken to be

$$\frac{\hbar n e \mu_m}{2B}$$

For sodium and $B = 1$ kG, the mass of a helicon is about equal to the mass of an electron. (For a detailed review, see (202.1)). In fact, Barkhausen's whistlers are helicons of the ionospheric plasma.

Owing to the unequal densities of electrons and holes, strong transverse currents occur with helicon waves. These currents in turn generate a large magnetic field. The electric field induced by the varying magnetic field is very small since the frequency is low. These waves represent therefore essentially an r.f. Hall effect and have been used for the measurement of the Hall coefficient (53).

The following general conditions for helicon waves are easily fulfilled,

$$\omega_p^2/\omega \omega_c > 1, \quad \omega/\omega_c \ll 1, \quad \text{and} \quad \omega_c \tau > 1$$

One can show that the damping is essentially determined by the product $\omega_c \tau$, which yields therefore one of the important conditions for helicons to propagate as stated above. This can be explained in physical terms: the existence of helicons is attached to the cyclotron rotation of the carriers around the magnetic field lines; if a particle can perform many cyclotron rotations between two successive collisions, the helicon is only slightly damped. This indicates that the best materials are high mobiltiy semiconductors. These waves have first been observed in InSb (171) at room temperature at f = 10 GHz, in Bi (88) at low temperatures, in sodium (37), and subsequently in other materials (237). There are two cases,

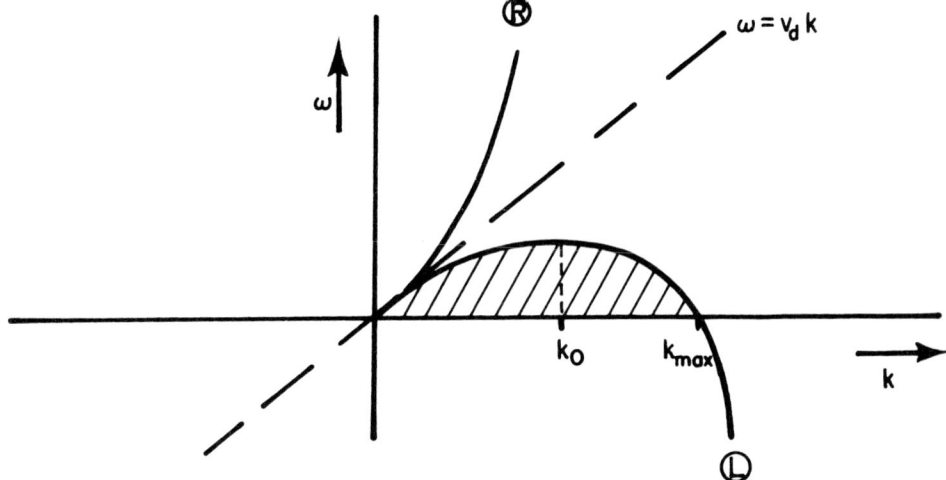

Fig. 4.28   Dispersion diagram of helicon waves (R=right-hand circularly polarized wave. L=left-hand circularly polarized wave; hatched region indicates negative energy).

depending on the sense of circular polarization. One wave is propagating almost freely and the other one is heavily attenuated. Their phase velocity v_H can be made much smaller than the speed of light and this fact seems to suggest amplification possibilities similar to those in travelling wave tubes, if electrons are made to drift with a velocity $v_d \approx v_H$.

The physical effect of a drift field in the direction of the magnetic field lines can be described as follows: As the magnetic field of the wave causes the initially straight lines of the applied magnetic field to become helical, the charge particles follow them now along a helical motion. It is not possible to achieve gain, however, with only one type of mobile carrier.

One can consider the situation in the same way as the resistive wall amplifier described in Chapter III [see equation (3.11)]. Of the two left- and right-polarized helicons propagating on electrons drifting with a velocity v_d, the former is the energy source, as it carries negative energy when the drift velocity exceeds the phase velocity. If such a negative energy-carrying wave is passed through a dissipative medium, energy will be extracted from the wave and it will grow. In fact, holes can act as a dissipative medium. The dispersion relation is shown in Fig. 4.28. The part of the diagram belonging to the left polarized wave and situated in the cross-hatched region represents a negative energy wave, for it has $\omega - v_d k < 0$ with v_d the electron drift velocity. In the region where $k < k_0$, one has a forward carrier wave which yields a convective instability. The region $k > k_0$ shows a backward wave giving an absolute instability (4).

An electron density $n = 7.10^{16}$ cm^{-3} could give an amplification up to 100 MHz. Nanney et $al.$ (209) have used n-PbTe with $n = 4.10^{17}$cm^{-3} and $\mu \simeq 10^6$ cm^2/Vsec at $4°$K and obtained gain in the GHz range.

However, it has been shown that boundaries introduce considerable damping at higher frequencies. The effect of boundaries is to shift k_{max} towards the origin in Fig. 4.28. Therefore, microwave emission from InSb (see pages 125-129) cannot be explained in terms of growing helicons, as the observed spectrum is too high. In fact one can say, that helicon waves in a finite semiconductor have a phase velocity larger than in the infinite case, so that they are usually too fast for any interaction to set in producing a negative energy wave. The above-mentioned experiment by Nanney et $al.$ (209) was performed with a material exhibiting a very high mobility at a large carrier density (n-PbTe has in fact exhibited one of the highest mobilities observed hitherto).

Klotzenberg et $al.$ (159) and Gueret (98) have derived the dispersion equation for helicons in finite plasmas. They found that it is necessary to take a secondary wave which has the properties of a surface wave, in order to match the fields in the semiconductor with those outside. This surface wave causes additional losses. It is very similar to electrostatic surface waves which can exist on a cylindrical plasma column (281). Crystal surfaces produce on helicons an effect which is analogous to that of electron-beam boundaries on the beam plasma, where a reduction in beam plasma frequency occurs. Experimental results have been reported by several authors (46).

The helicon-wave instability of Fig. 4.28 was first studied by Bok and Nozieres (33) for the left polarized wave for n-type and intrinsic materials. The drift velocity of the more mobile carrier types has to exceed the phase velocity of the helicon wave for gain to occur. Bers and McWhorter (28) showed that in this case an absolute instability can also occur, at whose frequency and wave number oscillations will set in, making the amplifier solution of Bok and Nozieres meaningless. However, as there are always boundary conditions involved in practice, these absolute instabilities will often be inhibited.

An experimental study of these effects has first been made in Bi (19) using the experimental set-up of Fig. 4.29. However, as $n = p$ for Bi, the measurements in fact relate to Alfvén waves. The magnetoresistance of the crystal in an axial field confines the current into a cylinder with a cross-section defined by the size of the

ohmic end contacts. The surrounding material forms a heat sink. The abrupt
boundary of the current cylinder acts like a boundary of a waveguide. The coupling
of the r.f. signals was performed by small coils through narrow slots in the end
contacts. A region of absolute instability and another with amplification was
measured, giving a verification of the theoretical work.

A detailed study of helicon-wave instabilities was performed by Misawa (196).
Hasegawa (112) investigated resistive instabilities for the slower helicon wave
carrying negative kinetic power of Fig. 4.28. S. Akai (4) calculated the generalized
dispersion relation for arbitrary directions of wave propagation, and applied
magnetic and electric fields, which gives the helicon-wave instability as a special
case, and produces the conditions for convective and non-convective instabilities
analytically.

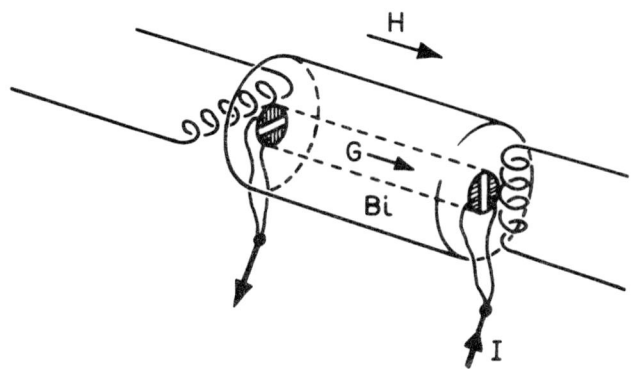

Fig. 4.29   Experimental set-up for the study of transverse-wave instabilities in Bi
(G gain).

Another method of producing gain for helicon waves was suggested by Grimes
and Buchsbaum, where the two species of charge carriers are separated spatially.
Carriers in one plasma layer would support the wave, while carriers in an adjacent
layer would be given a drift velocity greater than that of the phase velocity of
the wave. Baraff (16) has analysed this case theoretically and found indeed
instabilities.

Another way to overcome the collisional losses of helicon waves in single component plasmas was suggested by Baraff and Buchsbaum (16a, 16b). When a helicon
wave propagates in a medium of finite transverse dimensions, as discussed above,
it is accompanied by a surface wave, which decays exponentially away from the
plasma-vacuum interface. The penetration depth of the surface wave is propor-
tional to $(\omega_c \tau)^{-1}$ and its amplitude proportional to $\omega_c \tau$. This means that the
loss tends to a finite value, as $\omega_c \tau \to \infty$, provided that $\omega \tau < 1$. If the medium with
the helicon wave is one plasma region, bounded by two different plasma regions
in the form of a sandwich, then surface waves exist at the interfaces. The effective

dielectric constant in each plasma region can be changed by a drift velocity, such that the surface wave can be made to disappear. If the drift velocity is then further increased, the surface wave reappears, but with its phase reversed, and the losses are transformed to gain. If this surface-wave gain is larger than the losses of the helicon wave in the bounded plasma, then one has gain. The required drift velocity does not have to exceed the phase velocity of the wave.

Nanney *et al.* (209) in fact observed in their above-mentioned experiment an interaction between helicon waves and drift currents in a three-layer structure of PbTe. Although spatial growth of the helicon wave was not achieved, wave attenuation could be reduced by 15dB. Further theoretical studies on these surface-wave instabilities are reported by several authors (16b, 16c, 247, 247a, 289).

The instabilities in an electromagnetic field which has both transverse and longitudinal components of electric field, have been considered (288) and four possible non-convective instabilities for mm-waves have been found. Similar computations by Solymar and Lashmore-Davies (260b) suggest, however, only a decrease in attenuation of helicon propagation but no net gain. Other authors (24) studied also the interactions between various wave modes propagating at an angle to the d.c. magnetic field. Interactions were found to occur between two Alfvén-type modes, a longitudinal and a transverse plasmon mode. Plasmons are the quanta of plasma oscillations which are related to the plasma frequency ω_p (308). There are two branches; one is caused by electrons and holes moving out of phase, and the other one, a lower frequency mode, is given by the charge carriers moving in phase. In metals, plasmons possess such high frequencies that their energies are greater than the electron energies at the top of the Fermi distribution. These plasmons can therefore not be thermally excited and are usually generated by the bombardment of the metal with high-energy electrons. In a semiconductor, plasmons can exist in thermal-equilibrium conditions. For example, the plasmon energy in n-Ge with $n = 10^{16}$ cm^{-3} at temperatures where impurity scattering dominates, is about 2.10^{-3} eV. When the wavelength of a plasmon approaches the Debye length, Landau damping becomes very strong. Therefore, their frequencies are usually only a few per cent higher than ω_p.

Some first measurements seem to show helicon gain, on the other hand, if the angle between electric and magnetic field is about $25°$ (22). The case of helicon propagation at an angle ϕ_h to the external magnetic field H_0 can be considered as follows: The magnetic field of the helicon wave has, under these conditions, a component in the direction of H_0 and hence in the direction of the particle motion. The helicon field component along H_0 alternately adds to and subtracts from H_0, so that the local magnetic field oscillates in magnitude. Therefore, as the charge carriers drift along the field, they experience regions of alternately increasing and decreasing magnetic field. These 'ridges' in the magnetic field act as magnetic mirrors which tend to restrict the particle motion along the field. If a particle becomes trapped by the wave, in general there is an exchange of energy between the wave and the particle. Charge carriers which move initially along H_0 at a velocity less than $V_a/\cos \phi_h$ absorb energy from the wave. More rapidly-moving particles deliver energy to the wave. One can have, therefore, either damping or gain respectively. This theory does not include collisions, which introduce a further damping term.

Other workers have excited acoustic shear waves by means of helicons in Al, (169, 244) and Greebe (97a) has shown theoretically that helicon resonances can be excited by sliding along each other two metal plates which are orientated perpendicularly to an applied static magnetic field, provided that they are electrically connected along their circumferences. This is an example of interaction between helicons in solids and ultrasound, and can lead to various device applications. Helicon–phonon coupling was also observed in semiconducting PbTe at 4.2°K (249.1).

Of interest is a theoretical study by Bartelink (19a) who found the conditions for gain if a negative-energy carrying helicon wave reacts with a positive resistance background. He showed that under some conditions amplification occurs if the electronic drift velocity v_d is larger than the phase velocity v_H of the helicon. He pointed out, however, that the proper criterion for gain is not $v_d > v_H$, but that the negative-energy carrying wave must see a net positive resistance, and in some cases gain can be achieved even for $v_d < v_H$. A negative resistance on the other hand can lead to a second mode of amplification. Another result shows that there can exist an absolute instability, which does not depend critically on collisions. The frequency is determined by 'second-order' effects, like the difference in the anisotropy of the electron and hole mobilities.

Wisseman and Davies (302) have measured the boundary effects in n-type InSb cylinders at 54.2 MHz for temperatures from 81° to 373°K. The guided helicons had higher phase velocities and increased attenuation constants, in agreement with the theoretical results described above.

It should be mentioned that helicon propagation has been studied under various aspects, in order to study either their general properties or relevant material parameters. Helicons near the cyclotron resonance experience an absorption edge owing to the Doppler-shifted cyclotron resonance of the electrons moving in the field of the helicon wave (8, 51, 158, 195). For very large magnetic fields Landau levels have an effect on the propagation (86, 86a, 195a, 195b). Damped helicon oscillations have been measured in HgSe (94) and helicon propagation was determined in In (109). Seifert and Pötzl (250) have studied mobilities and carrier densities under hot-electron conditions by helicon attenuation, if a large electric field was applied perpendicularly to the wave vector. Helicon resonances have also been measured in superconducting media (186), and helicon spin wave interactions have been found in magnetic semiconductors, (see p. 38) (288a).

Interesting microwave techniques for the study of helicon propagation have been suggested. Vasile and Sucher (286) employed a new stripline technique, consisting of two orthogonal striplines, separated by a common ground plate and coupled through a hole containing the test sample. Seifert and Pötzl (250) used a rectangular

TE_{102} resonator where a part of the large wall can be replaced by a semiconductor without cutting any current lines by the insulated transition from conducting wall to semiconducting specimen.

If electromagnetic frequencies are increased high enough, intense power absorption appears at frequencies given by the cyclotron resonance of one of the carriers involved. As this gives a very accurate method of determining the mass of carriers, this experiment has commonly been performed for the measurement of electron and hole masses (248). However, cyclotron-resonance phenomena cannot be used for any plasma instability.

4.4.4. Other Instability Effects

A further phenomenon has been studied in gaseous and in semiconductor plasmas simultaneously. In 1958. Lehnert discovered surprising phenomena on electrical discharges in gases, and Ivanov and Ryvkin measured small oscillations of current when a large current was passed through a semiconductor. Because of the general interest in these results, the experiments were repeated in several other laboratories with more refined techniques. Theoretical work was performed to explain the discharge phenomena. In a magnetic field, electrons and ions spiral along the magnetic field within the discharge column. When the externally applied magnetic field is large enough, the discharge column twists in a helical fashion, because the magnetic field produced by the current flow causes a displacement of the column. The effect was therefore called helical instability. In 1960, Larrabee and Steele (168) showed that the same instability exists in a semiconductor plasma, and they called a device based on this oscillating phenomenon, an oscillistor. Soon it was realized, that this was also the reason for Ivanov and Ryvkin's results. Helical waves (6d) can develop particularly in materials with a long minority carrier lifetime such as Ge (93).

The effect can be understood in the following way: First helical density fluctuations of electrons and holes develop. The axial electric field tends to separate, or effectively 'unscrew', these helices with respect to one another giving rise to azimuthal electric fields. These fields, together with the axial magnetic field, cause radial flow of both carrier species which can produce a build-up of carrier densities near the surface. This results in growing oscillations (128). Frequencies reported are 10^5 Hz. Disturbances excited between a pair of probes on a long semiconductor filament grew as they propagated along the crystal.

Various experimental results belong to this class of oscillations. Ancker-Johnson (6) produced a solid-state plasma by injection from current contacts into p-InSb at $77°K$ under pulsed conditions. The oscillations occur in the absence of an applied magnetic field. They appear only at currents greater than that required for the onset of self-pinching in the plasma.

Systematic measurements of helical instabilities in p-InSb with external axial magnetic fields have been performed by Ancker-Johnson (6c).

A plasma is generally diamagnetic. However, the helical shape of the discharge column produces a large magnetic field inside the helix which increases the externally-applied magnetic field. This, however, means that this type of plasma is now paramagnetic. The external field can in fact now be reduced slightly without destroying the helix. Therefore a small displaced hystereses loop is generated. Whereas this loop is only a few tenths of a milligauss in gaseous plasma discharges, semiconductors showed more than 20 Gauss. Additionally, the loop is electronically tunable by means of the current. It has been suggested that these ferromagnetic-like loops might be used for digital-computer memories. Not only can their operating condition be adjusted electronically, but they would signal their 'on' condition by continuous oscillations.

The study of helical waves in semiconductors has led to another useful experiment. Controlled nuclear-fusion experiments require plasma-confining systems. One has suggested Joffe bars, which are four rods, placed along the plasma, with a large current flowing in the opposite directions in alternate bars, so that a magnetic quadrupole field is created. It is expensive to build a gas-plasma confined by this system and it is easier to place them along a semiconductor with a helical instability. In fact experiments have shown that Joffe bars are able to suppress the current instability, an indication that the discharge column has been confined successfully along a straight path. However, when the current through the Joffe bars was increased, in order to obtain further confinement, a new form of instability appeared. This would seem to indicate that there is a limit to the ultimate plasma confinement by Joffe bars. This is an important experimental result.

The class of oscillatory phenomena known as the oscillistor (168) effect also belongs to the helical instability. However the observed current oscillation at the crystal terminals cannot be explained fully by it. Arizumi and Umeno (9) studied the oscillistor effect by observing simultaneously a microwave signal transmitted through the crystal whose dimensions were much smaller than its skin depth, and the potential difference between two probes alloyed at axially-symmetrical positions on the sample. It was found that the terminal effect is caused by density waves travelling along the drift direction of the minority carriers. A theoretical analysis has been attempted by Schulz (249.2).

The phenomena of pinching or constriction of a plasma under the action of the self-magnetic field of the current has been studied in high-mobility semiconductors such as InSb (6a, 6b, 6c, 93a). In some cases oscillations have been observed between the pinched and unpinched states. Pinching of an electron-hole plasma in InSb has been observed directly by a microwave-probe technique (127, 127a). It could be seen, that there does not exist a critical current for pinching which sets in before the current-controlled negative dynamic resistance begins. It is shown that the full growth of a pinch occurs during about 1 μsec.

The madistor (192) employs the ability to produce a localized plasma within a semiconducting medium between an injecting and an ohmic contact. This is possible if the carrier life-time increases with injection level. In InSb the life-time is determined by trapping centres, which become filled at high injection levels. Once a plasma has been established, it can be steered by a weak magnetic field and be made to jump between a number of ohmic contacts, giving switching action. A disc-shaped semiconductor with an injecting contact at the centre and ohmic contacts along the periphery produces dekatron-action. †

Nakashima (208) performed measurements on a Ge disc with an injecting $p-n$ junction contact in the centre and an ohmic ring contact near the edge of the disc. When a voltage was applied between the inner and outer contact and a magnetic field H, oscillistor action was observed for H parallel to the surface of the disc and a new type of oscillation called spiral instability for H perpendicular to the Ge disc surface. The observation was made in p-type Ge at 77°K and in n-type Ge at 300°K; The frequencies ranged between 0.1 to 1.6 MHz (198a). The theory for these instabilities was developed by Miyai and Nakashima (198).

Toda (278, 278a) predicts a plasma density instability caused by the dependence of the plasma generation rate on the electric field. When the density of electrons and holes in an extrinsic semiconductor changes, a change in electric field is caused, which alters the generation rate. An external capacitance between the two end contacts of the crystal makes the phase of the electric field lag that of the density by up to 90°. The time during which the carriers gain or lose energy causes a further phase difference. This will cause growing oscillations. Damped oscillations were observed experimentally at 2–10 MHz in n-InSb at 77°K, if the plasma was shunted by an external capacitance.

When a strong transverse magnetic field is applied, 'transverse' breakdown might be used for a similar instability. The phase of the r.f. Hall electric field will lag that of the longitudinal r.f. electric field in the direction of the drift field. Thus the phase of the transverse generation rate will lag that of the longitudinal field, and an instability will occur. Microwave transmission measurements at 7–10 GHz seem to verify the theory for n-InSb. Toda suggests that Suzuki's results (269) could be explained by his theory (see page 126).

An interesting effect is caused by field-dependent recombination and trapping of carriers in certain semiconductors. This produces domains similar to those of the Gunn effect described in the first section of this chapter. It relies on the same effect, i.e. the differential volume conductance of an originally homogeneous semiconductor becomes negative. However, this time it is not the mobility which exhibits a negative slope with electric field, but the carrier density. Domains can be formed. They may move in the external field along the crystal and cause oscillation at domain-transit time frequencies (31, 69, 147, 147a).

---

† A dekatron is a classical counting and indicating tube where a glow discharge is transferred along electrodes.

On the other hand, this field-dependent carrier density can cause also different oscillations. It has been suggested that the moving high-field domains in InSb at $77°K$ might be caused by this recombination nonlinearity (9a). Current oscillations have also been observed in Cu-doped Si *pin* structures (265). The frequencies are in the 100 kHz range. The results illustrate that the charge condition in the traps is fundamental to the oscillations.

Some hot-carrier current oscillations have been observed by several authors (118, 143). They occur in the microwave region at $77°K$ when a large electric field is applied. Although various mechanisms have been suggested, the origin of these instabilities is unclear. They seem to be different from the results of McGroddy and Nathan (76, 78, 188), as too low a bias field is required in one case (118).

A current-controlled negative resistance in p-InSb at $77°K$ has been explained as a double injection phenomenon associated with avalanche breakdown (7). A similar effect has been observed with Ge photocells (71.1).

Muravski *et al.* (205) reported current oscillations at the contacts of a metal with the surface of Ge and Si and could provide evidence that the oscillations appeared due to charge exchange in the compensating impurity caused by a strong electric field. For example, if a compensating acceptor impurity was introduced into the surface layer of an *n*-type semiconductor, some electrons from the conduction band were captured by the levels of this impurity. Above a certain critical value of the applied voltage, the field in the surface layer became sufficient to transfer electrons to the conduction band. This reduced sharply the surface layer resistance and the field in it. Consequently, the electrons were again captured by the compensating impurity and the process was repeated. It demonstrates how the contacts of the semiconductor diodes can contribute to any instability phenomena.

Many other types of instability have been suggested (221), such as the concept that electrons could exhibit negative mass at certain electric fields (164), or the instability caused by an ionization rate which is strongly dependent on the carrier temperature (295). Various Soviet workers have studied the general effects of a negative conductivity (75, 131, 155). Oscillations seem also possible due to the strongly field-dependent interaction between optical phonons and electrons (141.1). Similarly, interactions between a magnetoplasma and spin waves have been discussed (286.1).

Of interest are studies of the magnetoresistance, which can become negative for certain conditions and which should be useful for various microwave devices (149, 207).

Many proposals have also been made which rely on an interaction between the semiconductor plasma with some external medium. An interaction of the drifting carriers in the semiconductor with an external slow-wave structure (268a) has been studied. Hammer (106) treated the same case for GaAs with a negative differential mobility. Other authors have investigated, how an external electron beam either excites a helicon wave in the semiconductor (152) or interacts with a plasma of a degenerate semiconductor (17). The problem of the excitation of surface waves has been discussed (151), in particular by an electron beam moving in vacuum along the surface.

Amplification has also been achieved by magnetic control of the skin depth in high-purity bismuth at $4.2°K$, resulting from magnetoconductivity (122).

Then one has the effects of plasma oscillations of valence electrons if an electron beam of several keV energy passes through a thin film of a solid. These oscillations are quantized in integral multiples between 15 and 20 eV, and their energy quantum hf_p is known as a 'plasmon'. If the energy of the electron beam is further increased so that its velocity is larger than the velocity of an electromagnetic wave in the solid (which is given by $v_l = 1/\sqrt{(\epsilon\mu)}$, where ϵ is about 12 times larger in many solids than in vacuum), then a radiation occurs, which is produced by the reorientation of the microscopic dipoles in the trail of an electron. This effect is called Czerenkov radiation and has been suggested as a submillimeter microwave source. It is commonly used nowadays for the detection and analysis of particle energies in high-energy physics. This could bring us to the many other effects of microwave generation by solids, like the Josephson (167) effect occurring between two superconducting media separated by a very thin insulating layer. However, these devices cannot be treated here in the limited scope of this book, although they might be of great technological importance in the future (see, for example, the interaction between the a.c. Josephson current and surface plasmons, discussed by Economou and Ngai (72)).

(For References to Chapter IV see Chapter VI.)

CHAPTER V

Devices

Research is always stimulated most if the prospect of commercial devices exists. This is certainly an important aspect for most of the instabilities discussed in the preceding chapter.

It remains now to describe the general devices which either have been developed already, or which may become available in the future. Such a treatment is a difficult task. One cannot deal with the subject exhaustively, as its content is very much a matter of the future. However, it is felt to be of importance for a study of semiconductor plasmas to look forward and answer the question of technological relevance. Therefore, the attempt is made here to review the device field.

5.1 The Transferred-Electron Effect

For some time, the most important application of the transferred electron effect seemed to be its use for oscillators. Then a formidable competitor appeared in the avalanche oscillator. Since then a further important field of devices emerged for the transferred-electron effect, namely, its use for pulse generation and processing.

5.1.1 Oscillators and Amplifiers

Since Gunn discovered his large oscillations under pulsed conditions (102), important increases in microwave power have been achieved, both under pulsed and CW operation.

Although the most spectacular developments have been suggested and partly obtained with the lsa mode (62c), devices have mainly been made with the domain-mode oscillators. These have given more than 200 W pulsed output power at 1.5 GHz (71, 71a) and up to 1 W at X-band (113, 156). Some 100 μW has been obtained from harmonics of the domain-fundamental at 31 GHz (50). On the other hand, 30 mW is a typical figure for CW output powers at X-band operation (291).

The efficiencies range from a few percent to more than 10%. They can be calculated approximately as long as the Q-factor of the cavity is large enough, by multiplying the electrostatic energy, stored by the domain capacitance, with the transit-time frequency and then dividing by the losses occurring in the diode outside the domain. The resulting expression for the efficiency η is:

$$\eta = \frac{V_D \mathscr{E}_R d_d}{3V_B[V_B - V_D + (\mathscr{E}_t - \mathscr{E}_R)d_d]} \tag{5.1}$$

It is possible to tune the oscillator by about an octave by altering the resonance frequency of the cavity without any appreciable decrease in η (39, 62d). By addition of an inductance in series with the diode, the performance of the oscillator could be increased to higher efficiencies, indicating how important the correct position of the diode is with respect to the resonating circuit (68, 71a).

An important property of an oscillator is often that of noise. A first attempt in the treatment of the noise phenomenon of the transferred-electron effect has been made by Shockley *et al.* (255a) by the development of the impedance-field method. There are several phenomena contributing to noise, such as the scattering of electrons

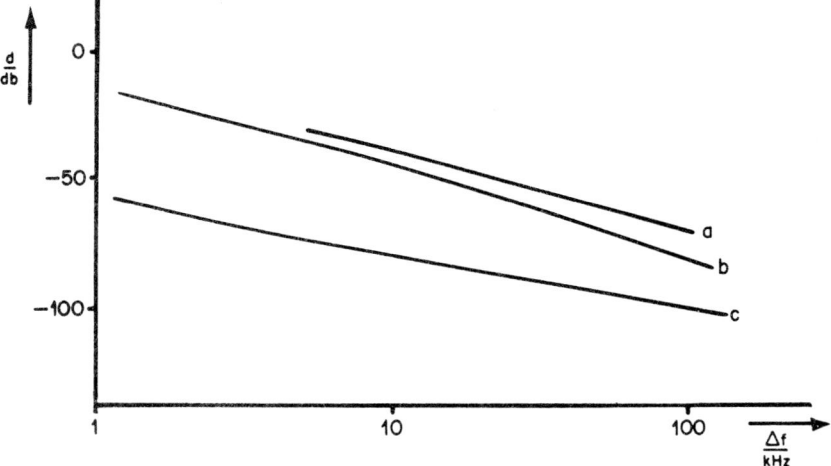

Fig. 5.1   F.M. noise power d for Gunn oscillators and local-oscillator klystron: (*a*) J-Band diode (13.1 GHz); (*b*) X-Band diode (9 GHz); (*c*) CV 2346 klystron (9.375 GHz) (Δf difference between carrier and measurement frequencies).

between the energy valleys, impact ionization by the high domain field, thermal noise, etc. An elementary theory of frequency modulation noise has been proposed by Hobson (125b). He assumed that the domain develops from a set of elemental domains, each with a cross-sectional area of several times the Debye length. Fluctuations of the electric field result in statistical variations of the time at which the field in the nucleation centre reaches the threshold value for the transferred electron effect. He has, in fact, restricted himself to one type of noise source, which can be observed with long Gunn-effect samples.

Measurements show that A.M. noise power is in fact lower than F.M. noise power (63, 144). The A.M. noise performance of Gunn oscillators is very similar to that of typical low-voltage klystrons (2). This shows that these domain-transit oscillators will be particularly useful as local oscillators (see Fig. 5.1). Improvements of F.M.

noise can be obtained by employing high Q resonators, and cavities with a high characteristic impedance. The latter requirement can be fulfilled by placing the Gunn diode in an overmoded cavity oscillating in a higher-order H-mode (63a).

Frequency tuning of the domain-mode oscillators is a simple matter and can be achieved either by changing the resonance frequency of the cavity (241) or by suitable diode properties. Cavity tuning has been performed by changing the cavity dimensions, or by a movable dielectric washer inside the cavity. Electronic tuning has been achieved by insertion of a varactor diode (166, 291), which represents a variable capacitance, whose value can be adjusted by an applied voltage. This technique can also be considered as a suitable way of frequency modulation, if the signal frequency is applied to the varactor. A ferrimagnetic sample has also been used so that the Gunn diode could be tuned by the application of a magnetic field over a wide frequency range (56, 306).

On the other hand, frequency changes can be obtained by diode tuning. The reactive components of the equivalent circuit of the diode depend on the applied voltage to a small degree, so that frequency changes can be obtained by changes in the biasing voltage (36, 156, 156b). On the other hand, the frequency can also be made variable for diodes operating with a resistive load by changing the applied voltage, as the domain voltage depends on the applied voltage.

Increased tunability can be achieved with diodes having a certain geometry, so that the domain trajectory length varies strongly with applied voltage. If one electrode is small and the other one large, the field varies considerably along the crystal. For a small voltage the domain will only travel along the region with maximum field-value, and the frequency is high. If the applied voltage is high enough, the domains travel along the whole length between the contacts and the frequency is decreased. This effect has been observed with planar diodes having circular geometries (139a).

Gunn oscillators can also be controlled by external microwave signals. If an external signal is near the natural operating frequency of the diode, it can pull the diode into synchronism with the signal frequency. In fact, the external signal power can be very much smaller than the Gunn-diode output power. The further the two frequencies are away from each other, the more external signal power is required for successful synchronization, as can be seen from Fig. 5.2. The experimental results (91, 104a, 145) agree fairly well with the general theory of synchronized oscillators (2). The diode with resistive load requires less input signal for successful synchronization than the resonant set-up. In fact, the higher the Q-factor, the higher is the required input power.

These effects enable one to obtain very large output powers with Gunn-diode arrays, feeding one load simultaneously. It is of great interest here that Carroll (50b) has managed to place several Gunn diodes in series in one coaxial oscillator and has obtained a correspondingly increased power output. This had previously not been thought possible, as one domain would absorb all other domains in series. However, by placing the diodes at suitable intervals inside an extended cavity, series operation is feasible.

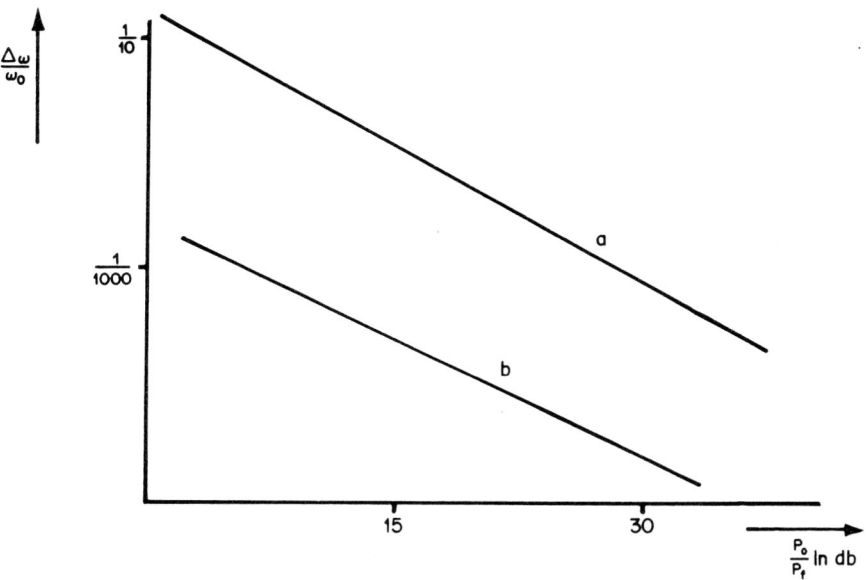

Fig. 5.2 Frequency pulling of Gunn diode by external signal: (a) results for resistive load; (b) results for diode in resonator with $Q=500$ (P_f= external signal power, P_0 =diode output power, ω_0 =signal frequency, $\Delta\omega$ =difference between signal and unsynchronized diode frequency).

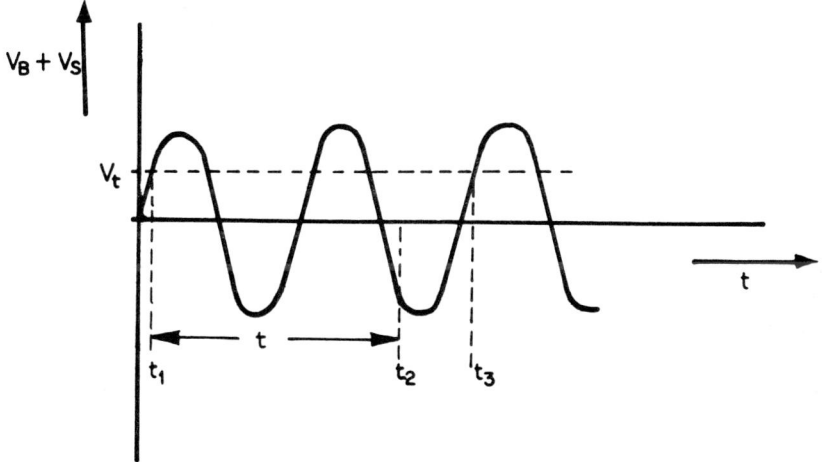

Fig. 5.3 Frequency synchronization on subharmonic of an external signal (t_1 and t_3 points of domain nucleation, t_2 time of domain extinction at anode, V_s voltage of external signal).

It is possible to obtain synchronization of the diode on a subharmonic of the external signal (228). The signal can then be applied to the diode via a high-frequency filter, whereas the load can be connected via a filter of correspondingly lower frequencies. As Fig. 5.3 shows, a domain is nucleated at t_1 and reaches the anode at t_2. The next domain can only be nucleated now at t_3, when the applied voltage, consisting of dc component and signal frequency, passes the value for domain nucleation threshold again. t_3 can in fact occur after several periods of the signal. It is even possible to obtain signal gain, as was shown by Pollmann and Bosch (228).

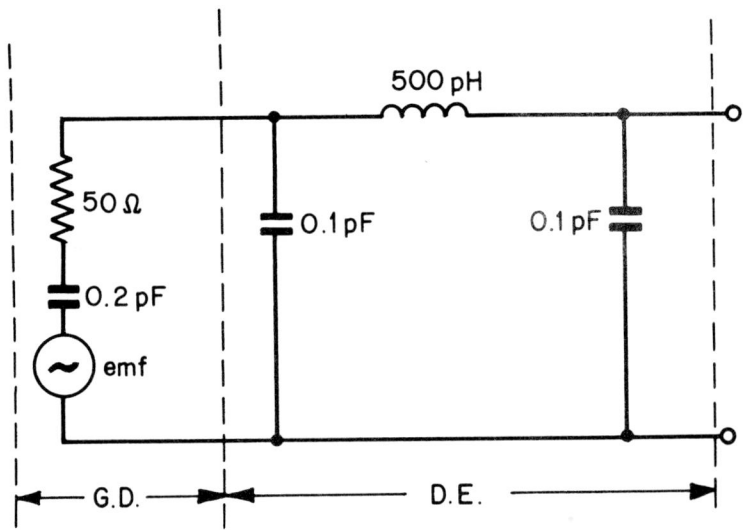

Fig. 5.4   Equivalent circuit of typical Gunn-diode oscillator (G.D. = Gunn diode, D.E. = diode encapsulation, f = 9.5 GHz).

Phase locking can be achieved with both the Gunn oscillator and the IMPATT device by an external signal (135). Often, it is useful to employ a weak external signal in order to help the onset of oscillations. This technique can be employed for synchronizing the regular onset of pulsed oscillations or for the starting of oscillations with diodes connected to load impedances which usually prohibit domain formation (228a).

The domain can be considered a capacitance, which alters its value periodically with the domain production and extinction. It has been suggested to employ this effect for parametric action (50a). This represents a very simple device, as the diode produces its own pump power.

Microwave amplification has been obtained with the small-signal gain effect (104b, 104c, 104d, 241a, 277, 277a, 277g) in the range 2–10 GHz with a maximum gain of 10 dB; and with the negative dynamic resistance of the domain formation process (277f). In the first case the noise figure was 23 dB and the saturated power output about 1 mW. Generally, the negative resistance occurs at those frequencies whose period is close to the time it takes electrons to drift through the crystal. Gain has been observed at frequencies up to 50 GHz. The second effect was obtained with diodes operating with a domain oscillation at 8 GHz. A gain of 9 dB was observed at 6 GHz with an output power of 60 mW. Only when the amplified output signal was 2 dB below the oscillation-output power, did a reduction in gain occur. The noise figures were about 20 dB. This amplifier has been called the 'Travelling Domain Amplifier' (TDA) (277f). The TDA-effect has also been employed for oscillations at lower frequencies (52) and has been observed by many workers as a spurious resonance oscillation. A Gunn diode, biased at post-threshold conditions, has also been operated simultaneously as an oscillator and a mixer (266).

Of practical importance is the equivalent circuit of Gunn oscillators in their domain-formation mode (50c, 108, 125a, 184). Figure 5.4 shows the equivalent circuit for a typical resonator consisting of a diode in a coaxial resonant circuit. Often it is more convenient to use a parallel connection as the representation of the Gunn diode G.D.

Although it is difficult to produce suitable crystals for successful lsa operation, it promises to give the most important devices for the future. A useful comparison with the domain oscillator can be performed by taking the product of microwave power P and load resistance R_L (140). It is easy to find this expression for the domain oscillator. It produces microwave power in accordance with the following expression:

$$P = \eta V_B \, n v_a e A = \frac{\eta V_B \, l v_a}{\mu_1 R_0} \tag{5.2}$$

where v_a is the average velocity of carriers, and μ_1 and R_0 are the low-field mobility and resistance respectively. Assuming that the highest frequency to be obtained with a reasonable efficiency is given by

$$f = 1.4 \frac{v_D}{l} \tag{5.3}$$

(v_D = domain velocity), one obtains

$$PR_L = \eta \bar{\mathscr{E}} \frac{R_L \, 2 v_\alpha v_D{}^2}{R_0 \mu_1 f^2} \tag{5.4}$$

with $\bar{\mathscr{E}} = V_B/l$. This expression decreases with $1/f^2$. A similar expression for the lsa mode, however, does not depend on frequency. Therefore, it represents a device ideally suited for high-frequency operation. At very high frequencies, two additional effects become relevant. Theory shows (62b, 62e) that one dimension of the crystal cannot be much larger than the h.f. wavelength in the material—i.e., the diode cross-sectional diameter must be smaller than about 4% of the wavelength in free space, in order to have reasonable efficiencies. For very high frequencies, a power limit is given by the scattering time of about 10^{-12} sec of the electrons required for the transferred electron effect and it seems that this can have some appreciable effect already at 100 GHz. Experimental results and pulsed operation of the lsa mode give about 350 W at 8 GHz, a little less than 1 W at 51 GHz. Extremely high pulse power of 400 kW has been proposed for lsa mode diodes for a pulse duration of 500 nsec and a repetition frequency of 340 Hz (150a). Such an achievement requires very homogeneous long crystals, in order to avoid any breakdown of the very high voltages required, and such crystals cannot yet be grown.

There exists an important difficulty with lsa diodes. They operate under such high bias voltages that an accidentally-formed domain would build up to very high fields which would destroy the crystal by voltage breakdown (150b). In fact, some theoretical work has suggested that domains would always form if $nl > 10^{12}$ cm^{-2} (277h), and that a high bias voltage would cause multiple-domain formation. However, multiple-domain operation seems to exhibit very similar phenomena to those of the lsa mode. Further clarification will certainly be obtained in the near future.

The theoretical efficiency of about 20% of lsa diodes is appreciably higher than for domain modes. The a.m. noise properties of lsa oscillators seem to be very good and promise to be of a similar value as the thermal noise of a load resistance at room temperature (62b).

The frequency of operation can possibly be changed by about one octave, although experiments have only shown a tunability of 15% (62c).

A whole range of applications is possible for the transferred-electron oscillator. The main advantages are given by its small weight and size, its relatively high efficiency and its usually small bias voltage for CW operation (of the order of 12 V d.c.). The output power is quite considerable for pulse operation. Therefore it is of advantage to employ Gunn oscillators in light-weight telecommunications systems, in teaching equipment, in portable radar systems (123d) (radar speed control, burglar alarms, ship docking, tug manoeuvring in harbours, non-contacting revolution counters and speed meters, collision avoidance on motorways, etc.) in telemetering and spectroscopical devices, phased array aerials, etc. (178).

As the operating frequency changes with temperature and mechanical pressure, such quantities could be telemetered (35a).

The frequency range 5-100 GHz will be of great commercial importance. For lower frequencies microwave-frequency transistors will become available. The Gunn effect will therefore become an important competitor for reflex klystrons in particular. Owing to its large tunability, it will replace also travelling-wave tube oscillators.

The trailing edge of the domain can be considered as a conducting electrode. If the other electrode is the negative contact electrode, a thin transmission line is formed along which a microwave can travel in a direction which is perpendicular to the domain-velocity direction. As one of the transmission-line electrodes moves periodically outwards, the transmission-line is varied periodically, thus pumping energy into the microwave and producing parametric amplification. This device has been called 'The Travelling Wave Parametric Amplifier' (287), however, no experimental results have been reported yet.

5.1.2 Pulse Generation and Processing

It has been realized that the Gunn-effect domain can be utilized for pulse production and processing. If the domain growth takes place during a shorter time than the domain transit, i.e. if

$$T_d < t_d$$

(see Section 4.1.2), a domain produces a steeply falling current drop, whose duration is the same as the domain transit time. The diode current can be fed through a resistance R_L, whose value must be sufficiently low. If it is much larger than the low-voltage diode resistance, the time T_d will increase and will finally prevent the production of a pulse.

The voltage drop occurring then across R_L, can be considered as a negative voltage pulse. When a domain approaches the anode, it is discharged during the time T_d, so that the rise and fall time of the pulse is equal.

In order to employ Gunn diodes for pulse production, they have to be operated in a non-dispersive circuit, such as a purely resistive load R_L. When the diode is biased above threshold V_t for domain nucleation, a succession of negative pulses is generated and one has an astable multivibrator.

If a diode is biased below V_t but above the value for domain extinction, it requires a positive pulse for domain nucleation, so that the applied voltage is temporarily raised above V_t. The applied pulse has to be longer than T_d, but can be shorter than t_d, so that a short triggering pulse can produce a long pulse if l is large.

In order to avoid the triggering pulse being short-circuited via the biasing-voltage supply, it is necessary to apply the bias via an inductive or resistive element.

The pulses produced by Gunn diodes are given by the domain speed and l, and have been observed with values as short as 50 psec. Pulses of 100 psec have been produced giving up to 0.5 A into a 50 Ω load (77,80.1).

A negatively-biased diode produces a positive pulse. If a second diode is to be triggered by this pulse, it will have to be biased differently. A positive bias voltage results in domains being nucleated at the terminal near R_L and travelling towards the diode contact near the biasing terminal. The result is the same, namely, a decrease in current flow. However, as the current travels in the opposite direction, this means that a negative voltage pulse is generated. We have, therefore, a device which can be triggered by a positive pulse and produces a negative one. We can, therefore, develop a chain of pulse devices, as shown in Fig. 5.5. The pulse duration is t_d, whereas the time it takes a pulse to travel along such a chain is given by the sum of all domain nucleation times T_d plus the time for the pulse to travel from one diode to the next one. The circuitry has to be built in microstrip technique (49). This consists of a grounded conducting plate, covered by a dielectric (e.g. semi-insulating GaAs with $\epsilon_r = 16$), on top of which is a conducting strip line. The signals travel between strip and conducting groundplate. A short delay of 100 psec can easily be achieved by

8 mm length using semi-insulating GaAs as dielectric. If no delay is required between the diodes, the interconnections must be as short as possible.

There exists one major difficulty, which is caused by the capacitors C in Fig. 5.5. They cause together with the diode resistance and R_L considerable delays of about $t_s = C(R_L + R_0)$ which are almost equal to the duration of the Gunn-diode pulses. One is able to develop circuits without capacitors, in a similar way as the dc amplifier. This will ultimately yield an enormous increase in speed of operation, which will then only be given by the domain growth time T_d.

It is of interest that a shortening of the pulse length can be achieved by shorter Gunn diodes, giving a reduced power consumption. This is in contrast to conventional circuitry where smaller pulses are usually obtained by a higher power consumption. If one wants to increase the rise time of the pulse, T_d, one will have to

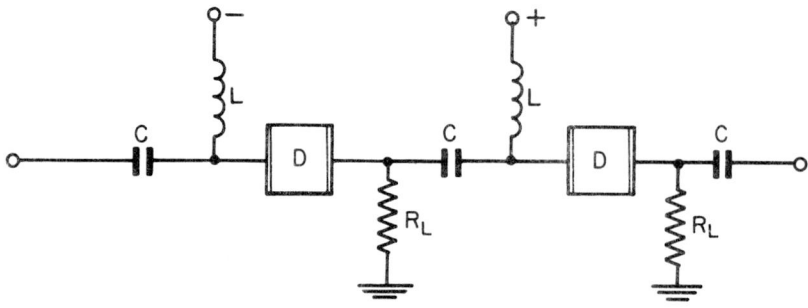

Fig. 5.5   A chain of two Gunn-effect pulse devices (D=Gunn diode).

decrease the resistivity of the material, which increases the power dissipation, as the threshold field $\mathscr{E}_t$ has to be obtained by a higher current.

Instead of employing a series connection with a constant-voltage source, it is also possible to use a parallel connection with a constant-current source (80.1). When a domain is formed, less current passes through the diode, so that the parallel load resistor has to take more current, producing a voltage pulse. The advantage of this circuit is the fact that the triggering pulse is of the same polarity as the output pulse.

An important advantage of these pulse devices is the inherent gain. An input pulse can be amplified by up to 20 dB (80.1, 136). This means that one will be able to obtain a considerable fan-out. A 'fan-out' indicates how many devices can be triggered by one generator.

A pulse oscillator producing short pulse spikes of subnanosecond duration with long pulse intervals has been developed (80.1) by using the series circuitry of Fig. 5.5, together with an inductor L in parallel to R_L. L keeps the anode electrode at a raised potential until the stored energy of L has been discharged via R_L, so that the nucleation of a new domain is delayed for some time. Ultimately, the whole circuitry will be built in monolithic structures.

An extensive range of basic logic elements has been developed already. An inclusive 'or' can be obtained by one diode with several parallel leads to the input contact. As soon as one of these leads carries a pulse to the crystal, a domain is formed and an output pulse is obtained.

There are several ways of producing an 'and'. If the voltage pulses from both input connections have the same amplitude, one can apply them via separate resistors R_a to the input electrode, such that one input signal alone does not suffice to raise the field above nucleation threshold owing to the voltage drop across R_a. Only when both input connections supply a pulse simultaneously, is the voltage at the input contact of the crystal raised high enough for domain nucleation [see also (99)].

On the other hand, if both pulse amplitudes cannot be made of equal value, one can use another 'and' device (62f). It is a long GaAs crystal with one contact at each end and an additional electrode at the side of the crystal, somewhere along the length of the domain trajectory. If no triggering pulse is applied at this third electrode, no domain will be triggered whatever the amplitude of the input voltage at one of the end-face contacts, as long as the crystal is not destroyed by too large voltages.

If there are two or more parallel small contacts at the same distance from the cathode, along the length of the diode, one can use these side contacts as the input terminals of an 'or', where the input terminals are isolated from each other. Similarly, this can be achieved by dividing the cathode electrode into several small ones.

A capacitive output contact will produce output pulses whose durations are of the order of the time that it takes the domain to pass under the contact, rather than the transit time for the whole device.

An epitaxial diode with semi-insulating substrate and two ohmic contacts on the free surface, can have, between these contacts, a capacitive control electrode. This structure would act in a similar way as MOS transistors (301).

A further device is an exclusive 'or' or 'comparator' (111a, 111b, 111c) whose output is shown by Table 5.1.

TABLE 5.1 Output Signals of a Comparator

Input signal		Comparator outputs
a	b	
0	0	0
1	0	1
0	1	1
1	1	0

A high-field and subsequent low-field region can be obtained inside a GaAs crystal if one electrode has a very small and the other a very large contact area. A domain can be nucleated in the high-field region, if its field value is above the threshold value $\mathscr{E}_t$, and will travel to the large-size electrode, as the domain-sustaining field can be smaller than $\mathscr{E}_t$. If a second small electrode is placed on the same surface as the original one, the effective electrode area is doubled. This causes a reduction of the field in the high-field region, so that no domains can be nucleated any more. The same effect can be achieved by first only applying the input pulse at one small contact, whereas the other one does not receive any pulse. Domains are formed now; however, if both small contacts receive input pulses simultaneously, the field near them can be sufficiently reduced to prevent domains nucleating. One therefore has the operation of an exclusive 'or'. It is essential that the amplitudes of the input pulses are not too large. This can be achieved easily if necessary by placing additional two terminal Gunn devices in front of the comparator-input connections.

A detailed study (111c) has shown that the comparator property relies on one of two different effects. Firstly, two parallel electrodes produce a steeper potential gradient near the large electrode, than only one small electrode. This phenomenon is most pronounced with small electrodes on one surface separated from each other by an optimum distance. Secondly, if the small contacts are increased to a certain size, the disconnected small electrode presents a conducting boundary to the crystal. The field lines from the other, negatively biased, small electrode will partly converge to the disconnected one. This causes a large field at the edge of the disconnected electrode between the two small contacts. This field is largest for a very small inter-electrode separation. It can act effectively as a domain nucleating centre, although the field vector is not directed towards the large electrode. When both parallel contacts are connected to the same biasing terminal, this local high field between the two small contacts disappears, so that comparator action is achieved if the interelectrode separation is small enough.

The comparator described always requires a negative biasing potential at its input terminals, and utilizes negative triggering pulses.

A comparator can also be built if two Gunn diodes both operate on one resistive load. If both input electrodes receive an input signal simultaneously, the greatly increased current through R_L produces a large voltage drop across R_L, so that the field in both diodes remains below $\mathscr{E}_t$. On the other hand, if only one input electrode receives a signal pulse, the voltage drop across R_L is smaller, with the result that the diode field becomes larger than $\mathscr{E}_t$.

An inhibitor, whose output is shown in Table 5.2, can be obtained by connecting a resistor in series with one of the small ohmic contacts. If the voltage is applied only to this electrode via the resistor, the field near the electrode cannot reach the full value required for domain nucleation and no output signal is obtained. Applying the voltage solely to the other small electrode, however, does produce a domain. If the voltage is finally applied to both small electrodes, (to one of them via the resistor) the high-field value can be reduced, far enough to prevent domain nucleation. Instead of having a resistor connected to one of the electrodes, one can use a pulse generator with high internal resistance for this electrode. This can usually be achieved with a Gunn diode and a small load resistance R_L.

A memory device has been proposed (62f) which is a diode in a resonant circuit. It is biased such that no domains are formed. However, a signal pulse nucleates a domain, which causes the resonator to oscillate. The voltage swing produced suffices to nucleate a further domain, when the voltage across the diode becomes larger than

TABLE 5.2 Inhibitor Output

Input signal		Inhibitor output
a	b	
0	0	0
1	0	1
0	1	0
1	1	0

V_t. The result is a continuous oscillation, triggered by one signal, which can be considered to be stored in the oscillation.

It is possible to develop further logic elements. However, it is also possible to design complex circuits. A few examples are now described (111a).

A pulse code modulator (217) is not only employed for code modulation, but can also be considered as a transformer of analogue into digital information.

A first approach has been made with the DOFIC (245), [see also (99)] which, however, does not yet produce digital information. It only gives a succession of pulses which still have to be added up. The number of pulses produced are proportional to the amplitude of the analogue voltage at the input.

It might sometimes, however, be easier to use the circuit described in Fig. 5.6, where the pulse production process is better controllable. The input voltage is applied at I and will travel along the chain of delay lines d_1, d_2, d_3, etc., with attenuating resistances R_1, R_2, R_3, etc. A capacitor C, which is large enough for the lowest frequency component at the input to pass, will bring the attenuated and delayed signals to Gunn diodes A_1, A_2, etc.

The capacitor C_1 sees the input signal undamped and without delay, and C_2 receives the signal attenuated by R_1 without delay. When a trigger-signal pulse is applied at S, all the Gunn diodes A will be opened by the trigger signal applied at the third electrode along the crystal (62f). This means, A_1 and A_2 produce an output pulse at O_1 and O_2 simultaneously, if the input signal is large enough. The capacitors C_3, C_4, etc., transmit delayed and attenuated signals to the Gunn elements A_3, A_4, etc., which receive the triggering signal from S with the same delay as the

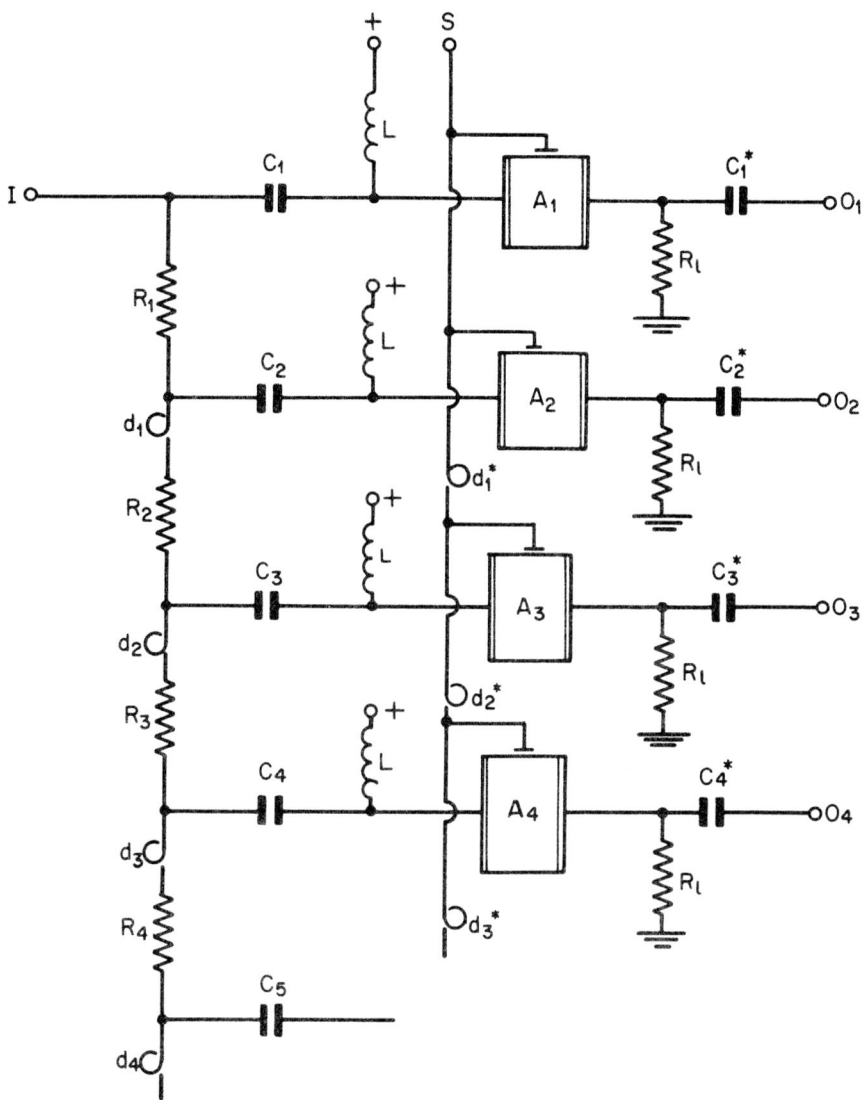

Fig. 5.6 System for transforming analogue voltage into a succession of pulses whose number is proportional to the input amplitude ($\frown$ = delay line).

analogue signal, because the delays are equal, i.e. $d_1 = d_1^*$, $d_2 = d_2^*$, etc. However, only those diodes A will produce domains which receive large enough signals via C. Therefore, only the first range of m 'and' devices $A_1, A_2 \ldots A_m$ will produce output pulses at $O_1, O_2 \ldots O_m$, whereas for the remaining ones, $A_{m+1}, A_{m+2}, \ldots$

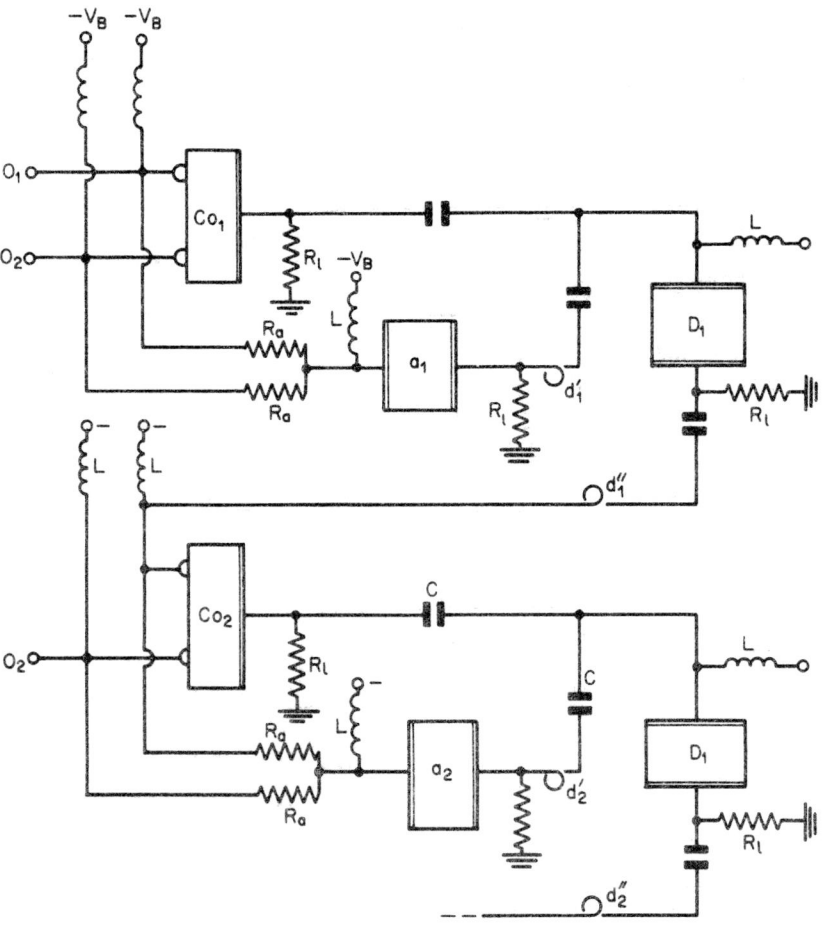

Fig. 5.7   First two elements of adder for pulse code modulation (C_0 = comparator).

A_n, the input signal will be too low for domain nucleation. The value m is thus proportional to the amplitude of the input signal.

The m pulses produced at O (or by the DOFIC) have to be added up (111d). This is achieved by the circuits of Figs 5.7 and 5.8. Let us first assume the case of a pulse only at O_1. This will produce a domain in the comparator C_{0_1} and it will fail to nucleate a domain in the 'and' of a_1. The domain from C_{0_1} produces a voltage pulse across R_L and a domain is triggered in D_1. The domain in D_1 produces a positive pulse in C_{0_2}, after a delay by d_1'', triggering a domain there too. The result is a domain being produced in all comparators, until an output pulse appears at the final output P after a delay produced by $n-1$ elements of d''.

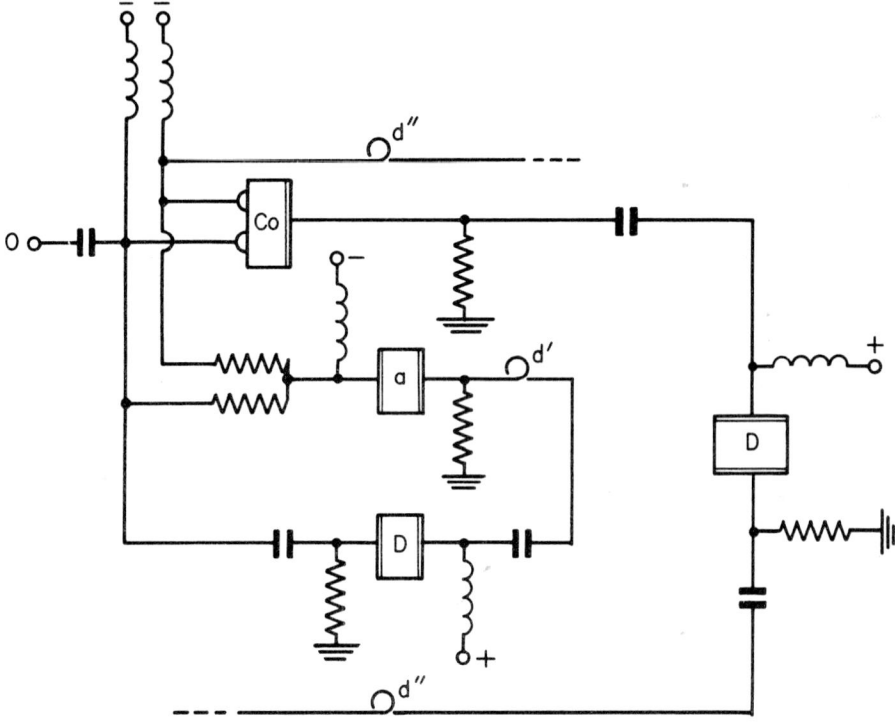

Fig. 5.8 P.C.M. adding element of higher order than two, to be used subsequently to the two elements of Fig. 5.7.

Now we assume the case of output pulses at O_1, O_2, and O_3. As the pulses from O_1 and O_2 appear simultaneously, no domain is created in C_{0_1}. However a_1 now receives a large enough voltage as pulses are supplied via both resistors R_a so that a domain is produced. Its output pulse is delayed by d_1'. The pulse at O_3 appears after a delay by d_1 (which is equal to that of d_1'). It produces a domain in C_{0_2}, as the pulse from a_1 has not yet arrived owing to the delay d_1''. The pulse produced by C_{0_2} will now travel down the line of comparators as no pulses are appearing at O_4, O_5, etc. After the delay in d_1'' the pulse from a_1 appears at C_{0_2} and produces another domain there. The voltage pulse generated thus by C_{0_2} along its load resistance will now travel down the line of comparators too. At the final output P, one will, therefore, obtain first a pulse which corresponds to the digit 2^0, and then a second pulse corresponding to 2^1.

The same description of the adding procedure can be given if the outputs O_1, $O_2 \ldots O_m$ produce a pulse. The binary addition will either produce an output pulse from a comparator C_0 or from the diode a. The pulse from a will be delayed by d'.

The output from the delays d_1' and d_2' is fed directly to the input of the subsequent Gunn diodes D. However, for the pulses from a_3, a_4, etc., a different arrangement has to be made, as from that point onwards, two or more subsequent 'carries' are possible. The outputs of d_3', d_4', etc., are therefore connected via an additional Gunn-diode pulse amplifier (which is required for a reversal of the pulse polarity) to those inputs of C_{0_3}, C_{0_4}, etc., which are connected to the terminals O_4, O_5, etc. (see Fig. 5.8). A pulse from d_3', d_4', etc., can therefore be properly added up with any pulses from d_2'', d_3'', etc. If a pulse arrives only from say, d_3' and none from d_2'', a domain is nucleated in C_{0_3} producing now a pulse in the diode D_3. However if a pulse arrives simultaneously from d_3' and d_2'', no domain is produced in C_{0_3} and the diode a_3 is now able to produce a further output pulse. The pulses from C_0 (and the delayed one from d_1' and d_2') will be fed into the Gunn diode D, in order to obtain the correct pulse polarity for the subsequent comparator. The pulses from d_3', d_4', etc., can be fed into the terminals O_4, O_5, etc., as they would never occur simultaneously with a pulse originating from A_4, A_5, etc., because the time interval between triggering pulses at S is much larger than the delay in d'. The output from D is fed to the subsequent combination of a comparator and an 'and' with diode a, after having been delayed by another delay line d''. The delay times in d, d^*, d' and d'' are of the same value. The output signals will finally arrive at P, where the pulses represent a set of p digits.

One set of p digits represents one value of the analogue voltage applied at I. The maximum value of input signal is quantized by (2^p-1) quanta. This requires a certain length of the modulator chain. In fact, one requires $n = (2^p-1)$ Gunn devices A; (2^p-2) Gunn devices C_0 and a, delays d', and attenuating elements R; (2^p-3) delays d, d'' and d^*, and Gunn diodes D.

If the time interval t_p between triggering pulses at S is the same as the time required for one set of p digits, the sets of digits follow without any interruption at P. This represents, therefore, a very fast modulator, as the pulse length is that of a domain transit through one of the Gunn diodes employed, i e., shorter than 500 psec. The whole chain of 'adders' operates continuously. An example is demonstrated in Table 5.3. A chain with seven O connections (i.e. $p = 3$) is shown, of which the terminals O_1 to O_5 receive pulses (denoted by '1'). The delay in any of the delay lines (d, d^*, d' or d'') is denoted by t and is the same as the transit time for a domain through any of the Gunn-effect crystals employed. The diagonal range of figures demonstrates how the resulting digits appear at the Gunn diodes D as a function of time. After the time $p \cdot t = t_p$, a new triggering pulse is applied at S, which will trigger off the next sequence of pulses for the next analogue-to-digitial conversion.

Decoding can be achieved with the following semi-conventional techniques for these ultrafast pulses. The p pulses of one sequence have to be differently amplified such that the pulse amplitudes are made proportional to $(q+1)$ for the pulses representing 2^q. This means, the pulse representing 2^1 is double the size of that of 2^0; and the pulse of 2^2 is three times as large. This weighting is performed with Gunn diodes of different lengths l, as l can be chosen such that it is approximately proportional to the pulse amplitude to be produced. The Gunn diodes can be triggered by suitable pulses with a third electrode along the length, in the same way as the diodes A

TABLE 5.3

Gunn diodes A	output from A	digital pulses at D as a function of time			Gunn diodes D
			$\Big\vert$ new pulse $t_p\!\downarrow$ at S		
A_1	1	$\longleftrightarrow$			
A_2	1	0 1 0			D_1
A_3	1	$\overset{\leftrightarrow}{t}$ 1 1 0			D_2
A_4	1	0 0 1			D_3
A_5	1	1 0 1			D_4
A_6	0	1 0 1			D_5
A_7	0	1 0 1			P

$\longrightarrow$

increasing time

in Fig. 5.6. These weighted pulses are applied to an integrating circuit, whose output is the reproduced analogue signal.

A further example of a Gunn-effect circuit is shown in Fig. 5.9, which is a memory device. When an input-signal pulse is applied at I, it nucleates a domain in the comparator C_0. This causes a pulse to travel along the delay d and a domain to be produced in the subsequent diode D_1. This generates a pulse at the other terminal of the comparator, where a further domain is created. The result is a signal stored in the loop, and it can be read out by applying a read-out signal at the terminal R. This signal will produce a domain in the 'and' of diode D_2, when the output pulse from C_0 appears simultaneously. The stored pulse can be erased when a second pulse is applied at I, so that no further domain is then produced in C_0.

It is easy now to develop further circuits such as a shift register consisting of a series of such memory loops (Fig. 5.10). A first pulse produces a rotating signal in the first loop. On application of a second input-signal pulse, the rotating pulse of the first loop is erased and a signal-pulse is stored in the second loop, instead. The two pulses applied so far have produced the binary number 10, where the first loop stores the second digit and the second loop the first digit. Further input pulses will produce further shifts of digits, such that an addition of all the pulses supplied is obtained, as the reader could check for himself (111a, 111e).

A 1350 Megabit/sec binary P.C.M. system, together with pulse repeaters, is the first application of Gunn-effect pulse devices to be developed (80.1a).

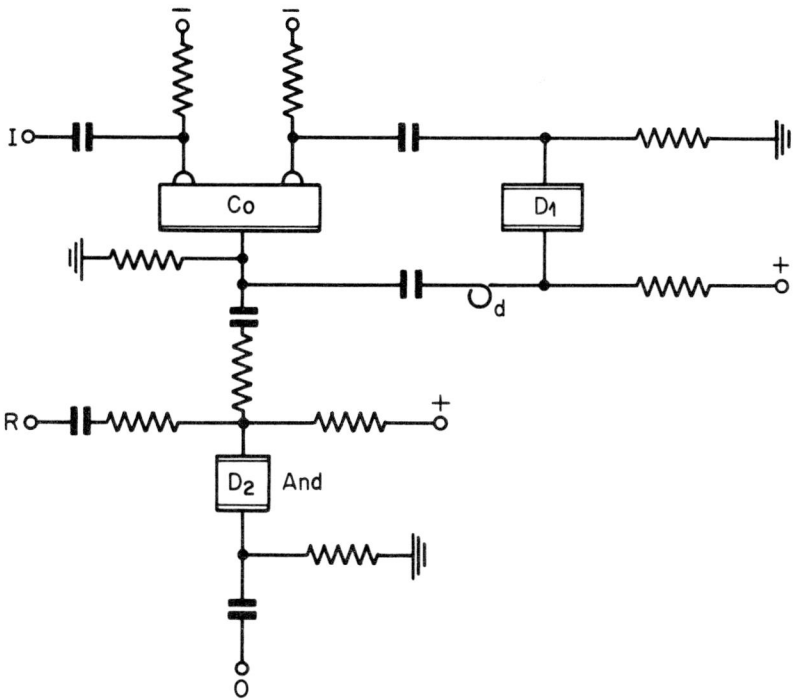

Fig. 5.9 Gunn-effect memory loop (I=input terminal, R=connection for read-out triggering signal, O = output terminal).

After having discussed the question of logic circuitry, one has to deal with the methods of producing pulses with differing wave-forms and their applications.

If any of the diode parameters change along the length l of the Gunn diode, the current through the diode is changed.

The diode current I is given as follows:

$$I = A.J \cong A\frac{dD_d}{dt} \cong A\epsilon\frac{d\mathscr{E}}{dt} \tag{5.5}$$

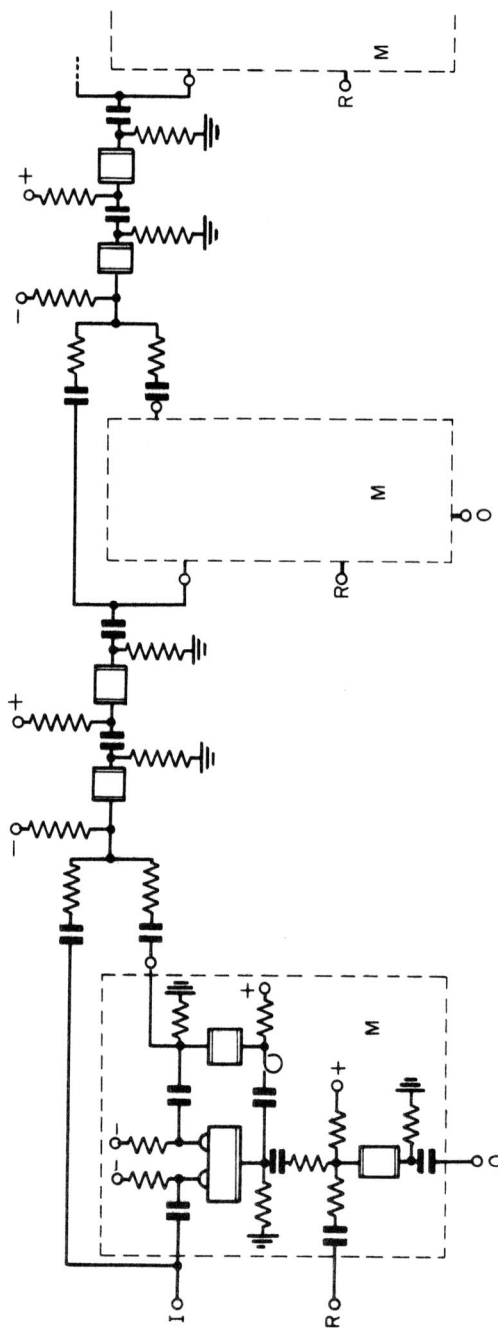

Fig. 5.10 Gunn-effect shift register (M=memory loop of Fig. 5.9, I=input to register, R=connection for read-out signal, O=output of each M).

where D_d is the electric displacement current density. Poisson's equation for the field inside the depletion layer (see Section 4.1.2) gives

$$\frac{n_0(x)}{\epsilon} = \frac{d\mathscr{E}}{dx} \tag{5.6}$$

with $n_0(x)$ the ionized donor density in the depletion layer. Expanding the expression for the field change of equation (5.5):

$$\frac{d\mathscr{E}}{dt} = \frac{\partial\mathscr{E}}{\partial x}\frac{\partial x}{\partial t} \simeq \frac{\partial\mathscr{E}}{\partial x} v(x)$$

one finds with some approximations:

$$I = ev(x_1)\, n_0(x_1)\, A(x_1) \tag{5.7}$$

where x_1 gives the instantaneous position of the accumulation layer of the domain, and v, n_0 and A the drift velocity, ionized donor density and diode cross-sectional surface respectively for the domain at x_1. A change of any of these three terms will cause I to alter.

This phenomenon can be understood in the following way. A fully developed domain acts as a wall of constant current density. Therefore, at any instant the total current through the device equals the product of this current density and A.

The shape of the current I during domain transit is therefore able to indicate for example, the doping gradient. On the other hand, it is possible now, to produce any desired pulse shape by one of the following methods (245):

(a) variation of doping by impurity diffusion along the crystal,
(b) changes of A,
(c) localized ionization of deeper-lying donors by very high domain fields (99a, 116a, 219),
(d) illumination of parts of the crystal, and
(e) placing some conducting contacts along the crystal.

The methods (a) and (b) are suitable for the production of waveforms, whose shape has been determined once and for all by the construction of the diode. The other three methods permit changes to occur during operation.

For example, Shoji (256a) has obtained very complex waveforms by a changing cross-section of the diode along l. Fig. 5.11 shows an example.

When a domain was nucleated near the cathode, it travelled first along a section with increasing A, causing an increase in current. When A decreases from a certain point onwards, the current decreases again. If the applied voltage is small, a domain will only travel a short distance away from the cathode; soon the field will have dropped below the value for domain sustaining and the domain is extinguished. A high-frequency mode results, as seen in Fig. 5.11b. Raising the applied voltage,

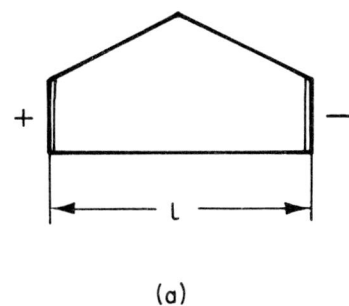

(a)

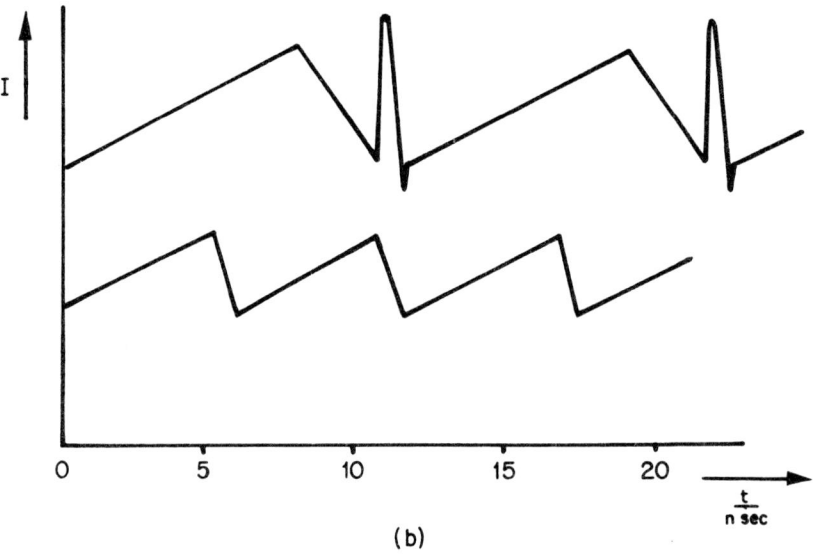

(b)

Fig. 5.11 Production of complex wave-forms by Gunn diodes: (a) changing cross-section of diode along length l; (b) current wave-forms produced as a function of bias voltage (top curve representing the current for domains travelling along total l, bottom curve giving the case for domains travelling less than $l/2$).

causes the domain to travel along the whole length of the crystal reproducing the entire geometry in its waveshape. Additionally, one finds sharp voltage pulses when the domain is discharged at the anode and a new one produced near the cathode. These spikes can be used for synchronizing purposes. With trapezoidal diodes, where the maximum field is near the cathode, the frequency of the pulses could be changed continuously by one octave if the bias voltage was varied. Frequency tuning could be obtained by an additional small electrode near one of the end contacts. When the voltage of this electrode was changed independently, a change in the electric field along the crystal length was achieved. This enables convenient electronic tuning (211, 223). A similar method was employed by Shoji, who attached a small contact halfway along the crystal and connected this to the anode via a variable resistor. Decreasing this resistor caused the field in the second half of the crystal to drop, so that the domain amplitude decreased there. The result is a two-step waveform, where the medium level of the pulse can be adjusted by the external resistor.

For some applications this technique can be utilized by applying a whole range of contacts along the crystal and connecting them to a resistive shunt path. When the domain passes beneath the shunt path, some current flows around the domain along the shunt path, increasing the total current output at the anode. Whenever the domain is not beneath a shunt path region, the total output current is just that permitted by the domain. In this way the domain can be used to 'read out' the state of external switches.

Instead of using switches one can, in fact, connect two neighbouring contacts to the two output terminals of digital circuits. If an output pulse is produced by one of the digital circuits, it produces, say, a decrease in field between the two contacts. This causes the domain-charge to be decreased which results in an increase of output current. During a transit, a domain can therefore read all the digital outputs successively and the device is suitable as a multiplexer, which is used in pulse transmission systems.

Another way of producing a multiplexer is as follows. A succession of high resistance electrodes is applied along the crystal. A digital signal will either shorten this contact to earth, or it will open it. For example, p-n junction devices could operate as such digital switches. The pulses at the high-resistance contacts can be as long as the transit time of the domain, whereas the multiplexed-signal pulses have a short duration only, which is about the time the domain travelled past the high-resistance contact. If, for example, a crystal is 300 microns long and has ten resistive electrodes, each about 20 microns long, one can interleave ten input pulse streams each of 3-nsec time slots, into a 3GHz output stream. The output pulses would each be about 200 psec long and a few volts in amplitude. This is about ten times that achievable with transistor circuits.

Of great device interest is the posibility of depositing a photoconductive material, say CdS, along the GaAs crystal. The conductance of the shunt resistor would depend on the light intensity. The current shape at the output is therefore a true representation of the light intensity variation along the diode. This effect can ultimately be employed for an ultrafast electrical read-in system for digital computers, or as a device which can scan light intensities, such as a high speed television camera.

A similar effect can be obtained directly by a change of conductivity owing to photon bombardment, making use of the method (d) (245) above. The method of localized ionization [see (c)], can be utilized for a device, where a first 'writing pulse' of high amplitude and of a given waveform produces a domain with a varying value of field amplitude. If this domain field is large enough, it will ionize the donors on its way. Varying the domain field by the externally-applied voltage enables one to obtain an ionization profile which yields a varying conductivity (116a, 219). The next domain, travelling with a much-reduced biasing voltage, will reproduce the original waveform. The recombination processes would cause the ionization profile to disappear only after about 1 μsec, so that the original pulse shape can be reproduced many times (261). Laser action of recombination radiation has been observed after ionization by the passage of domains (261a).

Gunn diodes can also be used for retiming and regenerating pulses in repeaters of high-capacity digital transmission systems. If the biasing voltage is sufficiently below threshold the presence of either a timing pulse or an information pulse alone will not raise the total voltage above threshold. However, the combination of the two pulses will cause a domain to form and an amplified output pulse is produced.

The three-terminal device by Copeland *et al.* (62f) described above can usefully be employed as a pulse regenerator, as a small triggering pulse applied at the third contact along the length of the diode produces a domain which yields a pulse of well-defined width and amplitude.

5.1.3 Gunn-Effect Technology

GaAs is most suited for Gunn-effect devices. A fairly substantial knowledge was available on GaAs technology from the beginning of the work on the transferred electron effect, as GaAs has been used for transistors, lasers, varactors and tunnel diodes. An essential requirement is for the crystals to be homogeneous and without dislocations. A mobility as high as possible is often aimed for. This means that a low degree of compensation is required, so that only few donor impurities are present which could act as trapping centres or which could be ionized easily by the domain field. Avalanche and impact ionization effects are important because they are relevant for the degree to which a device can be overdriven. It has also been suggested that some non-coherence of the oscillations might be caused by impact ionization of a deep donor level (156a). Deep donor levels are also responsible for the negative coefficient of resistivity above room temperature (73).

Another important aspect is the peak to valley current ratio, which is the ratio of the ohmic current at the applied field to the current when the domain is in transit. This ratio is important for high efficiencies. The usual donor concentration ranges from $\simeq 10^{14}$ to $\simeq 10^{16}$ cm^{-3}, and depends very much on the mode of operation in which it is intended that the diode should operate (see Section 4.1).

Both epitaxial and melt-grown GaAs is used for Gunn devices. High-frequency domain-mode operation requires very short values of l, often of a few microns only. Such thin samples are difficult to process from melt-grown material, and epitaxial crystals are of advantage with their thick supporting substrate. Devices from melt-grown material have often a strong negative coefficient of resistivity, so that they would be liable to suffer from thermal runaway. On the other hand, epitaxial layers have shown a positive coefficient for resistivities up to 2.5 Ω cm. (73). At 260°C the resistivity has been found rising at 0.075 % per °C (73).

The procedure of growing epitaxial GaAs out of the vapour phase has been described by various authors (39a) and requires much skill and experience.

There are various types of diode geometries. Epitaxial diodes can either have a conducting or an insulating substrate. In the first case, the substrate acts as a current carrying contact. Otherwise two ohmic contacts have to be deposited side by side on the free surface of the active layer (68.1). Often, a conductive layer is of great convenience for the preparation of ohmic contacts, as they can be obtained more easily on highly conducting material. Therefore, a thin conductive GaAs layer is frequently deposited (20, 39a) epitaxially. Devices have originally been prepared in the following way: Bulk crystals are first cut by a diamond-wheel cutter into suitable slices which are then lapped. These slices are now etched in boiling NaOCl acid, (which is suitably diluted) and subsequently ultrasonically cleaned, first with trichlorethylene and then in methyl alcohol. In epitaxial material, the substrate only has to be lapped before cleaning (36b). The two contacts have commonly been made of tin pellets, which are alloyed to the crystal under dry forming gas by raising the temperature to 400°C. Before reaching the maximum temperature, the forming gas is diverted through a bubbler with HCl which acts as a lubricant.

Tin and indium contacts, however, seem to reduce the life time of the diodes (40a, 139), and contact production with tin pellets is not very suited for mass production where vacuum evaporation techniques would be more convenient. It has even been observed that tin migrates under the action of large domain fields (99a). Tin acts as a donor impurity in GaAs, and an electric field acts on ionized tin donors which can migrate an average distance of 4 Å per domain transit. This means, the anode contact should not be made of tin if large domains are to be produced. Satisfactory contacts have been achieved with Au-Ge-Ni (40a), In-Au, In-Ni, Sn-Au (114.1), Sn-Ni (104), Sn-Ag (234), Ag-In-Ge (64), and several other materials. They are usually vacuum-deposited and subsequently alloyed in forming gas.

The maximal CW microwave power produced by Gunn diodes, is determined by the maximum temperature permitted inside the crystal. Therefore it is essential to use an efficient method for conducting the heat energy away (160).

Important advantages could be achieved here by employing a particular class of diamond as a heat sink, namely type IIa—diamond heat sinks, which have a much higher thermal conductivity than even copper (27). For example, at 200°K and

$300°K$, the thermal conductivity of type IIa-diamond is 45 W/cm$°K$ and 20W/cm$°K$ which exceeds the values for copper by factors of 10 and 5 respectively. Type IIa diamond, which constiutes only a few percent of all naturally occurring diamonds, is selected on the basis of its ultraviolet absorption properties (172). Its electrical resistivity is, however, that of an insulator. Therefore, the diamond crystals have to be metallized after polishing, so that a suitable current path is provided for by the metal film around the diamond.

For devices with complicated geometries like the DOFIC, one requires techniques of shaping the crystal to very small dimensions. This can be achieved by photo-etching of epitaxial layers, or by the use of abrasive powder (193) after having suitably masked the crystal.

Finally it should be mentioned that the operation under pulsed conditions requires generators giving pulses of very short duration. Mercury-wetted switches are employed here to discharge a delay line. The pulse duration is given by the time it takes a wave to travel backwards and forwards along the delay line. The switches operate at 8 atm. under the action of a magnetic field, which is often produced by a low-frequency current generator. The pulse repetition frequency is therefore given by the low frequency of the current generator. For further information, see Glasoe and Lebacqz (92.1).

5.2 Avalanche Devices

The most important competitor of the Gunn-effect oscillator is the avalanche diode, as described in section 4.2.Their abbreviated name 'IMPATT' derives from '*imp*act *a*valanche and *t*ransit *t*ime diodes'. It is of advantage that they can be produced with any semiconducting material. Therefore one was able to employ Silicon for high power oscillators as this material has a very large thermal conductivity, and together with diamond heat sinks as near as possible to the active junction, CW outputs of more than 2 W at 15 GHz with 9% efficiency have been obtained. The high-efficiency mode (258.1) gave 12 W at 1.2 GHz with 45% efficiency and represents a serious competitor for the microwave transistor.

Several IMPATT diodes have also been mounted on a common substrate, and the output power could be multiplied correspondingly, as the parallel avalanche regions oscillated in synchronism (271c). With this technique, the following CW results were obtained by Bell Telephone Laboratories in May 1967: 4.7 W at 14.6 GHz, 360 mW at 37 GHz, and 100 mW at 50 GHz. Noise figures measured so far on Ge and GaAs IMPATTs lie in the 25–28 dB range, while they have usually been about 10 dB higher for Si-devices (101).

Microplasmas could be suppressed by the application of a small external signal (60). It has also been shown that an avalanche oscillator modulated by a small external signal by phase locking has a reduced f.m. noise figure. Arrays of diodes have exhibited reduced noise. Further, the diodes with higher power and efficiency tended to be less noisy.

Synchronization of oscillators has been achieved by an external signal whose frequency is either a harmonic or a subharmonic of the oscillator (285). The signal power can be up to 15 dB lower than the oscillator power. This has been used as a frequency divider in the mm region. The low-frequency signal could be fed directly to the avalanche diode or by using an additional multiplier stage based on a varactor or some other multiplier diode. Synchronization of an avalanche diode of the cm region required a signal not exceeding 300 mW of the meter-region. Employing a quartz crystal, these circuits had a long-term frequency stability of 10^{-8} and a low level of phase fluctuations. The main advantages of these oscillator units with respect to conventional multiplier circuits using varactors were fewer intermediate stages, low cost, high reliability and more efficient operation.

The additional advantage of GaAs and Ge in contrast to Si is the good efficiency usually displayed, between 6 and 10% at 6 GHz.

As explained in Section 4.2, there are three types of avalanche diodes. The *pn* junction diodes have produced greater power than either the *pin* or Read diode. On the other hand, the operating frequency of *pin* and *pn* devices are more sensitive to changes in the applied voltage than the Read structure. This can be of advantage when a microwave signal is frequency-modulated, since the modulating voltage can be superimposed directly on the dc bias voltage. However, such sensitivity can also lead to some instability of the output frequency. The Read diode appears to be more efficient at lower current densities than either of the other two. In fact, operating under pulse conditions with a duty factor of approximately 10^{-3}, efficiencies as high as 25% and power outputs up to 435 W at 0.425 Ghz were reported for pnn^+ mesa structures (230). This is already very near to the efficiency originally calculated by Read (236).

In general, the available power output decreases sharply as frequency increases, since both the breakdown voltage and the active region are reduced as the frequency goes up. This means, that microwave power is more difficult to obtain at higher frequencies. So far, 0.13 W CW has been obtained at 70 GHz with Si diodes.

The power level of individual devices varies considerably. This appears to be largely due to non-uniform current flow caused by irregularities of the crystal structure and the distribution of impurities. Better efficiencies will ultimately be achievable by improved crystal preparation.

IMPATTs are very suitable for the many devices where they can replace reflex klystrons. Their applications will be in microwave radio systems, Doppler radar and for most of the other oscillator applications given for the Gunn oscillator in the previous section.

They can also be employed as amplifiers. However, whereas most negative-resistance devices—the tetrode vacuum tube and the tunnel diode for example—exhibit a negative resistance over a broad range of frequencies, the IMPATT shows this effect only in a narrow frequency range. Si *pn* junctions have been found to deliver 40 mW CW at X-band with 15 dB power gain, showing that large-signal amplification is possible at power levels comparable to those obtained under oscillating conditions (249).

Similarly, Bell laboratories have observed 20 dB gain at the same frequency range and with a bandwidth of 30 MHz. And Soviet (285) laboratories obtained several years ago regenerative amplification at bias voltages of 25–30 V and currents of 2–5 mA, where a single stage amplifier at X-band gave 25 dB for a bandwidth of up to 50 MHz and 15 dB for a bandwidth of 150 MHz. The amplitude characteristic remained linear at an input signal power of less than 1 μW. Unfortunately, the noise figure was 25–30 dB.

These IMPATT amplifiers will therefore be useful for high-gain, high power stages that follow a low-noise preamplifier.

It is worth mentioning here parametric effects in avalanche devices where signals interact via the pumping wave through the nonlinearity of the avalanche (85).

Avalanche diodes have also been developed as noise generators (285). When the avalanche breakdown develops uniformly over the area of the pn junction, a stable white noise of high intensity can be generated. Noise devices have been developed covering the decimetre and centimetre wavelength region. With a power supply of 10–100 mW, the effective noise temperature ranged from 10^5–$10^6\,°$K around X-band frequencies to 10^6–$10^7\,°$K in the MHz region. The noise temperature can be smoothly adjusted by a variation of the diode current. The noise-level stability is very good, the temperature coefficient of the spectral density of the noise power does not exceed 0.02 dB/°K. The noise can be modulated by μsec pulses. All these properties together with the small size make these noise generators very strong competitors of conventional devices using gas discharges, for example.

The device potentialities of avalanche diodes can be seen in the fact that portable radio-communication systems have already been developed in the U.S.S.R. These systems incorporate avalanche devices serving both as transmitting oscilllators and as a local oscillator for the heterodyne circuit (285). The possibility of phase-locking several oscillators (135, 253) enables the development of high-power microwave generators.

5.3. Applications of Electroacoustic and Other Effects

Many electroacoustic devices have been proposed and developed.

Electronic devices utilizing the properties of acoustic waves have been used for at least the past 30 years now. Quartz acoustic resonators, filters and various types of delay lines are commonly employed in many applications such as radar and communication systems. The conversion of electric into acoustic vibrations can be accomplished by transducers, which have been made to operate up to several GHz. Generally speaking, there are four categories of transducer materials, namely piezoelectric, magnetoelastic (magnetic field–stress field), magnetoacoustic (spin-phonon) and optoelastic (photon-phonon) interactions. The first type is the most commonly used, however.

Transducers are made of a suitable material (single crystal quartz, or zinc oxide, or the ceramics lead titanate zirconate, potassium sodium niobate), one-half wavelength thick, bonded on to the surface of the propagation medium. Transducer plates are limited in frequency up to about 100 MHz. Higher frequencies up to at least 3GHz can be obtained by thin-film transducers. The piezoelectric material, generally CdS, is vacuum deposited, which results in a high-resistivity polycrystalline oriented film. The orientation of the film determines the predominant stress mode to be generated. The electric field is applied via metallic thin-film electrodes, which have been deposited on and underneath the film. Similar results can be obtained with the compensated-layer transducer (58). A metallic acceptor impurity is diffused into a high conductivity n-type piezoelectric semiconductor material such as CdS, ZnO or GaAs. The high-resistivity layer thus produced, is made one-half wavelength thick. A metallic film is finally deposited on this layer, which acts as one of the electrodes, whereas the other one is the high-conductivity semiconductor. This type of transducer offers really good coupling properties. It has been operated up to 200 MHz. On the other hand, a depletion-layer transducer has been developed (232), which utilizes the charge-free depletion layer that can be formed at a metal-semiconductor junction under reverse bias. As the depletion layer is very thin, this device can be operated at frequencies above 2 GHz. It has the advantage that it can be tuned over a range of resonant frequencies by the bias voltage.

As a result of good coupling, the bandwidth of thin-film and semiconductor transducers is generally one octave in frequency, which is a significant improvement over typical 5% bandwidth available with the bonded type. Usually, however, an adequate impedance-matching network is required to counteract the small impedance bandwidth of these devices. This is particularly important for the electroacoustic amplifier whose gain is very broad band, in fact greater than 50% (30).

The acoustoelectric amplifier is not of great commercial interest as the optimum operating frequencies are below 500 MHz, where transistor amplifiers are readily available with the advantage of being suitable for monolithic structures. The electroacoustic amplifier has to be of considerable length in order to obtain appreciable gain. This also introduces a substantial time delay of the signal, as the ultrasonic sound velocity is relatively slow. However, this drawback can be exploited to create active delay lines. Owing to the gain in this case, the losses caused by the double conversion of the signal as well as the losses of the passage through the crystal can be compensated. Photoresistive CdS crystals have been used for this purpose under pulsed conditions and illumination. A time delay of 15 μsec was obtained from a 1.2 cm long crystal (226).

An interesting idea has been put forward which relies on the fact that wavelengths of sound waves in the GHz range are comparable with wavelengths of visible light. Using the geometrical theory of propagation, the focusing of acoustic beams for the application of an acoustic microscope has been studied, which could have higher resolution than a conventional light instrument (57).

The surface-wave amplifier was described in Section 4.3 as having the advantage of CW operation, as efficient heat sinking can be achieved. Surface waves may be launched and may propagate in any direction on transversely isotropic media. For example, the two coupling electrodes can be made to have such a geometry that surface waves are directed towards a focus so as to increase the wave amplitude, or in order to combine signals from independent sources and thus to perform logic functions. The interconnections of linear electrode pairs have been shown to produce interesting response patterns (299a). A range of electrode pairs has been used as input transducer and another system of electrodes as the output transducer. They act as 13-element Barker code sequences. A short input pulse produces a complex elastic-wave pulse. The electrode pairs of the output transducer act as appropriately-phased current sources whose separate outputs are summed, producing a pulse of a given shape. The output pulse is the autocorrelation of the propagating elastic wave pulse. Thus, filter action or complicated logic functions can be obtained.

Surface waves can be guided in similar ways as electromagnetic waves. Therefore devices resembling waveguides, directional couplers and other components can be developed for surface waves (11). The use of surface waves seems to be attractive, since it can make use of integrated semiconductor technology, where surfaces are used to the best advantage.

Bulk-waves have also been employed to obtain certain circuit functions by the use of space and time varying parameters. An example is the use of a CdS amplifier as a gate (239). The resistivity is made to vary along the crystal and a voltage is applied which varies exponentially with time. If a broad flat acoustic input pulse then enters the crystal via a transducer, only the part of the acoustic wave produced at the optimum electric-field amplitude will travel towards the anode, where one receives now a narrow acoustic pulse.

The photoresistive CdS oscillator requires a dark area near the positive electrode. A small displacement of this area leads to a strong frequency shift. This effect could be utilized for small-displacement measurements (21b).

The high-field domains of the semiconductor CdS oscillator can be employed for several applications, which are very similar to the ones described in Section 5.1.1 for the Gunn-effect domain. In particular, a Doppler-shift experiment of infrared waves from a CO_2–He laser has been suggested (283).

The electroacoustic domains have very similar properties to those of the Gunn-effect domain. It absorbs, for example, also any excess voltage so that the domain voltage can be made very large by increasing the applied bias voltage (48).

Of great interest is the development of a device relying on the acoustoelectric domain which is called 'SALS' (solid-state acoustoelectric light scanner) (104e). An n-CdS strip of 400 μ width, of less than 100 μ thickness and 0.2–0.4 cm long has a resistivity of 1 Ωcm. A layer of p-Cu_2S is deposited on one surface of the CdS strip. Photoresist techniques are then used to cut this layer into perpendicular strips. Ohmic contacts are applied on opposite ends of the CdS strip. When a large voltage is applied between them an electro-acoustic domain is formed and travels along the CdS crystal. On its trajectory it passes underneath the perpendicular p-Cu_2S strips which form a *p-n* junction with the n-CdS. The domain voltage causes a local breakdown in the junction and some current can by-pass the domain, increasing the output current momentarily. Furthermore the flow of current through the junction is accompanied by an emission of red light, which is produced by the reverse breakdown of the junction. The amount of current bypassing the domain depends very much on the resistivity of the p-Cu_2S layer. This, however, can be varied by light, so that the momentary increase in output current is a measure of the light intensity. The device can, therefore, be employed either as a scanned-light detector, in a similar way as the corresponding Gunn-effect light scanner described in Section 5.2, or it can be used as a light-emitting array for alphanumeric devices or image displays. Other types of light-emitting arrays require electrical circuits connected to each active element, but here an acoustic domain scans a row of arrays thereby emitting light sequentially from its elements. Therefore, the circuitry is reduced, because it is no more each element but only each row, which has to be supplied with external electrical circuitry.

The electroacoustic domain travels about 100 times slower than the Gunn-effect domain. If one produces a sandwich of CdS, insulator and GaAs, acoustoelectric domains can be made to travel in x-direction, whereas Gunn domains can be running in y-direction, perpendicular to x. By this technique, the point, where both domains overlap, is scanned across the whole sandwich in the same way as an electron beam is scanned across the screen of an oscilloscope. Such a sandwich might therefore be useful to reduce the supply circuitry for a two-dimensional display to only two connections. As a light beam can be modulated by a passing domain using Pockel's effect, a laser beam at a suitable frequency could possibly be modulated before being projected onto a screen.

Thin platelets of CdS with ohmic transparent contacts have shown (180b) oscillations in the U.H.F. range, when they were illuminated through the contacts and a sufficiently high voltage was applied. This is caused by round-trip gain of the acoustic wave. It has been found that single mode operation is possible up to 500 MHz with 0.2 mm thick crystals. As significant changes in sound velocity can be achieved by an electric field, the frequency of oscillation can be tuned externally by the applied voltage. Similarly, the frequency can be changed by conductivity, strain and temperature, where the conductivity can be altered by the illumination intensity. As the frequency is high enough, the device generates electromagnetic waves directly which can be transmitted and received on a conventional f.m. receiver. An essential increase in frequency (180c), (up to 5 GHz), has been reported for platelets with ZnO.

It should be mentioned that In is widely used for making electrical contacts to n-CdS. The contacts are applied by evaporation in vacuum and can be alloyed subsequently at a temperature of $400°C$ under some neutral gas.

So far, only a few devices have been suggested for the plasma instabilities described in Section 4.4 (286.1).

It has been shown that helicon waves have two modes, one of which is strongly damped while the other, which can be made to travel in the opposite direction, is very little attenuated. These properties have been used for a proposal of a microwave isolator, a non-reciprocal solid-state device (35b). The difficulty is to match the free-space wave to the helicon wave of the semiconductor. It has been suggested to use a GaAs crystal, which simultaneously supports a helicon wave and exhibits Gunn-effect negative-resistance gain. This would enable one to build a small-size microwave amplifier with an inherent circulator property, given by the helicon wave.

Circulator properties have been observed at 140 GHz in a wave-guide junction loaded with an InSb rod aligned with the principal symmetry axis of the junction (42). The junction was cooled to 77°K and a magnetic field of 10.5 kG was applied along the symmetry axis. A typical isolation of 14–17 dB was observed. The proposed theory relies on the fact that the anisotropic material removes the degeneracy associated with the two counter-rotating polarizations along the principal symmetry axis of the junction.

Microwave power absorbed by a rod of p-InSb in a Q-band waveguide decreased by up to 9 dB when electric fields of up to 126 V/cm were applied to it. This could be employed as a microwave switch or modulator (274).

It has been suggested to employ helicons also as delay lines, as the attenuation can be made very small under certain conditions.

Again, one of the difficulties would be to match the helicon wave to the free-space wave or to that in a waveguide. Larrabee (168d) has suggested a technique to overcome this problem. When a bar of semiconductor material which supports a wave with a longitudinal component of microwave electric field, is mounted as a central inductive post in a dominant mode waveguide, the energy coupling occurs via the electric field. The wave inside the post will have many wavelengths as compared to the guide wavelength. The contributions from alternate half-wavelength sections of the post will cancel. Therefore the post is only coupled to the waveguide very poorly. Now a system of alternate layers of an insulator and of a conductor is prepared, such that the thickness of each layer is the same as half a wavelength of the microwave inside the crystal. This system of stacked layers is made very thin, and placed inside a waveguide in front of the semiconductor rod. The result is a greatly increased transfer of microwave energy from the post to the waveguide and vice versa, as the many periods along the semiconductor no longer cancel one another. Experiments have demonstrated the suitability of this method.

Another solution to this problem of coupling between the helicon mode and the wave in a guide, has been developed by using a cone of high-dielectric material (272a).

It seems that new microwave components can be developed by using the Hall effect (149c). Kataoka et al. (149b) pointed out that an external reactance, connected to the Hall terminals, produces a reactive effect across the current terminals. They employed this phenomenon, using an InSb element, and developed a variable microwave impedance device.

The devices discussed in this chapter are only a small selection of the possible applications of semiconductor plasmas. The future will probably see a rapid development in this field.

CHAPTER VI

References for Chapters IV and V
(and Author Index)

Page number
of text where
reference is given

1. Acket, G. A., de Groot, J. 'Measurements of the Current-Field   82
Strength Characteristic of n-Type GaAs Using Various High-
Power Microwave Techniques', *I.E.E.E. Trans. El-Dev.* **ED-14**,
pp. 505-511, 1967.

1a. Acket, G. A., 't Lam, H., 'Behaviour of n-Type GaAs in Strong   82
Microwave Fields', *Electronics Letters,* **3**, p. 258, 1967.

2. Adler, R., 'A Study of Locking Phenomena in Oscillators', *Proc.*   143, 144
I.R.E., **34**, pp. 351-357, 1946.

3. Aigrain, P., *Proc. Int. Conf. Semiconductor Physics, Prague* (New   131
York, Academic Press), p. 224, 1960.

4. Akai, Shin-ichi, 'The Nature of Helicon-Wave Instabilities', *Jap. J.*   133, 134
Appl. Phys. **5**, p. 1227, Dec. 1966.

5. Allen, J. W., Shyam, M., Chen, Y. S., Pearson, G. L., 'Microwave   80
Oscillations in GaAs$_x$ P$_{1-x}$ Alloys', *Appl. Phys. Letters,* **7**, pp.
78-80, 1965.

5a. Allen J. W., Shockley, W., Pearson, G. L., 'Gunn Domain   82
Dynamics', *J.Appl. Phys.,* **37**, pp. 3191-3195, July 1966.

6. Ancker-Johnson, B., 'Some Observations of Growing Oscillations   137
in Electron-Hole Plasma', *Phys. Rev. L.* **9**, p. 485, Dec. 1962.

6a. Ancker-Johnson, B., Drummond, J. E., 'Thermal Pinching in   138
Electron-Hole Plasma, *Phys. Rev.,* **131**, pp. 1961-1965, 1963.

6b. Ancker-Johnson, B., Drummond, J. E., 'Thermal Pinching in   138
Electron-Hole Plasma, II.', *Phys. Rev.* **132**, pp. 2372-2373,
1963.

6c. Ancker-Johnson, B., 'Some Nonlinear Properties of Electron-Hole   138
Plasmas Sustaining the Helical Instability', *Phys. Rev.,* **135A**,
p. A1423, 1964.

6d. Ancker-Johnson, B., 'Hysteresis in Stability Conditions of   137
Electron-Hole Plasma', *Phys. Rev.,* **134A**, pp. A1465-1473,
1964.

6e. Ancker-Johnson, B., 'Avalanche Plasma Production and Instabili-   127
ties on Subnanosecond Time Scales', *Proc. Internat. Conf.*
Phys. Semiconductors, Kyoto, Japan, 1966, *J. Phys. Soc. Jap.,*
21, Suppl. p. 694, 1966.

6f. Ancker-Johnson, B., Berg, M. F., 'Microwave Radiation from   126
Electron-Hole Plasmas', *Bull. Am Phys. Soc., Ser. 2*, **11**, p. 570,
1966.

6g. Ancker-Johnson, B., 'Gigahertz Radiation from Magnetic-Field-   125
Free Electron-Hole Plasmas', *Phys. Rev.* **164**, pp 1050-1056,
1967.

6h. Ancker-Johnson, B., 'Avalanche Plasma Production and Insta-   111, 127
bilities on Subnanosecond Time Scales, II', *J. Phys. Soc. Jap.*
22, p. 1156, 1967.

6i. Ancker-Johnson, B., 'Microwave Emission from Non-equilibrium   127
Plasmas in InSb Subject to Magnetic Fields', *Boeing Sci. Res.
Lab. Doc.*, D1.82.0623, Boeing Labs. Seattle, Washington,
June 1967.

7. Ando, K., 'A Double Injection Negative Resistance in p-type InSb   140
at 77°K', *Jap. J. Appl. Phys.*, **3**, p. 757, 1964.

8. Antoniewicz P. R., 'Helicon Window Below the Absorption Edge',   136
Phys. L., **24A**, p. 83, 1967.

9. Arizumi, T., Umeno, M., 'Oscillation Modes of Oscillistors in Uni-   138
form Magnetic Field', *Jap. J. Appl. Phys.*, **4**, p. 485, 1965.

9a. Arizumi, T., Aoki, T., Umeno, M., 'Moving High-Field Domain   140
and Current Saturation in Optically Excited n-InSb', *J. Phys.
Soc. Jap.*, **23**, pp. 283-289, 1967.

9b. Arizumi, T., Aoki, T., Hayakawa, K., 'Microwave Emission from   122, 127
Acoustoelectrically Oscillating n-InSb', *J. Phys. Soc. Jap.*, **23**,
pp. 1251-1256, 1967.

10. Asai, S., Miura, N., Tanaka, S., 'Conductivity Change in CdS by   122
Microwave Phonons', *Phys. Rev. L.*, **16**, p. 991, 1966.

11. Ash, E. A., Morgan, D., 'Realisation of Microwave-Circuit Func-   170
tions Using Acoustic Surface Waves', *Electr. L.*, **3**, p. 462,
1967.

12. Aukerman, L. W., Millea, M. F., McColl, M., 'Diffusion Lengths of   82
Electrons and Holes in GaAs', *J.Appl. Phys.*, **38**, pp. 685-690,
1967.

13. Autin, B., Cahen, O., Dieulesaint, E., Gouvernelle, D., Tavernier, J.,   120
Bauduin, P., 'Two-Step Current Saturation in CdS Crystals',
phys. stat. sol. **22**, K135, 1967.

14. Baibakov, V. I., Pado, G. S., Kartushina, A. A., 'Continuous   119
Amplification of Ultrasound in CdSe', *Fisika Tverdogo Tela,*
8, pp. 3716-3718, 1966, Translated: Sovj. Phys.-Sol. St., **8**, p.
2986, 1967.

15. Balberg, I., Many A., 'Frequency Shifts during Growth of Ampli-   121
fied Acoustic Flux in CdS'. *Appl. Phys. L.* **13**, p. 100, 1968.

16. Baraff, G. A., 'Interaction of Helicon Waves with an Adjacent   134
Drift Current', *Bell Tel. Labs. Inc.* Murray Hill, N.Y. Internal
Report, 1966.

16a. Baraff, G. A., Buchsbaum, S. J., 'Surface Wave Instability in   134
Helicon Wave Propagation', *Appl. Phys. L.*, **6**, p. 219, June 1965.

16b. Baraff, G. A., Buchsbaum, S. J., 'Surface Wave Instability in   134, 135
Helicon Wave Propagation', *Phys. Rev.*, **144**, pp. 266-276,
April 1966.

16c. Baraff, G. A., 'Interaction of Helicon Waves with an Adjacent   135
Drift Current', *J. Phys. Chem. Solids*, **28**, pp. 1037-1053, 1967.

17. Baramidze, G. A., Pkhakadze, M. G., 'Modulation of the Charge   141
Density of a Beam Resulting from Interaction with a Plasma in
a Solid', *Fizika Tverdogo Tela*, **9**, pp. 382-383, 1967, Trans-
lation: *Sov. Phys. Sol. St.*, **9**, p. 293, 1967.

18. Barkhausen, H., 'Zwei mit Hilfe der neuen Verstärker entdeckte   129
Erscheinungen', *Phys. Zs.*, **20**, p. 401, 1919.

19. Bartelink, D. J., 'Amplification of Transverse Plasma Waves in   133
Bismuth', *Phys. Rev. L.*, **16**, p. 510, 1966.

19a. Bartelink, D. J., 'Propagation and Instability of Transverse Waves   136
in Current-Carrying Electron-Hole Plasmas', *Phys. Rev.* **158**,
pp. 400-414, 1967.

20. Bass, J. C., Edridge, A. L., Knight, J. R., 'Gunn-Effect Oscillators   165
with Vapour-Grown Contact Layers', *Electronics L.*, **3**, p. 24,
1967.

21. Bauduin, P., 'Oscillations de Courant dans le Sulfure de Cadmium'.   121
Phys. L., **23**, p. 12, 1966.

21a. Bauduin, P., Buchy, F., 'Oscillations de Courant dans le Sulfure   121
de Cadmium Photoconducteur', *phys. stat. sol.*, **17**, p. 517,
1966.

21b. Bauduin, P., Buchy, F., 'Suggestions for New Acoustoelectric   170
Devices', *Proc. I.E.E.E.*, **54**, p. 1624, 1966.

22. Baynham, A. C., 'Off-Axis Helicon Amplification', *R.R.E. News-*   135
letter, p. 23, 1967, Royal Radar Est., Malvern, England.

23. Beale, J. R. A., 'Acoustoelectric Effects with Hypersonic Waves   123
of Large Amplitude', *Phys. Rev.*, **135**, pp. A1761-1766, 1964.

24. Beaudet, P. R., Houghton, A., 'Interaction of Magnetoplasma   135
Waves in a Two-Component Solid-State Plasma', *Phys. L.*, **23**,
p. 658, 1966.

25. Bekefi, G., Bers, A., Brueck, S. R. J., 'Microwave Emission from   126
n-Type InSb at 4.2 and 77°K', *Phys. Rev. L.*, **19**, p. 24, 1967.

25a. Bekefi, G., Bers, A., Brueck, S. R. J., 'Microwave Instability in   127, 128
n-Type Indium Antimonide', *I.E.E.E. Trans. El.Dev.*, **ED-14**,
pp. 593-596, 1967.

26. Berlincourt, D., Jaffe, H., Shiozawa, L. R., 'Electroelastic Proper-   118
ties of the Sulfides, Selenides and Tellurides of Zinc and
Cadmium', *Phys. Rev.*, **129**, pp. 1009-1017, 1963.

27. Berman, R. (Ed) 'Physical Properties of Diamond', Clarendon   165
Press, (Oxford), p. 387, 1965.

28. Bers, A., McWhorter, A. L., 'Absolute Instabilities with Drifted   133
Helicons', *Phys. Rev. L.*, **15**, p. 755, Nov. 1965.

29. Blakemore, J. S., 'Semiconductor Statistics', Pergamon Press,   129
New York, 1962.

30. Blötekjaer, K., Quate, C. F., 'The Coupled Modes of Acoustic   116, 169
Waves and Drifting Carriers in Piezoelectric Crystals', *Proc.*
I.E.E.E., **52**, p. 360, 1964.

30a. Blötekjaer, K., 'Cooled Electrons in Polar Semi-conductors', *Phys.*   125
L., **24A**, p. 15, 1967.

31. Böer, K. W., Ward, J. J., 'New Kind of Field Instability in CdS in   139
the Range of Negative Differential Resistivity', *Sol. St. Comm.*,
5, p. 467, 1967.

32. Bogachev, V. S., Berozashvili, Yu. N., Vul, B. M., 'Observation of   121, 122
Electric 'Domains' in High-Resistance GaAs with the Aid of
the Electrooptic Effect', *Zh. E.T.F.*, **6**, p. 464, 1967.

33. Bok, J., Nozieres, P., 'Instabilities of Transverse Waves in a Drifted   133
Plasma', *J. Phys. Chem. Solids*, **24**, p. 709, 1963.

34. Bonch-Bruevich, V. L., 'Motion of Electrical Domains in Semi-   82
conductors Containing Hot Electrons', *Fisika Tverdogo Tela*,
8, p. 1753, 1966, Translated in *Sov. Phys. Sol. State.* **8**,
p. 1397, 1966.

34a. Bonch-Bruevich, V. L., 'On the Theory of Electrical Domains in   82
Hot Electron Semiconductors', *phys. stat. sol.* **22**, p. 267, 1967.

35. Bosch, B. G., 'Gunn-Effekt-Elektronik', Telefunkenröhre, Dec.   78
1967.

35a. Bosch, B. G., Pollmann, H., 'Frequency Synchronization of Gunn   148
Effect Oscillators', *I.E.E.E; Trans. El.Dev.* **ED-13**, pp. 194-
196, 1966.

35b. Bosch, B., Pollmann, H., 'Elektronisches Festkörperelement mit   171
negativem differentiellem Widerstand', Deutches Bundespatent
12 35 457.

36. Bott, I. B., Hilsum, C., Taylor, B. C., 'Amplitude and Frequency   144
Modulation of Transferred Electron Microwave Generators',
I.E.E.E. Trans. El.-Dev., **ED-13**, pp. 193-194, 1966.

36a. Bott, I. B., Hilsum, C., 'An Analytic Approach to the lsa Mode',   98
I.E.E;E. Trans. El.Dev., **ED-14**, pp. 492-497, 1967.

36b. Bott, I. B., Hilsum, C., Smith, K. C. H., 'Construction and   165
Performance of Epitaxial Transferred-Electron Oscillators',
Sol. St. Electronics, **10**, pp. 137-144, 1967.

37. Bowers, R., 'Plasmas of Solids', *Scientific American*, **209**, p. 46,   132
Nov. 1963.

38. Bowman, L. S., Burrus, C. A., 'Pulse-Driven Si p-n Junction   113
Avalanche Oscillators for the 0.9 to 20 mm Band', *I.E.E.E.*
Trans El.Dev., **ED-14**, pp. 411-418, 1967.

39. Brady, D. P., Knight S., Lawley, K. L., Uenohara, M., 'Recent   143
Results with Epitaxial GaAs Gunn Effect Oscillators', *Proc.*,
I.E.E.E., **54**, p. 1497, 1966.

39a. Brady, D. P., Knight, S., Lawley, K. L., Uenohara, M., 'Character-   165
istics of Epitaxial GaAs Gunn Oscillators', Proc. Internat.
Symp. On GaAs, Reading, England, Sept. 1966, *Inst. of Phys.*
Soc. London, Conf. Ser. **3**, pp. 162-167.

40. Braslau, N., 'Velocity-Field Characteristic of GaAs from Measure-   82
    ment of the Conductivity in a Microwave Field', *Phys. L.* **24A**,
    pp. 531-533, 1967.

40a. Braslau, N., Gunn, J. B., Staples, J. L., 'Metal-Semiconductor   165
    Contacts for GaAs Bulk Effect Devices', *Sol. St. Electronics*,
    10, pp. 381-383, 1967.

41. Bray, R., Kumar, C., Ross, J., Sliva, P., 'Acoustoelectric Domain   121, 122
    Effects in III-V Semiconductors', *Proc. Int. Conf. Semicon-
    ductor Physics*, Kyoto, p. 483, 1966.

42. Brodwin, M., Kahn, S., 'Circulator Action at 140 GHz in a Semi-   172
    conductor Loaded Waveguide Junction', *I.E.E.E. Trans.
    Microw. Theory and Techniques*, **MTT-15**, p. 530, 1967.

43. Buchsbaum, S. J., Chynoweth, A. G., Feldmann, W. L., 'Micro-   126, 127
    wave Emission from InSb', *Appl. Phys. L.* **6**, p. 67, 1965.

43a. Buchsbaum, S. J., Galt, J. K., 'Alfvén Waves in Solid-State   129
    Plasmas,' *Phys. Of Fluids*, **4**, p. 1514, 1961.

44. Buchy, F., Bauduin, P., 'Relaxation-Type Oscillations in a High   121
    Conductive CdS Crystal', *Jap. J. Appl. Phys.*, **6**, p. 115,
    1967.

45. Buki, S., Nojima, K., 'Continuous Oscillations in CdS', *Jap. J.   119
    Appl. Phys.* **4**, p. 71, 1965.

46. Burke, B. E., Kino, G. S., 'Helicon-Wave Propagation in InSb',   133
    J. Appl. Phys. **38**, pp. 4888-4892, 1967.

47. Butcher, P. N., Fawcett, W., 'Intervalley Transfer of Hot Elec-   80, 82
    trons in Gallium Arsenide', *Phys. L.* **17**, pp. 216-217, 1965.

47a. Butcher, P. N., Fawcett, W., 'Calculation of the Velocity-Field   80, 82
    Characteristic for Gallium Arsenide', *Phys. L.* **21**, pp. 489-490,
    1966.

47b. Butcher, P. N., Fawcett, W., Hilsum, C., 'A Simple Analysis of   82
    Stable Domain Propagation in the Gunn Effect', *Brit. J. Appl.
    Phys.*, **17**, p. 841, 1966.

47c. Butcher, P. N., Fawcett, W., 'Stable Domain Propagation in the   82
    Gunn Effect', *Brit. J. Appl. Phys.* **17**, pp. 1425-1432, 1966.

47d. Butcher, P. N., Fawcett, W., Ogg, N. R., 'Effect of Field-Depend-   82
    ent Diffusion on Stable Domain Propagation in the Gunn
    Effect', *Brit. J. Appl. Phys.*, **18**, pp. 755-759, 1967.

48. Butler, M. B. N., Sandbank, C. P., 'Characteristics and Applica-   170
    tions of Domains in Semi-insulating CdS', *I.E.E.E. Trans.
    El.Dev.* **ED-14**, pp. 663-668. 1967.

49. Carlton, M., Hughes, J. J., Sobol, D. H., 'Measurements on the   149
    Properties of Microstrip Transmission Lines for Microwave
    Integrated Circuits', *R.C.A. Rev.* p. 377, 1966.

50. Carrol, J. E., 'Oscillations Covering 4 GHz to 31 GHz from a   142
    Single Gunn Diode', *Electronics Letters*, **2**, p. 141, 1966.

50a. Carroll, J. E., 'Resonant Circuit Operation of Gunn Diodes: A   146
    Self-Pumped Parametric Oscillator', *Electronics Letters*, **2**,
    p. 215, 1966.

50b. Carroll, J. E., 'Series Operation of Gunn Diodes for High R.F.   144
     Power', *Electronics Letters*, **3**, p. 455, 1967.
50c. Carroll, J. E., Giblin, R. A., 'A Low-Frequency Analog for a   147
     Gunn-Effect Oscillator', *I.E.E.E. Trans. El.Dev.* **ED-14**, pp.
     640-656, 1967.
51. Carter, D. L., Picard, J. C., 'Resonances in Submillimetric Alfvén   136
     Wave Propagation in Bismuth', *Sol. State Comm.*, **5**, pp. 719-
     722, 1967.
52. Cawsey, D., 'V.H.F. and U.H.F. Gunn Effect Oscillators',   147
     Electronics L., **3**, p. 550, 1967.
53. Chambers, R. G., Jones, B. K., 'Measurement of the High-Field   131
     Hall Effect by an Inductive Method', *Proc. Roy. Soc.* **A270**,
     p. 417, 1962.
54. Chang, D. M., Moll, J. L., 'Direct Observation of the Drift   82
     Velocity as a Function of the Electric Field in Gallium
     Arsenide', *Appl. Phys. L.*, **9**, pp. 283-285, 1966.
55. Chang, J. J.,'Frequency Response of PIN Avalanching Photo-   110
     diodes', *I.E.E.E. Trans. El.Dev.* **ED-14**, pp. 139-145, 1967.
56. Chang, N. S., Hayamizu, T., Matsuo, Y., 'YIG-Tuned Gunn   144
     Effect Oscillator', *Proc. I.E.E.E.*, **55**, p. 1621, 1967.
57. Chodorow, M., Auld, B. A., Wilkinson, J., 'Geometrical Optics of   169
     Acoustic Waves', Microwave Lab Report No. 1410, Stanford
     University, Calif. p. 9, 1966.
58. Chubachi, N., Wada, M., Kikuchi, Y., 'A New Ultrasonic Ampli-   169
     fier Device of CdS Crystal with Integrated Diffusion-Layer
     Transducers', *Jap. J. Appl. Phys.*, **3**, pp. 777-779, 1964.
59. Cipolla, F., Prudenziati, M., 'Spontaneous Oscillations of 2N708   115
     Transistors in Avalanche Condition with Open Emitter', *Proc.
     I.E.E.E.*, **55**, p. 460, 1967.
60. Cohen, B. G., 'Deep Impurity Band Effects on Transient   166
     Behaviour of GaAs PIN Devices', Solid State Device Res. Conf.,
     June 1967, Santa Barbara, California, Summary:*I.E.E.E. Trans.
     El.Dev.* **ED-14**, p. 634, 1967.
61. Conwell, E. M., Vassell, M. O., 'Variation of Drift Velocity with   80
     Field in GaAs', *Appl. Phys. L.*, **9**, pp. 411-413, 1966.
61a. Conwell, E. M., Vassell, M. O., 'Effect of Nonparabolicity on   82
     Drift Velocity in GaAs', *Phys. L.*, **25A**, pp. 302-303, 1967.
61b. Conwell, E. M., Vassell, M. O., 'High-Field Distribution   88
     Function in GaAs', *I.E.E.E. Trans. El.Dev.* **ED-13**, pp. 22-27,
     1966.
62. Copeland, J. A., 'Stable Space Charge Layers in Two-Valley   82, 96
     Semiconductors', *J. Appl. Phys.*, **37**, pp. 3602-3609, 1966.
62a. Copeland, J. A., 'A New Mode of Operation for Bulk Negative   96
     Resistance Oscillators', *Proc. I.E.E.E.*, **54**, pp. 1479-1480,
     1966.
62b. Copeland, J. A., 'LSA Oscillator Diode Theory', *J. Appl. Phys.*,   96, 147,
     38, pp. 3096-3101, 1967.   148

62c. Copeland, J. A., 'CW Operation of LSA Oscillator Diodes—44 to   98, 142,
88 GHz', *B.S.T.J. Briefs*, **46**, p. 284, 1967.   148

62d. Copeland, J. A., 'Theoretical Study of a Gunn Diode in a Reson-   143
ant Circuit', *I.E.E.E. Trans. El.Dev.* **ED-14**, pp. 55-58,
1967.

62e. Copeland, J. A., 'Doping Uniformity and Geometry of LSA   147
Oscillator Diodes', *I.E.E.E. Trans. El.Dev.*, **ED-14**, pp. 497-500,
1967.

62f. Copeland, J. A., Hayashi, T., Uenohara, M., 'Logic and Memory   151, 153,
Elements using Two-Valley Semiconductors', *Proc. I.E.E.E.*,   164
55, p. 584, 1967.

63. Court, W. P. N., Daysey, D. W., Bott, I. B., 'Noise Performance of 143
Gunn Microwave Generators in X and J-Bands', *Electronics L.*,
2, pp. 125-126, 1966.

63a. Court, W. P. N., Herman, P., Hilsum, C., Holliday, H. R., Warner, 144
F. L., 'Reduction of Frequency-Modulation Noise from Gunn
Oscillators', *Electronics L.*, **3**, p. 567, 1967.

64. Cox, R. H., Strack, H., 'Ohmic Contacts for GaAs Devices', *Sol.* 165
St. Electronics, **10**, pp. 1213-1218, 1967.

65. Davis, E. A., Drews, R. E., 'Effects of Transverse and Longitu-   118
dinal Non-Uniformities in Conductivity on Ultrasonic Propagation in CdS', *J. Appl. Phys.*, **38**, p. 2663, 1967.

66. Davis, E. M., 'Rieke Diagrams for Avalanche Diodes Show Per-   115
formance as a Function of Load', *Proc. I.E.E.E.*, **55**, p. 1521,
1967.

67. Dawson, R. W., Marinaccio, L. P., 'High-Q Microwave Filters   115
Employing IMPATT Active Elements', *I.E.E.E. Trans. Microw.*
Theory and Techniques, **MTT-15**, p. 272, 1967.

68. Day, G. F., Dow, D. G., Mosher, C. H., Vane, A. B., 'The   143
Achievement of High Efficiency in Gunn-Effect Devices',
Proc. Conf. GaAs Technology, Reading, England, 1966.

68.1. Dienst, J. F., Dean, R., Enstrom, R., Kokkas, A., 'Coplanar-   165
Contact Gunn-Effect Devices', *RCA Rev.*, **28**, pp. 585-594,
1967.

69. Döhler, G., 'On the Field Emission of Minority Carriers in Photo- 139
conductors', *phys. stat. sol.*, **19**, p. 555, 1967.

70. Domer, F. R., Kyle, R. H., 'Phase Locking an IMPATT Device in   113
the Pulsed Mode', *Proc. I.E.E.E.*, **55**, p. 1753, 1967.

71. Dow, D. G., Mosher, C. H., Vane, A. B., 'High-Peak Power   142
Gallium Arsenide Oscillators', *I.E.E.E. Trans. El.Dev.*, **ED-13**,
pp. 105-110, 1966.

71a. Dow, D. G., Mosher, C. H., Vane, A. B., 'High-Pulsed Power Using 142, 143
the Gunn-Effect', MOGA-Conf., Cambridge, England, 1966,
I.E.E. Conf. Publ. No. 27, p. 273, 1966.

71.1. Driedonks, F., Zijlstra, R. J., Alkemade, C. Th., 'Double Injection 140
and High Frequency Noise in Germanium Diodes', *Appl. Phys.*
L., **11**, pp. 318-319, 1967.

72. Economou, E. N., Ngai, K. L., 'Interaction of the ac Josephson   141
    Current with Surface Plasmons' *Phys. Rev. L.* **20**, pp. 547-550,
    1968.
73. Edridge, A. L., 'The Fabrication of Gunn Devices', Proc. Internat.   164, 165
    Symp. On GaAs, Reading, England, 1966, Inst. Phys. and Phys.
    Soc., London, Conf. Ser. 3, pp. 168-171, 1966.
74. Eidson, J. C. Kino G. S., 'A New Type of Oscillation in InSb',   126
    Appl. Phys. L., **8**, p. 183, 1966.
75. Elesin, V. F., Manykin, E. A., 'Stability of the State of a Semi-   140
    conductor with Absolute Negative Conductivity', *Fizika
    Tverdogo Tela*, **8**, pp. 3621-3625, 1966. Transl: *Sov. Phys.
    Sol St.*, **8**, p. 2891, 1967.
76. Elliott, B. J., Gunn, J. B., McGroddy, J. C., 'Bulk Negative   80, 140
    Differential Conductivity and Travelling Domains in n-Type
    Germanium,' *Appl. Phys. L.*, **11**, pp. 253-255, 1967.
77. Engelbrecht, R. A., 'Bulk-Effect Devices for Future Transmission   149
    Systems', *Bell Lab. Record*, p. 192, June 1967.
78. Fawcett, W., Paige, E. G. S., 'Negative Differential Resistance in   80, 140
    n-Type Germanium', *Electronics L.*, **3**, pp. 505-507, 1967.
79. Ferry, D. K., Young, R. W., Dougal, A. A., 'Frequency Range   126
    of the Microwave Emission from InSb', *Z. Naturforschg.*, **22a**,
    p. 576, 1967.
79a. Ferry, D. K., Dougal, A. A., 'Microwave Emission from Bulk   129
    n-Type InAs', *Appl. Phys. L.*, **7**, p. 318, 1965.
80. Fisher, S. T., 'Small-Signal Impedance of Avalanching Junctions   110
    with Unequal Electron and Hole Ionization Rates and Drift
    velocities', *I.E.E.E. Trans. El.Dev.*, **ED-14**, pp. 313-322,
    1967.
80.1.Fisher, R. E., 'Generation of Subnanosecond Pulses with Bulk   149, 150
    GaAs', *Proc. I.E.E.E.*, **55**, p. 2189, 1967.
80.1a. Fisher, R. E., 'A Proposed 1350 Megabit/Sec Binary PCM   159
    Repeater Using Bulk GaAs Devices', Paper presented at
    I.E.E.E. Internat. Communications Conf., June, 1968.
81. Fleming, P. L., 'Further Observations Above and Below Twice the   96
    Gunn Threshold', *Proc. I.E.E.E.*, **55**, p. 1538, 1967.
81.1.Fossum, H. J., Rannestad, A., 'Field Distribution and Current   121
    Saturation in Photoconductive CdS', *J. Appl. Phys.*, **38**, pp.
    5177-5182, 1967.
82. Foyt, A. G., McWhorter, A. L., 'The Gunn Effect in Polar Semi-   79, 80,
    conductors', *I.E.E.E. Trans. El.Dev.*, **ED-13**, pp. 79-87, 1966.   84
83. Friedman, L., 'Spatially Inhomogeneous Phonon Amplification in   116
    Solids', *Phys. Rev.*, **163**, pp. 712-719, 1967.
84. Froom, J., 'An Analysis of Current Instabilities in Semi-Insulating   121
    Piezoelectric Crystals', *I.E.E.E. Trans. El.Dev.*, **ED-14**, pp.
    656-663, 1967.
85. Fukatsu, Y., 'Parametric Effects in a Microwave Read Avalanche   110, 168
    Diode', *I.E.E.E. Trans. El.Dev.*, **ED-14**, pp. 251-259, 1967.

86. Furdyna, J. K., 'Helicons, Magnetoplasma Edge and Faraday   136
    Rotation in Solid-State Plasmas at Microwave Frequencies',
    Appl. Optics, **6**, p. 675, 1967.
86a. Furdyna, J. K., 'Microwave Faraday Rotation in Semiconductor   136
    Plasmas in the High Magnetic Field Limit', *Sol. State Comm.,*
    5, p. 539, 1967.
87. Furukawa, Y., Ishibashi, Y., 'Trapping Effects in Au-n-Type   82
    GaAs Schottky Barrier Diodes', *Jap. J. Appl. Phys.,* **6**, p. 503,
    1967.
87a. Furukawa, Y., Kajiyama, K., Seki, Y., Sugane, K., 'Trap Density   82
    in Epitaxially Grown GaAs', *Jap. J. Appl. Phys.,* **6**, p. 413, 1967.
88. Galt, J. K., Yager, W. A., Merritt, F. R., Cetlin, B. B., Brailsford   129, 132
    A. D., 'Cyclotron Absorption in Metallic Bismuth and its
    Alloys', *Phys. Rev.,* **114**, p. 1396, 1959.
89. Gantsevich, S. V., Gurevich, V. L., 'Theory of Sound Amplifica-   116
    tion in Many Valley Semiconductors', *Phys. Rev.,* **161**, pp.
    736-745, 1967.
90. Gay, R. K. L., Hartnagel, H., 'New Oscillation Phenomena with   121
    Piezoelectric CdS', *Sol. Stat Electr.,* **11**, pp. 407-410, 1968.
90a. Gay, R. K. L., 'Current Oscillations in Photoconductive CdS',   121
    Thesis of M.Eng. Sheffield University, England, June 1967.
91. Gelbwachs, J., Mao, S., 'Phase Locking on Pulsed Gunn Oscilla-   144
    tors', *Proc. I.E.E.E.,* **54**, pp. 1591-1592, 1966.
92. Gilden, M., Hines, M. E., 'Electronic Tuning Effects in the Read   112, 113
    Microwave Avalanche Diode', *I.E.E.E. Trans. El.Dev.,* ED-13,
    p. 169, 1966.
92.1. Glasoe, G. N., Lebacqz, J. V., 'Pulse Generators', M.I.T.   166
    Radiation Laboratory Series, No. 5, McGraw-Hill, 1948.
93. Glicksman, M., 'Instabilities of a Cylindrical Electron-Hole Plasma   137
    in a Magnetic Field', *Phys. Rev.,* **124**, p. 1655, 1961.
93a. Glicksman, M., Powlus, R. A., 'Observations of Electron-Hole   138
    Current Pinching in InSb', *Phys. Rev.,,***121**, p. 1659, 1961.
94. Gobrecht, H., Tausend, A., Danckwerts, J., 'Helicon Oscillations   136
    in HgSe', *Sol. State Comm.,* **5**, p. 551, 1967.
95. Gordeyev, G. V., 'Undamped Plasma Oscillations in Nonpolar   125
    Semiconductors', *Radiotech. i. Elektron.* **11**, 1966, Translation:
    Rad. Eng. and El. Phys. **11**, p. 1408, 1966.
96. Grace, M. I., 'Injection Locking of Pulsed Avalanche Diode   113
    Oscillators', *Proc. I.E.E.E.,* **55**, p. 713, 1967.
97. Greebe, C. A. A. J., 'The Influence of Trapping on the Acousto-   118
    Electric Effect in CdS', *I.E.E.E. Trans. Sonics and Ultrason.,*
    SU-13, pp. 54-61, 1966, *Philips Res. Rep.,* **21**, pp. 1-15, 1966.
97a. Greebe, C. A. A. J., 'Mechanical Excitation of Helicon Waves',   136
    Phil. Res. Rep., **22**, pp. 133-141, 1967.
98. Gueret, P., 'Wave Propagation and Instabilities in Semiconductors',   127, 133
    Microwave Lab. Report No. 1533, Stanford University, Calif.,
    pp. 79-99, 1967.

98a. Gueret, P., Burke, B., Kino, G. S., 'Collision Dominated Instabi-   127
lities', Solid State Development and Research Conference,
Santa Barbara, California, 1967, Summary: *I.E.E.E. Trans.
El.Dev.*, **ED-14**, p. 635, 1967.

99. Guetin, P., 'Gunn Effect with Two Samples in Parallel',   151, 153
Electronics Letters, **4**, No 4, p. 63, 1968.

99a. Guetin, P., 'Contribution to the Experimental Study of the Gunn   161, 165
Effect in Long GaAs Samples', *I.E.E.E. Trans. El.Dev.*, **ED-14**,
pp. 552-562, 1967.

100. Gulyaev, Yu. V., 'Negative Differential Conductivity in a Semi-   123
conductor Under Sound Instability Conditions', *Phys. L.* **25A**,
p. 320, 1967.

101. Gummel, H. K., Blue, J. L., 'A Small-Signal Theory of Avalanche   166
Noise in IMPATT Diodes', *I.E.E.E. Trans. El.Dev.*, **ED-14**, pp.
569-580, 1967.

102. Gunn, J. B., 'Microwave Oscillations of Current in III-V Semicon-   78, 142
ductors', *Sol. State. Comm.*, **1**, pp. 88-91, 1963.

102a. Gunn, J. B., Elliott, B.J., 'Measurement of the Negative Differen-   82
tial Mobility of Electrons in GaAs', *Phys. L.*, **22**, p. 369,
1966.

102b.Gunn, J. B., 'Effect of Domain and Circuit Properties on Oscilla-   93
tions in GaAs', *I.B.M. Journal*, **4**, pp. 310-320,
1966.

102c. Gunn, J. B., 'Properties of a Free Steadily Travelling Electrical   85, 89
Domain in GaAs', *I.B.M. Journal.* **4**, pp. 300-309, 1966.

103. Haitz R. H., Goetzberger, A., Scarlett, R. M., Shockley, W.,   101
'Avalanche Effects in Silicon p-n Junctions I. Localized Photo-
multiplication Studies on Microplasmas', *J. Appl. Phys.*, **34**,
p. 1581, 1963.

103a. Haitz, R. H., 'Noise Theory for the Read Type Avalanche Diode',   113
J. Appl. Phys., **38**, pp. 2935-2946, 1967.

104. Hakki, B. W., Knight, S., 'Microwave Phenomena in Bulk GaAs',   165
I.E.E.E. Trans. El.Dev., **ED-13**, pp. 94-105, 1966.

104a. Hakki, B. W., Beccone, J. P., Plauski, S. E., 'Phase Locked GaAs   144
CW Microwave Oscillators', *I.E.E.E. Trans. El.Dev.*, **ED-13**,
pp. 197-199, 1966.

104b.Hakki, B. W., 'Amplification in Two-Valley Semiconductors',   93, 146
J. Appl. Phys. **38**, pp. 808-818, 1967.

104c. Hakki, B. W., Beccone, J. P., 'Microwave Negative Conductance   146
of Bulk GaAs', *Proc. I.E.E.E.*, **54**, p. 916, 1966.

104d.Hakki, B. W., 'GaAs Post Threshold Microwave Amplifier, Mixer   146
and Oscillator', *Proc. I.E.E.E.*, **54**, p. 299, 1966.

104e. Hakki, B. W., 'Solid-State Acoustoelectric Light Scanner', *Appl.*   170
Phys. L., **11**, p. 153, 1967.

105. Hamaguchi, C., Ishida, A., Inuishi, Y., 'Build-up Time and Oscilla-   121
tion of Acoustoelectric Current in CdS', *J. Phys. Soc. Jap.*,
20, p. 1279, 1965.

105a. Hamaguchi, C., Ishida, A., Inuishi, Y., 'Microwave Attenuation   122
by Supersonic Electrons in CdS', *Proc. I.E.E.E.*, **53**, p. 1259,
1965.

105b. Hamaguchi, C., Ishida, A., Inuishi, Y., 'Interaction of Supersonic   122
Electrons with Strong Microwaves in CdS.', *Jap. J. Appl. Phys.*,
5, p. 1250, 1966.

105c. Hamaguchi, C., Kono, T., Inuishi, Y., 'Microwave Measurement of   82
Differential Negative Conductivity due to Intervalley Transfer
of Hot Electrons in n-Type GaAs', *Phys. L.*, **24A**, pp. 500-501,
1967.

106. Hammer, J. M., 'Coupling Between Slow Waves and Convective   140
Instabilities in Solids', *Appl. Phys. L.*, **10**, p. 358, 1967.

107. Hanlon, J. T., 'Noise Induced Gain Saturation in the Ultrasonic   118
Travelling Wave Amplifier', *Proc. I.E.E.E.*, **55**, pp. 1128-1135,
1967.

108. Hanson, D. C., Rowe, J. E., 'Microwave Circuit Characteristics of   147
Bulk GaAs Oscillators', *I.E.E.E. Trans. El.Dev.*, **ED-14**, pp.
469-476, 1967.

109. Harding, G. N., Thonemann, P. C., 'A Study of Helicon Waves in   136
In.', *Proc. Phys. Soc.*, **85**, p. 317, 1965.

110. Harrison, M. J., 'Collective Excitation of Degenerate Plasmas in   125
Solids', *J. Phys. Chem. Solids*, **23**, p. 1079, 1962.

111. Hartnagel, H., Gay, R., 'Modulation Effect of Continuous Current   121
Oscillations in CdS.', *Phys. L.*, **24A**, p. 158, 1967.

111a. Hartnagel, H. L., Izadpanah, S. H., 'High-Speed Computer Logic   151, 159
with Gunn-Effect Devices', *Rad. Electronic Eng.*, **36**, pp. 247-
255, 1968.

111b. Hartnagel, H., 'Digital Logic-Circuit Applications of Gunn Diodes',   151
Proc. I.E.E.E., **55**, p. 1236, 1967.

111c. Hartnagel, H., 'Theory of Gunn-Effect Logic', *Sol. State Electro-*   151, 152
nics., **12**, pp. 19-30, 1969.

111d. Hartnagel, H., 'Gunn-Effect Pulse Code Modulation', *Archiv der*   155
Elektr. Übertragung, pp. 225-229, 1968.

111e. Hartnagel, H., 'Some Basic Logic Circuits Employing Gunn-Effect.   159
Devices', *Sol. State Electronics*, **11**, pp. 568-572, 1968.

112. Hasegawa, A., 'Resistive Instabilities in Semiconductor Plasmas',   127, 134
J. Phys. Soc. Jap., **20**, p. 1072, 1965.

112a. Hasegawa, A., 'Microinstabilities in Transversely Magnetized   127
Semiconductor Plasmas', *J. Appl. Phys.*, **36**, p. 3590, 1965.

113. Hasty, T.,E., Cunningham, P. A., Wisseman, W. R., 'Microwave   142
Oscillations in Epitaxial Layers of GaAs', *I.E.E.E. Trans.*
El.Dev., **ED-13**, pp. 114-117, 1966.

114. Hayakawa, H., Kikuchi, M., Abe, Y., 'Continuous Current   119
Oscillation in GaAs Caused by Acoustoelectric Effect', *Jap. J.*
Appl. Phys., **5**, p. 734, 1966.

114.1. Hayashi, T., Uenohara, M., 'Tin-Gold Contacts for Planar Bulk   165
GaAs Devices', *J. Phys. Soc. Jap.* **24**, pp. 110-114, 1968.

115. Haydl, W. H., Harker, K., Quate, C. F., 'Current Oscillations in   120, 121
      Piezoelectric Semiconductors', *J. Appl. Phys.*, **38**, pp. 4295-
      4309, 1967.

116. Heeks, J. S., 'Some Properties of the Moving High-Field Domain in   99, 114
      Gunn-Effect Devices', *I.E.E.E. Trans. El.Dev.*, **ED-13**, p. 68,
      1966.

116a. Heeks, J. S., Woode, A. D., 'Localized Temporary Increase in   161, 164
      Material Conductivity following Impact Ionization in a Gunn-
      Effect Domain', *I.E.E.E. Trans. El.Dev.*, **ED-14**, pp. 513-517,
      1967.

117. Heinle, W., 'Principles of a Phenomenological Theory of Gunn-   82, 94
      Effect Domain Dynamics', *Brit. J. Appl. Phys.*, **18**, p. 1537,
      1967.

117a. Heinle, W., 'Simple Theory for lsa Operation of Gunn-Effect   98
      Semiconductors', *Electronics L.*, **3**, p. 429, 1967.

118. Heinrich, H., Ferry, D. K., 'Hot Carrier Current Oscillations in   140
      n-Type Germanium', *Appl. Phys. L.*, **11**, p. 126,
      1967.

119. Hervouet, C., 'Comment on Acoustoelectric Saturation of Ultra-   118
      sonic Gain', *Phys. L.*, **24A**, p. 638, 1967.

119a. Hervouet, C., Kebailly, J., Leroux Hugon, P., Veilex, R., 'Current   122
      Oscillations in GaAs under Acoustic Amplification conditions',
      Solid. St. Comm., **3**, p. 413, 1965.

119b. Hervouet, C., 'Magnetic-Field Dependence of Current Oscillations   121
      in Piezoelectric Semiconductors', *phys. stat. sol.*, **21**, p. 117,
      1967.

120. Hickernell, F. S., 'The Electroacoustic Gain Interaction in III-V   118
      Compounds: GaAs', *I.E.E.E. Trans. Sonics and Ultrason.*,
      SU-13, pp. 73-77, 1966.

121. Higgins, V. J., Brand, F. A., Baranowski, J. J., 'Characteristics of   112
      Varactors Biased into Avalanche', *I.E.E.E. Trans. El.Dev.*,
      ED-13, p. 210, 1966.

122. Hille, P. F., Reid, F. J., Beer, A. C., 'Amplification by Magnetic   141
      Control of Skin Depth', *Sol. State Comm.*, **9**, pp. 453-458,
      1966.

123. Hilsum, C., 'Transferred Electron Amplifiers and Oscillators',   78, 80
      Proc. I.R.E. **50**, pp. 185-189, 1962,

123a. Hilsum, C., Rose Innes, A. C., 'Semiconducting III-V Compounds',   79
      Pergamon Press, New York, 1961.

123b. Hilsum, C., 'A Simple Analysis of Transferred Electron Oscilla-   82
      tors', *Brit. J. Appl. Phys.*, **16**, pp. 1401-1403, 1965.

123c. Hilsum, C., Holeman, B., 'Carrier Lifetime in GaAs', Proc.   94
      Internat. Conf. Semicond. Physics, Prague; p. 962, 1966.

123d. Hilsum, C., 'Miniaturizing Radar', *Science Journal,* **3**, pp. 74-79,   148
      1967.

124. Hines, M. I., 'Noise Theory for the Read Type Avalanche Diode',   113
      I.E.E.E. Trans. El.Dev. **ED-13**, pp. 158-163, 1966.

125. Hobson, G. S., Paige, E. G., 'Transmission of Microwave Radiation 121
Through Acousto-Electrically Amplifying CdS', Proc. Internat.
Conf. Phys. Semicond., Kyoto, Japan, 1966: J. Phys. Soc. Jap.,
21, Suppl. p. 464, 1966.

125a. Hobson, G. S., 'Small-Signal Admittance of a Gunn Effect Device', 147
Electronics L., 2, p. 207, 1966.

125b. Hobson, G. S., 'Source of f.m. Noise in Cavity Controlled Gunn- 143
Effect Oscillators', Electronics L., 3, p. 63, 1967.

126. Höfflinger, B., 'Wirkungsweise und einige Hochfrequenzunter- 78
suchungen des Gunn-Effektes', Archiv El. Übertragung, 20,
pp. 657-671, 1966.

126a. Höfflinger, B., 'High-Frequency Oscillations of $p^{++}-n^+-n-n^{++}$ 102
Avalanche Diodes Below Transit-Time Cutoff', I.E.E.E. Trans.
El.Dev., ED-13, p. 151, 1966.

126b. Höfflinger, B., 'Oscillation in p^+n n^+ Avalanche Diodes at Inter- 114
mediate Frequencies', Proc. I.E.E.E. 55, p. 425, 1967.

127. Hübner, K., Zuber, H., Markus, M., 'Some Remarks on Z-Pinch 138
Onset In an Electron-Hole Plasma in n-InSb', Phys. L., 25A,
p. 62, 1967.

127a. Hübner, K., Schneider, W., 'Direct Observation of Z-Pinching in 138
Electron-Hole Plasma in InSb at 0.8A', Phys. L. 25A, p. 343,
1967.

128. Hurwitz., C. E., McWhorter, A. L., 'Growing Helical Density 137
Waves in Semiconductor Plasmas', Phys. Rev.,L., 10, p. 20,
1963.

129. Hutson, A. R., McFee, J. H., White, D. L., 'Ultrasonic Amplifi- 115
cation in CdS', Phys. Rev. L., 7, p. 237, 1961.

129a. Hutson, A. R., Jayaraman, A., Coriell, A. S., 'Effects of High 79
Pressure, Uni-axial Stress, and Temperature on the Electrical
Resistivity of n-GaAs', Phys. Rev., 155, pp. 786-796, 1967.

130. Ibuki, S., Nojima, K., 'Continuous Oscillation in CdS.' Jap. J. 121
Appl. Phys., 4, p. 71, 1965.

131. Iglitsyn, M. I., Pel, E. G., Pervova, L. Ya., Fistul V. I., 'Instability 140
of the Electron-Hole Plasma in a Semiconductor due to the
Nonlinearity of the Current-Voltage Characteristics', Fizika
Tverdogo Tela, 8, pp. 3606-3612, 1966, Transl: Sov. Phys.
Sol. State, 8, p. 2880, 1967.

132. Ikoma, H., 'On The Threshold of Current Saturation in GaAs', 120
Jap. J. Appl. Phys., 6, pp. 495-502, 1967.

133. Irvin J. C., 'GaAs Avalanche Microwave Oscillators', I.E.E.E. 112
Trans. El.Dev., ED-13, p. 208, 1966.

134. Ishida, A., Hamaguchi, C., Inuishi, Y., 'Note on Current Satura- 120
tion in CdS. Crystals', J. Phys. Soc. Japan, 21, p. 192, 1966.

134a. Ishida, A., Inuishi, Y., 'Higher-Order Effect in Phonon Buildup of 120
CdS.', J. Phys. Soc. Japan, 21, p. 2078, 1966.

134b. Ishida, A., Inuishi, Y., 'Current Oscillations and High-Field Domains 121
in Dark Conductive CdS. Crystals', Appl. Phys. L., 8, p. 235, 1966.

134c. Ishida, A., Inuishi, Y., 'Current Oscillations in CdS caused by   121
      Acoustoelectric Domain Motion', *I.E.E.E. Trans. El.Dev.*,
      ED-14, pp. 600-607, 1967.

134d. Ishida, A., Hamaguchi, C., Inuishi, Y., 'Current Saturation and   121
      Instabilities in CdS Crystals', Proc. Internat. Conf. Phys.
      Semicond., Kyoto, 1966; *J. Phys. Soc. Jap.*, **21**, p. 469, 1966.

134e. Ishida, A., Hamaguchi, C., Inuishi, Y., 'Potential Probe Measure-   121
      ments along Current-Oscillating CdS Crystals', *J. Phys. Soc.
      Jap.*, **21**, p. 186, 1966.

135. Isobe, T., Tokida, M., 'Effects of Phase Locking on Modulation   146, 168
      Characteristics', *Proc. I.E.E.E.*, **55**, p. 453, 1967.

136. Izadpanah, S. H., Hartnagel; H., 'Pulse Gain and Analogue-to-   150
      Pulse Conversion by Gunn Diodes, *Electronics L.*, **4**, pp. 315-
      316, 1968.

137. Jackson, J. D., 'Longitudinal Plasma Oscillations', *J. Nuclear   124
      Energy C*, **1**, p. 171, 1960.

138. Jaskolski, S. V., Ishi, T. K., 'Simultaneous Low-Frequency Relaxa-   99
      tion and High-Frequency Microwave Oscillation of a Bulk
      GaAs CW Oscillator', *Electronics L.*, **3**, p. 12, 1967.

139. Jeppson, B., Marklund, I., 'Failure Mechanisms in Gunn Diodes',   165
      Electronics L., **3**, p. 213, 1967.

139a. Jeppson, B., Marklund, I., Olsson, K., 'Voltage Tuning of Concen-   144
      tric Planar Gunn Diodes', *Electronics L.*, **3**, p. 498, 1967.

140. Johnson, E. O., 'Physical Limitations on Frequency and Power   147
      Parameters of Transistors', *RCA Rev.*, **26**, pp. 163-177, 1965.

141. Johnston, R. L., de Loach Jr., B. C., Cohen, B. G., 'A Silicon   102
      Diode Microwave Oscillator', *Bell Syst. Techn. J., Briefs*, **44**,
      p. 369, 1965.

141.1. Jones, B. L., Beaudet, P. R., 'Negative Photoconductivity and   140
      Electrical Instabilities in Semiconductors', *Canadian Journal of
      Physics*, **45**, pp. 4091-4101, 1967.

142. Jonscher, A. K., 'Solid-State Plasma Phenomena', *Brit. J. Appl.*   115
      Phys., **15**, p. 365, 1964.

143. Jörgensen, M. H., Meyer, N. I., Quate, C. F., 'Microwave Emission   140
      from Germanium Crystals', *Phys. L.*, **25A**, p. 143, 1967.

144. Josenhans, J., 'Noise Spectra of Read Diode and Gunn Oscillators', 113, 143
      Proc. I.E.E.E., **54**, pp. 1478-1479, 1966.

144a. Josenhans, J., Misawa, T., 'Experimental Characterisation of a   112
      Negative-Resistance Avalanche Diode', *I.E.E.E. Trans. El.Dev.*,
      ED-13, p. 206, 1966.

145. Judd, S. B., Hewitt, S. J., 'Phase Locking of Gunn-Effect Oscilla-   144
      tors', *Electr. L.*, **3**, p. 107, 1967.

146. Kakihana, S., 'Oscillations in PIN Germanium Diodes in Crossed   115
      Fields', *J. Appl. Phys.*, **37**, p. 5002, 1966.

146a. Kakihana, S., Buchmiller, L., 'Two-Stream Instability in   125
      Anisotropic Semimetals', *J. Appl. Phys.*, **38**, pp. 5376-5387,
      1967.

147. Kalashnikov, S. G., Bonch-Bruevich, V. L., 'The Wave Velocity 139
of the Space Charge (Electrical Domains) in Semiconductors',
Rad. Eng. and Electronic Phys. 11, pp. 1514-1516, 1966.

147a. Kalashnikov, S. G., Kagan, M. S., Vdovenkov, V. A., 'Some 139
Properties of Electrical Domains in n-Type Germanium Doped
with Copper', *Fizika i. Tekhnika Poluprovodnikov*, 1, pp.
116-122, 1967. Transl: *Sov. Phys.-Semicond.*, 1, p. 88, 1967.

147b. Kalashnikov, S. G., Morosov, A. I., Proklov, V. V., 'Some Data on 121
Acousto-Electrical Domains in Photoconductive CdS.', *phys.
stat. sol.*, 23, p. K9, 1967.

147c. Kalashnikov, S. G., Morosov, A. I., Stankovskii, B. A., 'Effect of 118
Traps on the Amplification of Ultra-sound in CdS.', *Fizika
Tverdogo Tela*, 9, pp. 859-863, 1967. Transl: *Sov. Phys.-Sol.
St.*, 9, pp. 670-673, 1967.

147d. Kalashnikov, S. G., Lyubchenko, V. E., Skvortsova, N. E., 'Nega- 82
tive Differential Conductivity of GaAs when the Electrons are
Heated by a Microwave Field', *Fizika i Tekhnika Poluprovodnikov*, 1, pp. 1445-1447, 1967, Transl: *Sov. Phys.-Semicond.*
1, pp. 1206-1207, 1967.

148. Kastal'skii, A. A., Ryvkin, S. M., 'Gunn Effect in Uniaxially 80
Compressed Germanium', *Fizika i Tekhnika Poluprovodnikov*,
1, p. 622, 1967, Transl: *Sov. Phys.-Semicond.*, 1, p. 523, 1967.

149. Kataoka, S., Naito, H., 'Magnetoresistance Microwave Devices', 140
Sol. State Electronics, 9, pp. 459-464, 1966.

149a. Kataoka, S., Tacano, M., 'Angular Dependence of Microwave 126
Emission from InSb on the Magnetic Field', *Proc. I.E.E.E.*,
55, p. 1080, 1967.

149b. Kataoka, S., Hashizume, N., Iida, S., 'Magnetoreactive Element 172
and New Solid-State Inductor', *Solid State Electronics*, 11,
pp. 155-162, 1968.

149c. Kataoka, S., Fujisada, H., 'Magnetoresistance Effect in InSb at 172
Millimeter Wavelength', *Solid-State Electronics*, 11, pp. 163-
171, 1968.

150. Kennedy, W. K., M.Sc. Thesis, Cornell University, U. S. A., 96
Sept. 1966.

150a. Kennedy, W. K., Eastman, L. F., 'High Power Pulsed Microwave 148
Generation in GaAs', *Proc. I.E.E.E.*, 55, p. 434, 1967.

150b. Kennedy, W. K., Eastman, L. F., Gilbert, R. J., 'LSA Operation 96, 148
of Large Volume Bulk GaAs Samples,' *I.E.E.E. Trans. El.Dev.*,
ED-14, pp. 500-504, 1967.

151. Khankina, S. I., Yakovenko, V. M., 'Excitation of Surface Electro- 141
magnetic Waves in Semiconductors', *Fizika Tverdogo Tela*, 9,
pp. 578-582, 1967. Transl: *Sov. Phys.-Sol. St.*, 9, p. 443, 1967.

152. Kheifets, M. I., 'Excitation of Electromagnetic Waves in Ionic 140
Semiconductors by an Electron Beam', *Fizika Tverdogo Tela*,
9, pp. 322-329, 1967, Transl: *Sov. Phys.-Sol. St.*, 9, p. 241,
1967.

153.	Kikuchi, M., 'Continuous Oscillation in CdSe Observed by Local	121
Illumination', *Jap. J. Appl. Phys.*, 2, p. 812, 1963.

153a. Kikuchi, M., 'Experimental Observations of Undamped Current	119
Oscillations in CdSe Single Crystals', *Jap. J. Appl. Phys.*, 3,
p. 448, 1964.

153b. Kikuchi, M., 'Current Saturation and Undamped Oscillation in	119
CdTe Single Crystals', *Jap. J. Appl. Phys.*, 4, p. 233,
1965.

153c. Kikuchi, M., Hayakawa, H., Abe, Y., 'Sound Velocity Transit of	121, 122
High-Field Domain in GaAs under Acoustoelectric Oscillation',
Jap. J. Appl. Phys., 5, p. 735, 1966.

153d. Kikuchi, M., Hayakawa, H., Abe, Y., 'Acoustoelectric Current	122
Oscillation in InSb and its Dependence on the Transverse
Magnetic Field', *Jap. J. Appl. Phys.*, 5, p. 1259, 1966.

153e. Kikuchi, M., Hayakawa, H., Abe, Y., 'Dependence of Acousto-	121, 122
electric Current Oscillation in InSb on Azimuthal Angle of
Transverse Magnetic Field', *Jap. J. Appl. Phys.*, 5, p. 1260,
1966.

153f. Kikuchi, M., Hayakawa, H., Abe, Y., 'Phonon-Piling-Up Mode of	127
Acoustoelectric Oscillation in InSb', *Solid State Comm.*, 5,
pp. 581-584, 1967.

153g. Kikuchi, M., Okada, M., Iizima, S., 'Comments on the Selection	121
of CdSe Crystals for Getting Good Acoustoelectric Current
Oscillations', *Jap. J. Appl. Phys.*, 6, p. 658, 1967.

154.	Kikuchi, Y., Chubachi, N., Iinuma, K., 'Temperature Dependence	118
of Ultrasonic Amplification in Cadmium Sulfide', *Jap. J. Appl.
Phys.*, 5, p. 835, 1966.

154a. Kikuchi, Y., Chubachi, N., Iinuma, K., 'Temperature Dependence	120
of Electron Drift Mobility for Ultrasonic Amplification in
CdS. in Relation to Electron Trapping Effects', *Jap. J. Appl.
Phys.*, 6, p. 1251, 1967.

155.	Kikvidze, R.R., Rukhadze, A. A., Fetisov, E. P., 'Excitation of	140
Electromagnetic Waves in a Solid-State Plasma in the Presence
of a Negative Current-Voltage Characteristic', *Fizika Tverdogo
Tela*, 9, pp. 1349-1356, 1967, Transl: *Sov. Phys.-Sol. St.*, 9,
p. 1055, 1967.

156.	King, G., Wasse, M. P., 'High-Power Gunn-Effect Oscillators	142, 144
Using Expitaxial GaAs', *Electronics L.*, 2, pp. 314-315, 1966.

156a. King, G., Wasse, M. P., Sandbank, C. P., 'An Assessment of	164
Epitaxial Gallium Arsenide for Use in Gunn-Effect Devices',
Proc. Internat. Symp. on Gallium Arsenide, Reading, England,
Sept. 1966, Inst. Phys. and Phys. Soc., London, Conf., Series
3, pp. 184-188.

156b. King, G., Wasse, M. P., 'Frequency Modulation of Gunn-Effect	144
Oscillators', *I.E.E.E. Trans. El.Dev.*, ED-14, p. 717, 1967.

157.	Kino, G. S., Route, R., 'Sound Wave Interactions in InSb', *Appl.
Phys. L.*, 11, p. 312, 1967.	127

158. Kirsch, J., Miller, P. B., 'Doppler-shifted Cyclotron Resonance   136
     and Alfvén Wave Damping in Bismuth', *Phys. Rev. L.*, **9**,
     p. 421, 1962.
159. Klozenberg, J. P., McNamara, B., Thonemann, P. C., 'The Dis-   133
     persion and Attenuation of Helicon Waves in a Uniform
     Cylindrical Plasma', *J. Fluid Mech.*, **21**, p. 545, 1965.
160. Knight, S., 'Heat Flow in n^{++}–n–n^+ Epitaxial GaAs Bulk Effect   165
     Devices', *Proc. I.E.E.E.* **55**, p. 112, 1967.
161. Köchner, W., 'Experimentelle Untersuchung der Zweistrom-   125
     Instabilität in InSb', *Archiv. El. Übertr.*, **19**, pp. 619-628,
     1965.
162. Kohn, A. N., 'New Microwave Emission Effect in InSb', *Proc.*   126
     I.E.E.E., **55**, p. 695, 1967.
163. Konstantinov, O. V., Perel. V. I., 'Possible Transmission of   131
     Electromagnetic Waves Through A Metal in a Strong Magnetic
     Field', *J. Exptl. Theor. Phys. (U.S.S.R.)*, **38**, p. 161, 1960,
     Transl: *Sov. Phys. J.E.T.P.*, **11**, p. 171, 1960.
164. Krömer, H., 'The Physical Principle of a Negative-Mass Amplifier',   140
     Proc. I.R.E., **47**, p. 397, 1959.
164a. Krömer, H., 'Detailed Theory of the Negative Conductance of   94
     Bulk Negative Mobility Amplifiers, in the Limit of Zero Ion
     Density', *I.E.E.E.*, *Trans. El.Dev.*, **ED-14**, pp. 476-492,
     1967.
165. Kurokawa, K., 'Transient Behaviour of High-Field Domains in   82
     Bulk Semiconductors', *Proc. I.E.E.E.*, *Letters*, **55**, pp. 1615-
     1617, 1967.
166. Kuru, I., 'Frequency Modulation of the Gunn Oscillator', *Proc.*   144
     I.E.E.E., **53**, p. 1642, 1965.
166a. Kuru, I., Robson, P. N., Kino, G. S., 'Some Measurements of the   84
     Steady State and Transient Characteristics of High-Field
     Dipole Domains in GaAs', *I.E.E.E. Trans. El.Dev.*, **ED-15**,
     pp. 21-29, 1968.
167. Langenberg, D. N., Scalapino, D. J., Taylor, B. N., 'The Josephson   141
     Effects', *Scientific American*, **214**, p. 30, 1966.
168. Larrabee, R. D., Steele, M. C., 'The Oscillistor–New Type of   137, 138
     Semiconductor Oscillator', *J. Appl. Phys.*, **31**, p. 1519,
     1960.
168a. Larrabee, R. D., 'Observation of Microwave Emission from InSb',   125, 126
     Bull. Amer. Phys. Soc., Ser. II, **9**, No. 3, p. 258, 1964.
168b. Larrabee, R. D., Hicinbothem Jr. W. A., 'Observation of Micro-   125, 126
     wave Emission from Indium Antimonide', Proc. Internat. Conf.
     Phys. Semicond., vol. 2: 'Plasma Effects in Solids', Paris, 1964,
     Academic Press, New York, and Dunod, Paris, paper P.E.-21,
     pp. 181-187.
168c. Larrabee, R. D., Hicinbothem, W. A., 'Current Oscillations and   126
     Microwave Emission in InSb', *I.E.E.E. Trans. El.Dev.*, **ED-13**,
     pp. 121-131, 1966.

168d. Larrabee, R. D., Hicinbothem, W. A., 'A Laminar Slow-Wave   172
       Coupler and Its Application to InSb', *I.E.E.E. Trans. Microw.
       Theory and Techn.* **MTT-15**, p. 382, 1967.
169. Larson, P. K. Saermark, K., 'Helicon Excitation of Acoustic   136
       Waves in Al.' *Phys. L.,* **24A**, p. 374, 1967.
170. Lee, C. A., Batdorf, R. L., Wiegmann, W., Kaminsky, G., 'The   101
       Read Diode—an Avalanching, Transit-Time Negative-Resistance
       Oscillator', *Appl. Phys. L.,* **6**, p. 89, 1965.
170a. Lee, C. A., Batdorf, R. L., Wiegmann, W., Kaminsky, G., 'Techno-   101
       logical Developments Evolving from Research on Read Diodes',
       I.E.E.E. Trans. El.Dev., **ED-13**, pp. 175-180, 1966.
170b. Lee, C. A., Batdorf, R. L., Wiegmann, W., Kaminsky, G., 'Time   110
       Dependence of Avalanche Processes in Silicon', *J. Appl. Phys.,*
       38, pp. 2787-2796, 1967.
170c. Lee, C. A., Batdorf, R. L., Wiegmann, W., Kaminsky, G., 'Analysis   110
       of the Q-Factor, Efficiency, Stability and the Design of Read
       Structures in the Nonlinear Range', *J. Appl. Phys.,* **38**, pp.
       2797-2809, 1967.
171. Libchaber, A., Veilex, R., 'Wave Propagation in a Gyro-   132
       magnetic Solid Conductor: Helicon Waves', *Phys. Rev.,* **127**,
       p. 774, 1962.
172. Lightowlers, E. C., Dean, P. J., 'An Efficient Method for Selecting 166
       Type II and Intermediate-Type Diamonds', *Industrial Diamond
       Rev.,* **25**, p. 143, 1965.
173. Liu, S. G., 'Infrared and Microwave Radiations Associated with a   99
       Current-Controlled Instability in GaAs', *Appl. Phys. L.,* **9**,
       pp. 79-81, 1966.
174. Llewellyn, F. B., Peterson, L. C., 'Vacuum Tube Networks',   111
       Proc. I.R.E., **32**, pp. 144-166, 1944.
175. de Loach, B. C., Johnston, R. L., 'Avalanche Transit-Time Micro- 111, 114
       wave Oscillators and Amplifiers', *I.E.E.E. Trans. El.Dev.,*
       ED-13, p. 181, 1966.
175a. de Loach, B. C., 'Recent Advances in Solid-State Microwave   78
       Generators', *Advances in Microwaves,* **2**, ed. L. Young,
       Academic Press, N. Y., U.S.A., 1967.
176. Ludwig, G. W., 'Gunn-Effect in CdTe', *I.E.E.E. Trans. El.Dev.,*   80
       ED-14, pp. 547-551, 1967.
176a. Ludwig, G. W., Aven, M., 'Gunn Effect In ZnSe', *J. Appl. Phys.,*   80
       38, pp. 5326-5331, 1967.
177. Lyamov, V. E., Sapogin, L. G., 'Trapping of Particles by Waves',   123
       Zh. Technich. Fiziki, **37**, pp. 624-632, 1967, Transl: *Sov.
       Phys.-Techn. Phys.,* **12**, pp. 449-454, 1967.
178. Magarshack, J., 'Gunn Oscillator Used as a Phased-Array Aerial   148
       Element', *Electr. L.,* **3**, pp. 556-557, 1967.
179. Mahrous, S., Robson, P. N., Hartnagel, H. L., 'The Stability and   93, 94,
       Reflection Gain of Subcritically Doped Gunn Diodes',   96
       Sol. State Electronics, **11**, pp. 965-977, 1968.

179a. Mahrous, S., Hartnagel, H. L., 'Gunn Effect Domain Formation   94
Controlled by a Complex Load' *Brit. J. Appl. Phys. Ser. 2*,
2, pp. 1-5, 1969.

180. Maines, J. D., 'Measurement of the Spatial Variation of Electric   118
Field in Amplifying CdS. Using the Electrooptic Effect',
Appl. Phys. L., 8, p. 67, 1966.

180a. Maines, J. D., 'Ultra-High Frequency Oscillations in Amplifying   122
CdS', *Sol. State Comm.*, 5, p. 271, 1967.

180b. Maines, J. D., Paige, E. G. S., 'Acoustoelectric U.H.F. Oscillator: 122, 171
Frequency Modulation', *Electronics L.*, 3, p. 459, 1967.

180c. Maines, J. D., Marshall, F. G., Paige, E. G. S., Stuart, R. A., 122, 171
'Gigahertz Acoustoelectric Oscillations in ZnO', *Phys. L.*,
26A, p. 388, 1968.

181. Manasse, F. K., Shapiro, J. S., 'Current-Dependent Modes in   114
Pulsed Avalanche Diodes', *Proc. I.E.E.E.*, 55, p. 702, 1967.

182. Many, A., Balberg, I., 'Field Distribution in Semiconducting CdS.   120
Under Acoustic Gain Conditions', *Phys. L.*, 21, p. 486, 1966.

183. Mason, I. M., Farvis, W. E. J., 'High-Frequency Current Oscilla-   118
tions in Vapour-Deposited CdS. Thin Films', *Electronics L.*,
3, p. 247, 1967.

184. Matino, H., Kuru, I. 'Reactance of GaAs Bulk Oscillator', *Proc.*   147
I.E.E.E., 54, p. 291, 1966.

185. Mauro, R., Wang, W. C., 'Multiple-Wave Interactions in Piezo-   118
electric Semiconductors', *Phys. Rev. L.*, 19, p. 693, 1967.

186. Maxfield, B. W., 'The Damping of Helicon Resonances in Pure   136
Type II Superconductors', *Sol. State Comm.*, 5, p. 585, 1967.

187. McCumber, D. E., Chynoweth, A. G., 'Theory of Negative-Con-   93
ductance Amplification and of Gunn Instabilities in "Two-
Valley" Semiconductors', *I.E.E.E. Trans. El.Dev.*, ED-13,
pp. 4-21, 1966.

188. McGroddy, J. C., Nathan, M. I., 'A New Current Instability in 80, 140
n-Type Germanium', *I.B.M. J. Res. and Dev.*, 11, p. 337, 1967.

189. McFee, J. H., Tien, P. K., 'Acoustoelectric Current Distribution   120
and Current Saturation in CdS.', *J. Appl. Phys.*, 37, pp. 2754-
2763, 1966.

189a. McFee, J. H., Tien, P. K., Hodges, H. L., 'Transient Approach to 120, 121
Current Saturation in Photoconductive CdS.', *J. Appl. Phys.*,
38, pp. 1721-1729, 1967.

190. McNeill, P. R., 'Instabilities in a Drifting Semiconductor Plasma',   127
Proc. I.E.E.E., 54, p. 1596, 1966.

191. McWhorter, A. L., May, W. G., 'Acoustic Plasma Waves in Semi-   124
metals', *I.B.M. Journal*, p. 285, 1964.

191a. McWhorter, A. L., Foyt, A. G., 'Bulk GaAs Negative Conductance   93
Amplifiers', *Appl. Phys. L.*, 9, pp. 300-302, 1966.

192. Melngailis, I., Rediker, R. H., 'The Madistor—A Magnetically-Con-   138
trolled Semiconductor Plasma Device', *Proc. I.R.E.*, 50,
p. 2428, 1962.

193. Merrett, G., Carroll, J. E., 'The Use of Airbrasion in the Con-   166
struction of Gunn Diodes', Proc. Int. Symp. On GaAs, Inst.
Phys. and Phys. Soc., London, England, Conf. Series No. 3
Reading, England, pp. 193-196, 1966.

194. Mikoshiba, N., 'Interaction of Conduction Electrons with Acoustic   116
Waves in Many-Valley Semiconductors', *J. Phys. Soc. Japan,* **15,**
p. 1189, 1960

195. Miller, P. B., Haering, R. R., 'Cyclotron Resonance in Metals with   136
H Perpendicular to the Surface', *Phys. Rev.,* **128,** pp. 126-
130, 1962.

195a. Miller, P. B., 'Giant Oscillatory Attenuation of Helicon and Alfvén   136
Waves', *Phys. Rev. L.,* **11,** p. 537, 1963.

195b. Miller, P. B., Kwok, P. C., 'Quantum Oscillations in Helicon   136
Attenuation', *Phys. Rev.,* **161,** pp. 629-632, 1967.

196. Misawa, T., 'Transverse Instabilities in Solid-State Plasmas under   134
Steady Electric and Magnetic Fields', *Jap. J. Appl. Phys.,* **2,**
p. 500, 1963.

196a. Misawa, T., 'Negative Resistance in p-n Junctions under Avalanche   99, 103,
Breakdown Conditions', Parts I & II. *I.E.E.E. Trans. El.Dev.,*   109, 110,
ED-13, p. 137, and 143, 1966.   111

196b. Misawa, T., 'Multiple Uniform Layer Approximation in Analysis   111
of Negative Resistance in p-n Junction in Breakdown', *I.E.E.E.
Trans. El.Dev.,* **ED-14,** pp. 795-808, 1967.

197. Miya, M., Terai, M., 'Microwave Emission from CdS.', *Jap. J.*   122
Appl. Phys. **5,** p. 186, 1966.

198. Miyai, Y., Nakashima, S., 'Theory of Spiral Instabilities in Semi-   139
conductor Plasmas in Transverse Magnetic Fields', *J. Phys. Soc.
Jap.,* **21,** p. 106, 1966.

198a. Miyai, Y., Nakashima, S., 'Spiral Instabilities in Semiconductor   139
Plasmas', *J. Phys. Soc. Japan,* **21,** p. 1142, 1966.

199. Miyake, T., 'Carrier and Potential Distribution at High Electric   120
Field in Semiconductive CdS.', *Jap. J. Appl. Phys.,* **5,** p. 728,
1966.

199a. Miyake, T., Onuki, M., 'High-Field Hall Effect of Semiconducting   121
CdS.', *Appl. Phys. L.,* **10,** p. 128, 1967.

200. Mizushima, Y., Okamoto, Y., 'Properties of Avalanche Injection   115
and Its Application to Fast Pulse Generation and Switching',
I.E.E.E. Trans. El.Dev., **ED-14,** pp. 146-157, 1967.

201. Moore, A. R., 'Acoustoelectric Current Saturation in CdS. as a   120
Fluctuation Process', *J. Appl. Phys.,* **38,** pp. 2327-2339,
1967.

202. Moore, R. M., de Pian, L., 'The Effective Elastic Constant Theory   116
of Acoustic Amplification', *Proc. I.E.E.E.,* **55,** p. 107, 1967.

202a. Moore, R. M., de Pian, L., 'The Coupled-Mode Theory of Acoustic   116
Amplification', *Proc. I.E.E.E.,* **55,** pp 238, 1967.

202.1. Morgan, D. P., 'Helicon Waves in Solids', *phys. stat. sol.* **24,** pp.   131
9-36, 1967.

203. Morisaki, H., Inuishi, Y., 'Hall Mobility and Microwave Emission   126
in InSb Plasma', *Jap. J. Appl. Phys.*, **5**, p. 637, 1966.

203a. Morisaki, H., Inuishi, Y., 'Two Types of Microwave Emission from   126
InSb', *J. Phys. Soc. Jap.*, **23**, pp. 269-275, 1967.

204. Müller, G. O., Peibst, H., Schürer, E., Thiel, H., 'The Influence of   122
High-Phonon Flux Densities on the X-Ray Reflectivity of
Nearly Ideal CdS. Crystals', *phys. stat. sol.*, **20**, p. K173, 1967.

205. Muravskii, B. S., Gusakov, V. S., Kruzhilina, N. G., Shved, A. G.,   140
'Current Oscillations in Compensated Ge and Si.', *Fizika
Tverdogo Tela*, **7**, p. 3412, 1965, Transl: *Sov. Phys.-Sol. St.* **7**,
p. 2478, 1966.

206. Musha, T., Bers, A., 'Stimulated Emission of Phonons by Electrons   127
Drifting along the Magnetic Field', Quart. Progr. Rpt. No. 79,
M.I.T. Res. Lab. of Electronics, P. 99, 1965.

206a. Musha, T., Lindvall, F., Hagglund, J., 'Microwave Emission from   126, 127
InSb for Low Electric Fields', *Appl. Phys. L.*, **8**, pp. 157-159,
1966.

207. Nag, B. R., Engineer, M. H., 'On A Method for Measurement of   140
Microwave Hall Mobility of Semiconductors', *Int J. Electronics*, **18**, p. 529, 1965.

208. Nakashima, S., 'Spiral Instabilities in Semiconductor Plasmas in   139
Transverse Magnetic Fields', *J. Phys. Soc. Jap.*, **21**, p. 100,
1966.

209. Nanney, C. A., Libchaber, A., Garno, J. P., 'Helicon Drift Current   133, 135
Interaction in a Layered Semiconductor Structure', *Appl. Phys.
L.*, **9**, p. 395, 1966.

210. van Nieuwland, J. M., Vlaardingerbroek, M. T., 'Cyclotron Waves   130
in InSb', *I.E.E.E. Trans. El.Dev.*, **ED-14**, pp. 596-599, 1967.

211. Nordbotton, A., 'Gunn Oscillator with one Electrode Split',   163
I.E.E.E. Trans. El.Dev., **ED-14**, p. 608, 1967.

212. Ogawa, T., Kojima, A., 'Changes in Piezoelectric Constants of a   118
CdS. Crystal due to Carrier Injection', *Appl. Phys. L.*, **8**, p.294,
1966.

213. Ogg, N. R., 'Acoustic Amplification in Materials with Strain-   123
Dependent Dielectric Constants', *Phys. L.*, **24A**, p. 472,
1967.

214. Ohkubo, K., Yanai, H., 'Read-Type Oscillations from Silicon   114
pvn Diodes', *Proc. I.E.E.E.*, **55**, p. 1761, 1967.

215. Ohmi, T., 'A Limitation on Frequency of Gunn Effect due to the   88
Intervalley Scattering Time', *Proc. I.E.E.E.*, **55**, p. 1739, 1967.

216. Okada, J., Matino, H., 'Continuous Oscillations of Acoustoelec-   119
tric Current in CdS.', *Jap. J. Appl. Phys.*, **3**, p. 698, 1964.

217. Oliver, B. M., Pierce, J. R., Shannon, C. E., 'The Philosophy of   153
P.C.M.', *Proc. I.R.E.*, p. 1324, 1948.

218. Oliver, M. R., McWhorter, A. L., Foyt, A. G., 'Current Runaway   111
and Avalanche Effects in n-CdTe.', *Appl. Phys. L.*, **11**, p. 111,
1967.

219. Owens, J., Kino, G. S., 'Avalanche Effects in Gunn Diodes',   161, 164
    Solid State Device Res. Conf. June 1967, Santa Barbara,
    California, Summary: *I.E.E.E. Trans. El.Dev.*, **ED-14**, p. 629,
    1967.

220. Ozaki, H., Mikoshiba, N., 'Nonlinear Theory of Current Satura-   120
    tion in Piezoelectric Semiconductors', *J. Phys. Soc. Jap.*, **21**,
    pp. 2486-2496, 1966.

221. Paranjape, B. V., Paranjape, V. V., 'Density Waves in an Electron-   140
    Hole Plasma', *J. Phys. Chem. Solids*, **28**, p. 2106, 1967.

222. Pekar, S. I., 'Electron-Phonon Interaction Proportional to the   123
    External Applied Field and Sound Amplification in Semicon-
    ductors', *J. Exp. Theoret, Phys. (U.S.S.R.)*, **49**, pp. 621-629,
    1965. Translation in: *Sov. Phys. J.E.T.P.* **22**, p. 431, 1966.

223. Petzinger, K., Hahn, A., Matzelle, A., 'CW Three Terminal GaAs   163
    Oscillator', Internat. Electron Devices Meeting, Washington
    D.C., Oct. 1966.

224. Pines, D., Schrieffer, J.R., 'Collective Behaviour in Solid-State   124
    Plasmas', *Phys. Rev.*, **124**, p. 1387, 1961.

225. Poehler, T. O., Apel, J. R., Hochberg, A. K., 'Millimeter Wave   126
    Radiation from InSb', *Appl. Phys. L.*, **10**, p. 244, 1967.

225a. Poehler, T. O., 'Temperature Dependence of Microwave Emission   126
    from InSb', *Appl. Phys. L.*, **10**, p. 356, 1967.

226. Pogorelova, N. N., 'Active Ultrasonic Delay Line', *Radio Eng. and*   169
    Electronic Phys. pp. 498-500, 1967.

227. Pohlendt, E., Wettling, W., 'Velocity of Electron-Phonon Packets   121
    in Low Resistivity CdS. Crystals', *Phys. L.*, **25A**, p. 22,
    1967.

228. Pollmann, H., Bosch, B. G., 'Frequency Division with Power Gain   146
    in Gunn Oscillators', *Electronics Letters*, **3**, p. 513, 1967.

228a. Pollmann, H., Bosch, B. G., 'Injection Priming of Pulsed Gunn   146
    Oscillators', *I.E.E.E. Trans. El.Dev.*, **ED-14**, p. 609, 1967.

229. Pomerantz, M., 'Amplification of Microwave Phonons in   115, 116
    Germanium', *Phys. Rev. L.*, **13**, p. 308, 1964.

230. Prager, H. J., Chang, K. K. N., Weisbrod, S., 'High-Power, High-   113, 167
    Efficiency Si Avalanche Diodes at Ultra High Frequencies',
    Proc. I.E.E.E., **55**, p. 586, 1967.

231. Prohofsky, E. W., 'Acoustoelectric Saturation of Ultrasonic Gain',   118
    Phys. L., **24A**, p. 342, 1967.

232. Proklov, V. V., Kreinin, O. L., Morozov, A. L., Bondarenko, V.S.,   169
    'Ultrasonic Transducers Employing a Depletion Layer in
    CdS.', *Rad. Eng. and Electr. Phys.* pp. 831-834, 1966.

233. Quentin, G., Thuillier, J. M., 'Contribution of Acoustoelectric   120
    Current to Current Saturation in Piezoelectric Semiconductors',
    Phys. L., **23**, p. 42, 1966.

234. Ramachandran, T. B., Santosuosso, R. P., 'Contacting n-Type   165
    High Resistivity GaAs for Gunn Oscillators', *Sol. St. Electro-*
    nics, **9**, pp. 733-734, 1966.

235. Rannestad, A., 'Current Saturation and Trap-Controlled Electron   120
     Drift Mobility in Photo-conductive CdS.', *Phys. Rev.*, 155, pp.
     744-749, 1967.

236. Read, Jr., W. T., 'A Proposed High-Frequency Negative-Resist-   99, 101,
     ance Diode', *Bell Syst. Techn. J.*, 37, p. 401, 1958.   109, 111,
                                                                         167

237. Reed, W. A., Meincke, P. P. M., 'Excitation of Helicon Waves   132
     in Copper by an Alternating Current', *Phys. Rev.*, 163,
     pp. 664-666, 1967.

238. Ridley, B. K., Watkins, T. B., 'The Possibility of Negative Resist- 78
     ance Effects in Semiconductors', *Proc. Phys. Soc.*, 78, pp.
     293-304, 1961.

238a. Ridley, B. K., 'The Inhibition of Negative Resistance Dipole   88, 93,
     Waves and Domains in n-GaAs', *I.E.E.E., Trans. El.Dev.*,   94
     ED-13, pp. 41-43, 1966.

238b. Ridley, B. K., Wisbey, P. H., 'Non-Linear Theory of Electrical   82
     Domains in the Presence of Trapping', *Brit. J. Appl. Phys.*,
     18, pp. 761-771, 1967.

239. Robertson, G. I., Ash, E. A., 'Acoustic Amplification in CdS. with 119, 170
     Space- and Time-Varying Parameters', *Electronics L.*, 3,
     p. 427, 1967.

240. Robinson, B. B., Swartz, G. A., 'Two-Stream Instability in Semi-   125
     conductor Plasmas', *J. Appl. Phys.*, 38, pp. 2461-2465,
     1967.

240a. Robinson, B. B., 'A Collision-Induced Instability in Semiconduc-   127
     tor Plasmas', *R.C.A. Rev.*, p. 366, 1967.

241. Robson, P. N., Mahrous, S. M., 'Some Aspects of Gunn Effect   144
     Oscillators', *The Radio and Electronic Engineer*, 30, pp. 345-
     352, 1965.

241a. Robson, P. N., Kino, G. S., Fay, B., 'Two-Port Microwave   146
     Amplification in Long Samples of GaAs', *I.E.E.E. Trans.
     El.Dev.*, ED-14, p. 612, 1967.

242. Route, R., Kino, G. S., 'Phonon Interactions in InSb', *I.E.E.E.*   127
     Trans, El.Dev., ED-14, p. 630, 1967. (Paper given at Sol. St.
     Dev. Res. Conf., 1967, Santa Barbara, Calif.).

243. Ruch, J. G., Kino, G. S., 'Measurement of the Velocity-Field   82
     Characteristics of GaAs', *Appl. Phys. L.*, 10, p. 40, 1967.

244. Saermark, K., Larsen, P. K., 'Helicons and Acoustic Shear Waves   136
     in Al.', *Phys. L.*, 24A, p. 668, 1967.

245. Sandbank, C. P., 'Synthesis of Complex Electronic Functions by   153, 161,
     Solid-State Bulk Effects', *Sol.-St. Electronics*, 10, p. 369, 1967. 164

246. Sasaki, A., Takagi, T., 'Conditions for Space-Charge-Wave Growth   94
     and Differential Negative Resistance in "Two-Valley" Semi-
     conductors', *Proc. I.E.E.E.*, 55, p. 732, 1967.

247. Saunders, L. M., Baraff, G. A., Buchsbaum, S. J., 'High-Frequency   135
     Behaviour of the Surface-Wave Helicon Instability', *J. Appl.
     Phys.*, 37, pp. 2935-2936, 1966.

247a. Saunders, L. M., Baraff, G. A., 'Surface-Wave Instability in Heli-   135
con-Wave Propagation, III: Theory of Multilayered Struc-
tures', *J. Appl. Phys.* **37**, pp. 4551-4556, 1966.

248. Sawamoto, K., 'Cyclotron Resonance in CdS.', *J. Phys. Soc. Jap.,*   137
19, pp. 318-322, 1964.

249. Scherer, E. F., 'Large-Signal Amplification with Avalanche   114, 167
Devices' *Proc. I.E.E.E.,* **55**, p. 464, 1967.

249.1. Schilz, W., 'Experimental Evidence of Bulk Helicon-Phonon   136
Coupling in PbTe', *Phys. Rev. L.,* **20**, pp. 104-105,
1968.

249.2. Schulz, M., 'Helical Density Waves and The Oscillistor Effect   138
in the Electron Hole Plasma of the n-Type Ge, (Theory)',
phys. stat. sol. **25**, pp. 521-530, 1968.

250. Seifert, F., Pötzl, H. W., 'The Influence of a Transverse Electric   136
Field on Helicon Wave Propagation in InSb at 35 GHz', *Proc.
I.E.E.E.,* **55**, p. 1499, 1967.

251. Sewell, K. G., Boatner, L. A., 'Multimode Operation in Gunn   99
Oscillators Induced by Cooling and Illumination', *Proc.
I.E.E.E.,* **55**, p. 1228, 1967.

252. Shaw, M. P., Shuskus, A. J., 'Current Instability above the Gunn   96
Threshold', *Proc. I.E.E.E.,* **54**, pp. 1580-1581, 1966.

253. Shaw, R. C., Stover, H. L., 'Phase-Locked Avalanche Diode   113, 168
Oscillators', *Proc. I.E.E.E.,* **54**, p. 710, 1966.

254. Sher, A., Thornber, K. K., 'Resonant Electron-Phonon Scattering   82
in Polar Semiconductors', *Appl. Phys. L.,* **11**, p. 3, 1967.

255. Shockley, W., 'Negative Resistance Arising from Transit-Time in   111
Semiconductor Diodes', *Bell Syst. Techn J.,* **33**, pp. 799-826,
1954.

255a. Shockley, W., Copeland, J. A., James, P. R., 'The Impedance Field   143
Method of Noise Calculation in Active Semiconductor Devices',
Quantum Mechanics of Atoms, Molecules and the Solid State,
ed. P.O. Lowdin, Academic Press, N. Y., pp. 537-563,
1966.

256. Shoji, M., 'Small-Signal Impedance of Bulk Semiconductor   94
Amplifier Having a Nonuniform Doping Profile', *I.E.E.E. Trans.
El.Dev.,* **ED-14**, pp. 323-329, 1967.

256a. Shoji, M., 'Functional Bulk Semiconductor Oscillators', *I.E.E.E.*   161
Trans. El.Dev., **ED-14**, pp. 535-547, 1967.

257. Shyam, M., Allen, J. W., Pearson, G. L., 'Effect of Variation of   79, 80
Energy Minima Separation on Gunn Oscillations', *I.E.E.E.,
Trans. El.Dev.,* **ED-13**, p. 63, 1966.

258. Sliva. P., Bray, R., 'Oscillatory Current Behaviour in GaSb and its   122
Relation to Spontaneous Generation and Amplification of
Ultrasonic Flux', *Phys. Rev. L.,* **14**, p. 372, 1965.

258.1. Snapp, C. P., Stark, L. A., Höfflinger, B., 'Experimental Analysis   111
of High-Efficiency Avalanche-Resonance Pumped Oscillators',
Electronics L., **4**, pp. 595-596, 1968.

259. Socci, R. J., Fleri, D. A., 'Relative Phase Shift in Frequency-Locked Avalanche Oscillators', *Proc. I.E.E.E.*, **55**, p. 1649, 1967.   114

260. Solymar, L., 'Gain Mechanisms of Acoustic Amplification', *Solid State Electronics*, **9**, pp. 879-884, 1966.   116

260a. Solymar, L., Ash, E. A., 'Acoustic and Electromagnetic Interaction with Arbitrary Collision Frequencies', Internat. Conf. Microwave Behaviour, Ferrimagn. and Plasmas, London, England, 1965. *I.E.E. Conf. Proc.* pp. 84-1 to 84-5, Sept. 1965.   119

260b. Solymar, L., Lashmore-Davies, C. N., 'Interaction of Helicon Waves with Longitudinal Carrier Waves when the Applied Magnetic Field is at an Angle to the Direction of Carrier Drift', 6th Internat. Conf. Microw. Opt. Gen. Ampl. (MOGA), Cambridge, England, 1966, paper 22/4.   135

261. Southgate, P. D., 'Recombination Processes Following Impact Ionization by High-Field Domains in Gallium Arsenide', *J. Appl. Phys.*, **38**, pp. 4589-4595, 1967.   82, 99, 164

261a. Southgate, P. D., 'Laser Action in Field-Ionized Bulk GaAs', *Appl. Phys. L.*, **12**, p. 61, 1968.   99, 164

262. Spector, H. N., 'Amplification of Microwave Phonons in a Many-Valley Semiconductor', *Appl. Phys. L.*, **7**, p. 82, 1965.   116

262a. Spector, H. N., 'Solution of the Boltzmann Equation for Electrons Interacting with Acoustic Waves in Strong Electric Fields', *Phys. Rev.*, **165**, pp. 562-565, 1968.   116

263. Stanley I. W., 'Damping of Sustained Current Oscillations in Semiconducting CdS. at High Fields', *Appl. Phys. L.*, **10**, p. 76, 1967.   121

263.1. Steele, M. C., 'Magnetic Field Effect on Acoustoelectric Gain in Semiconductors', *RCA Rev.*, **28**, pp. 58-63, 1967.   123, 127

264. Stix, T. H., 'Theory of Plasma Waves', N. York, McGraw-Hill, 1962.   129

265. Streetman, B. G., Blouke, M. M., Holonyak, Jr. N., 'Current Oscillations in Co-Doped Si PIN Structures', *Appl. Phys. L.*, **11**, p. 200, 1967.   140

266. Sugimoto, S., 'Up-Conversion with Gunn-Effect Diode', *Proc. I.E.E.E.*, **55**, p. 1520, 1967.   147

266a. Sugimoto, S., 'Millimeter-Wave Amplification by Avalanching Varactor Diodes', *Proc. I.E.E.E. Letters*, **55**, p. 2165, 1967.   114

267. Suhl, H., Shockley, W., 'Concentrating Holes and Electrons by Magnetic Fields', *Phys. Rev.*, **75**, p. 1617, 1949.   127

268. Sumi, M., 'Current Oscillations by Coherent Excitation of Optical Phonons', *I.E.E.E. Trans. El.Dev.*, **ED-13**, p. 53, 1966.   123

268a. Sumi, M., 'Travelling-Wave Amplification by Drifting Carriers in Semiconductors', *Jap. J. Appl. Phys.*, **6**, pp. 688-698, 1967.   140

269. Suzuki, K., 'The Generation of Microwave Radiation from InSb', *Jap. J. Appl. Phys.*, **4**, p. 42, 1965.   126, 139

270. Suzuki, T., 'Microwave Emission and Low-Frequency Instabilities   126
       in InSb', *Jap. J. Appl. Phys.*, **4**, p. 700, 1965.
270a. Suzuki, T., 'Instabilities of Semiconductor Plasmas in Crossed   127
       Electric and Magnetic Fields', *J. Phys. Soc. Jap.*, **21**, pp. 2000-
       2010, 1966.
271. Swan, C. B., Misawa, T., Bricker, C. H., 'Continuous Oscillations at   113
       mm Wavelengths with Si Avalanche Diodes', *Proc. I.E.E.E.*,
       55, p. 1747, 1967.
271a. Swan, C. B., 'The Importance of Providing a Good Heat Sink for   113
       Avalanching Transit-Time Oscillator Diodes', *Proc. I.E.E.E.*,
       p. 451. 1967.
271b. Swan, C. B., 'Improved Performance of Si Avalanche Oscillators   113
       Mounted on Diamond Heat Sinks', *Proc. I.E.E.E.*, p. 1617,
       1967.
271c. Swan, C. B., Misawa, T., Marinaccio, L., 'Composite Avalanche   166
       Diode Structures for Increased Power Capability . *I.E.E.E.*
       Trans. El.Dev., **ED-14**, pp. 584-589, 1967.
272. Swartz, G. A., Robinson, B. B., 'Coherent Microwave Emission   126
       from InSb Structures', *Appl. Phys. L.*, **9**, p. 232, 1966.
272a. Swartz, G. A., 'Microwave Power Coupling to the Helicon Mode   172
       in Indium Antimonide', *RCA. Rev.*, **29**, pp. 64-74, 1968.
273. Takagi, T., Mizushima, Y., 'Properties of Breakdown and Switch-   119
       ing in CdS. Single Crystals', *Proc. I.E.E.E.*, **55**, p. 477, 1967.
274. Tan, B. T. G., 'Hot-Carrier InSb Microwave Modulation', *Electro-*   172
       nics L., **3**, p. 504, 1967.
275. Tarnay, K., 'The Domain Transit-Time in Gunn-Diodes', *Proc.*   82
       I.E.E.E., Letters, **54**, pp. 2001-2002, 1966.
276. Terai, M., Miya, M., 'Microwave Emission from CdS.' *Jap. J. Appl.*   122
       Phys., **6**, p. 896, 1967.
277. Thim, H. W., Barber, M. R., Hakki, B. W., Knight, S., Uenohora,   93, 146
       M., 'Microwave Amplification in a Bulk Semiconductor',
       Appl. Phys. L., **7**, p. 167, 1965.
277a. Thim, H. W., Barber, M. R., 'Microwave Amplification in a GaAs   146
       Bulk Semiconductor', *I.E.E.E. Trans. El.Dev.*, **ED-13**, pp. 110-
       114, 1966.
277b. Thim, H. W., Potential Distribution and Field-Dependence of   82
       Electron Velocity in Bulk GaAs Measured with a Point-Contact
       Probe', *Electronics L.*, **2**, pp. 403-405, 1966.
277c. Thim, H. W., 'Temperature Effects in Bulk GaAs Amplifiers',   94
       I.E.E.E. Trans. El.Dev., **ED-14**, pp. 59-62, 1967.
277d. Thim, H. W., 'Linear Negative Conductance Amplification with   99
       Gunn Oscillators', *Proc. I.E.E.E.*, **55**, pp. 446-447, 1967.
277e. Thim, H. W., Knight, S., 'Carrier Generation and Switching   99
       Phenomena in n-GaAs Devices', *Appl. Phys. L.*, **11**, pp.
       83-85, 1967.
277f. Thim, H. W., 'Linear Microwave Amplification with Gunn Oscilla-   146
       tors', *I.E.E.E. Trans. El.Dev.*, **ED-14**, pp. 517-522, 1967.

277g. Thim, H. W., Lehner, H. H., 'Linear Millimeter Wave Amplification   146, 147
with GaAs Waves', *Proc. I.E.E.E.*, **55**, p. 718, 1967.

277h. Thim, H. W., 'Computer Study of Bulk GaAs Devices with   98, 148
Random One-Dimensional Doping Fluctuations', *J. Appl.
Phys.*, **39**, pp. 3897-3904, 1968.

278. Toda, M., 'A Plasma Instability Induced by Electron-Hole Genera-   139
tion in Impact Ionization', *J. Appl. Phys.*, **37**, p. 32, 1966.

278a. Toda, M., 'Theory of a Microwave Plasma Instability due to   139
Transverse Breakdown' *J. Appl. Phys.*, **37**, p. 37, 1966.

279. Tokumaru, Y., Kikuchi, M., 'Current Saturation and Oscillation   121
in Photosensitive GaAs', *Jap. J. Appl. Phys.*, **6**, p. 654, 1967.

280. Tosima, S., Hirota, R., 'New Type of Two-Stream Plasma Insta-   125
bility', *J. Appl. Phys.*, **34**, p. 2993, 1963.

281. Trivelpiece, A. W., Gould, R. W., 'Space-Charge Waves in Cylin-   133
drical Plasma Columns', *J. Appl. Phys.*, **30**, p. 1784, 1959.

282. Trodden, W. G., 'Space-Charge-Limited Currents in CdS. with   120
more than one discrete Trapping Level', *Brit. J. Appl. Phys.*,
18, pp. 401-404, 1967.

283. Tsai, C. S., 'Elastic Wave and Infrared Light Interactions with a   170
Moving High-Field Domain in a Piezoelectric Semiconductor',
Appl. Phys. L., **9**, p. 400, 1966.

284. Turner, C. W., Crow, J., 'Acoustoelectric Oscillations with Field-   121, 122
Dependent Period in InSb', *Appl. Phys. L.*, **11**, p. 187, 1967.

284a. Turner, C. W., van Duzer, T., Weller, K., 'Acoustic-Wave Ampli-   123
fication in High-Mobility Semiconductors at Microwave Frequencies', *Electronics L.*, **3**, p. 162, 1967.

285. Val'd-Perlov, V. M., Krasilov, A. V., Tager, A. S., 'The Avalanch-   109, 110,
ing Transit-Time Diode—A New Semiconductor Microwave   113, 166,
Device', *Radiotechn. i Elektron.*, **11**, pp. 2008-2023, 1966.   167, 168
Transl: *Rad. Eng. and Electron. Phys.*, **11**, pp. 1764-1777,
1966.

286. Vasile, C. F., Sucher, M., 'Convenient Method of Studying   136
Helicon Waves in Solids' *Electronics L.*, **3**, p. 133, 1967.

286.1. Veselago, V. G., Glushkov, M. M., Prokhorov, A. M., 'Microwave   129, 140,
Properties of Solid State Plasma', *Radiotechnika i Elektronika*,   171
12, Transl: *Radio Eng. El. Phys.*, **12**, pp. 1134-1140, 1967.

287. Vinney, D. J., 'Possible Travelling-Wave Parametric Amplifier   148
Using The Gunn-Effect', *Electronics L.*, **2**, 357-358, 1966.

288. Vural, B., Steele, M. C., 'Possible Two-Stream Instabilities of   135
Drifted Electron-Hole Plasmas in Longitudinal Magnetic Fields',
Phys. Rev., **139**, p. A300, 1965.

288a. Vural B., Thomas, E. E., 'Helicon-Spin Wave Interaction in the   136
Magnetic Semiconductor $Ag_xCd_{1-x}Cr_2Se_4$', *Appl. Phys.
Letters*, **12**, pp. 14-17, 1968.

289. Wallace R. N., Baraff, G. A., 'Surface-Wave Instability in Helicon   135
Propagation, II: Effect of Collisional Losses', *J. Appl. Phys.*,
37, pp. 2937-2944, 1966.

290. Wang, Wen-Chung, 'Current Oscillations and Acoustic Flux   119
     Generation in CdS.', *Appl. Phys. L.,* **6**, p. 81, 1965.
291. Warner, F. L., Herman, P., 'Miniature X-Band Gunn Oscillator   78, 142
     with a Dielectric-Tuning System', *Electronics L.,* **2**, pp. 467-   144
     468, 1966.
292. Wasse, M. P., Lees, J., King, G., 'The Effect of Pressure on Gunn   79
     Phenomena in GaAs', *Sol. St. Electronics,* **9**, p. 601, 1966.
293. Weinreich, G., Sanders, T. M., White, H. G., 'Acoustoelectric   115
     Effect in n-Type Germanium', *Phys. Rev.,* **114**, p. 33, 1959.
294. Weiser, K., Drougard, M., Fern, R., 'Avalanching in GaAs pπp   114
     Structures', *J. Phys. Chem Solids,* **28**, pp. 171-183, 1967.
295. Weissglas, P., Andersson, B., 'Ionization Waves in Semiconductors 140
     and Gaseous Plasmas', *J. Appl. Phys.,* **38**, pp. 2185-2191, 1967.
296. Weller, K., Turner, C. W., van Duzer, T., 'Interaction of an   123
     Acoustic Wave with Electrons Drifting in Crossed Electric and
     Magnetic Fields in InSb', *Electronics L.,* **3**, p. 418, 1967.
296.1. van Welzenis, R. G., van den Dries, J. G., 'Microwave Emission   125
     During Plasma Formation in InSb', *Appl. Phys. L.,* **11**, p. 374,
     1967.
297. Wettling, W., 'Brillouin Scattering from Electron-Phonon Packets   121
     in Low-Resistivity CdS.', *Phys. L.,* **25A**, p. 193, 1967.
298. White, D. L., 'Amplification of Ultrasonic Waves in Piezoelectric 116
     Semiconductors', *J. Appl. Phys.,* **33**, p. 2547, 1962.
298a. White, D. L., Wang, W. C., 'Active CdS. Ultrasonic Oscillator',   122
     Phys. Rev., **149**, pp. 628-630, 1966.
299. White, R. M., 'Some Effects of Heating and Dispersion in the   118
     Ultrasonic Amplifier', *I.E.E.E. Trans. Sonics and Ultrasonics,*
     SU-13, pp. 69-73, 1966.
299a. White, R. M., 'Surface Elastic-Wave Propagation and Amplifica-   119, 170
     tion', *I.E.E.E. Trans. El.Dev.,* **ED-14**, pp. 181-189, 1967.
300. Williams, G. A., Smith, G. E., 'Alfvén Wave Propagation in Bis-   130
     muth: Quantum Oscillations of the Fermi Surface', *I.B.M.
     Journal,* p. 276, 1964.
301. Winteler, H. R., Steinemann, A., 'GaAs Field Effect Transistors'   151
     Proc. Internat Symp. on GaAs, Reading, England, 1966.
     Inst. Phys. and Phys. Soc., London, Conf. Series 3, pp. 228-
     232.
302. Wisseman, W. R., Davies, E. J., 'Investigation of Strong Guiding   136
     Effects in Helicon Propagation', *J. Appl. Phys.,* **38**, pp. 3940-
     3948, 1967.
303. Yamamoto, R., 'Current Oscillations in CdS.', *Jap. J. Appl. Phys.* 121
     5, pp. 351-357, 1966.
304. Yamashita, A., 'High-Field Effects Above the Gunn Threshold in   99
     n-Type GaAs', *Jap. J. Appl. Phys.,* **6**, p. 1011, 1967.
305. Yoshimura, H., 'Space-Charge-Limited and Emitter-Current-   111
     Limited Injections in Space-Charge Region of Semiconductors',
     I.E.E.E. Trans. El.Dev., **ED-11**, pp. 414-422, 1964.

306. Zieger, K., 'Frequency Modulation of a Gunn-Effect Oscillator by   144
      Magnetic Tuning', *Electronics L.,* **3**, p. 324, 1967.
307. Zil'berman, P. E., 'Nonlinear Theory of Acoustic Instability in   120
      Piezoelectric Semiconductors', *Fizika Tverdogo Tela,* **9**, pp.
      309-316, 1967. Transl: *Sov. Phys.-Sol. St.,* **9**, pp. 231-236,
      1967.
308. Ziman, J. M., 'Principles of the Theory of Solids', *Cambridge*   135
      University Press, p. 142, 1965.
309. Zucker, J., Zemon, S., 'Frequency Spectrum of Giant Acoustic   118
      Wave Packets Generated in CdS. by High Electric Fields',
      Appl. Phys. L., **9**, p. 398, 1966.

Index